TELEVISION THEORY AND SERVICING

TELEVISION THEORY AND SERVICING:
Color and Black/White

Clyde N. Herrick

RESTON PUBLISHING COMPANY, INC., Reston ,Virginia

PREFACE

Television devices, circuits, and systems have evolved rapidly within the past several years. The bipolar and field-effect transistor, the integrated circuit, the silicon controlled rectifier, and related devices have obsoleted the traditional TV building blocks. Concomitantly, circuitry has become more sophisticated, and circuit operation has become more efficient. Relevance to the state of the art requires concentration upon solid-state circuitry, to the exclusion of vacuum-tube technology. A need for systems analysis is also apparent, particularly in teaching the principles of cable television (CATV) and color television.

To provide a broad foundation of understanding, and to facilitate transfer of training by the student, the conceptual approach has been emphasized in this text. On the other hand, the "hardware" aspect of the discipline has not been entirely ignored, inasmuch as the tangible aspects of the television system make a legitimate contribution to the overall perspective of the student. Mathematics has been judiciously introduced, to provide ample rigor at the introductory level. Prerequisite courses in mathematics are arithmetic, algebra, geometry, and trigonometry. It is assumed that the student has also taken courses in basic electricity and electronics.

This book is intended for college-preparatory classroom use. However, the needs of the vocationally-oriented student have also been recognized, with respect to television installation and servicing techniques. Modern troubleshooting procedures require practical knowledge of test-instrument application, and this topic is accorded appropriate coverage. Inasmuch as the student may terminate his study of television, an introductory treatment of the NTSC system has been included. Similarly, basic color-TV test-equipment applications are discussed.

Grateful acknowledgement is made to the manufacturers who have been credited in the text for their cooperation and their generosity in providing photographs, diagrams, and technical data. Acknowledgement is also made to the faculty of San Jose City College, who have provided numerous constructive criticisms. An author does not work in a vacuum, and in a significant sense, this text represents a team effort. It is appropriate that this book be dedicated as a teaching tool to the instructors and students of our technical schools and junior colleges.

Clyde N. Herrick

CONTENTS

Section
ONE

THE TELEVISION
SYSTEM

Chapter **1**

TELEVISION TRANSMISSION AND RECEPTION

1.1 Basic Optics

Throughout the course of history, man has contrived in various ways to extend his sense of sight. The telescope, microscope, and camera were important landmarks along the way. In 1905, a major breakthrough was achieved when Thomas A. Edison introduced the moving-picture camera and projector. These inventions are based upon a characteristic of the human eye called "persistence of vision." That is, when photographs of an activity are taken at a rate of 16/sec, and then projected on a screen at the same rate, a viewer does not see the "jump" from one picture to the next. Instead, an illusion of continuous motion is produced. The same illusion is produced in animated cartoons, where

3

each frame shows a moving object as successive still pictures, as depicted in Fig. 1-1.

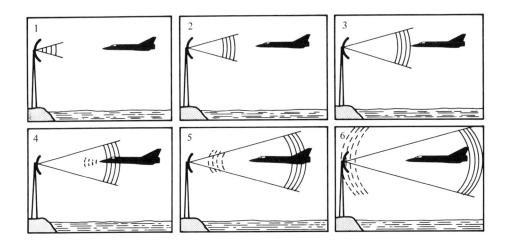

Fig. 1-1   Example of an animated cartoon sequence.

Although 16 pictures/sec provides a satisfactory illusion of continuous motion for slow-speed and medium-speed action, high-speed action, such as a batted ball, will appear "jerky" and discontinuous. Therefore, motion-picture projectors use 24 frames/sec and break up the basic 24 frames into 48 projected frames. This is done by quickly passing a shutter past each frame as it is being projected. Television frames are displayed in the same basic manner, except that the projection is faster. As explained in greater detail on p. 18 , 30 frames/sec are utilized, thus providing 60 fields/sec. As a result there is no visible flicker, even when fast-action images are being displayed.

Although "jerkiness" and flicker are eliminated in the foregoing projection process, a side effect called strobo-scopic display may appear occasionally. For example, if a spoked wheel is rolling across the scene at a certain speed, the spokes may appear to stand still, or the wheel may appear to be rotating in reverse, although its progress is actually in a forward direction. The basis of the stroboscopic effect is depicted in Fig. 1-2. In this classroom demonstration, two

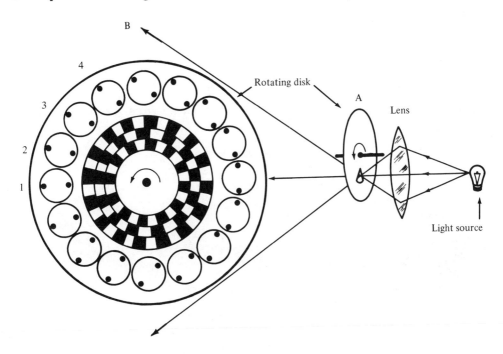

Fig. 1-2 Experiment for demonstrating stroboscope effect.

disks are mounted on the shafts of two separate motors. A narrow slot is provided in the smaller disk A to interrupt the light beam that illuminates the large disk. Thus, if disk A rotates 16 times/sec, disk B is illuminated by 16 short flashes of light/sec. Analyze the images that will be displayed.

With reference to Fig. 1-2, if B makes one revolution/sec, one flash of light strikes the disk in the position shown. With respect to circle 1, the enclosed dots are one above the other. When the second flash of light occurs, circle 2 will have moved into position 1. In turn, the two dots appear to have shifted slightly clockwise. Then, circle 3 moves into position 1, and the following flash of light makes

it appear that the dots have shifted still farther clockwise.
Thus, the circles have the appearance of standing still, while
the dots that they enclose appear to revolve clockwise. In the
television system, functional design is such that the strobo-
scopic effect is minimized.

Another important factor in basic optics concerns
picture elements. A printed picture is built up from dots,
as exemplified in Fig. 1-3. Each of the dots is a picture

Fig. 1-3 A television picture can be made up of
various sizes of dots.

element. Some dots are light, others are medium, and still
others are dark. Together they form various shades of gray
in accordance with the light and dark portions of the picture. The amount of detail displayed in an image depends
upon the number of picture elements that are utilized. The
retina of the human eye (Fig. 1-4) has approximately
1,000,000 picture elements, or fibers, in the optic nerve.
Although we can see a speck of dust, we cannot see an amoeba.
The image of an amoeba is smaller than an individual retinal
element.

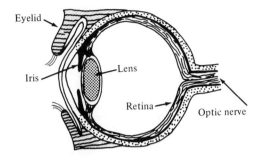

Fig. 1-4 There are approximately one million picture elements in the retina.

Reflection and refraction are important processes in television technology. For example, a television camera forms an image from reflected light. This image is produced by refraction of light rays through the camera lens. It is possible to recognize the difference between regular and diffused reflection, as depicted in Fig. 1-5. Thus, a mirror

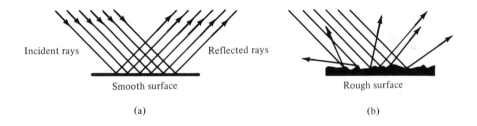

Fig. 1-5 Basic reflection processes: (a) regular reflection, (b) diffused reflection.

image is produced by regular reflection. On the other hand, when light strikes a rough surface, irregular reflection occurs, and the light is said to be diffused. In turn, an illuminated rough surface is visible, but it forms no images.

A fundamental law of optics states that the angle of incidence is equal to the angle of reflection. For example, when we observe a mirror image (Fig. 1-6), angle α is equal to angle β. Note that a light ray always travels through air

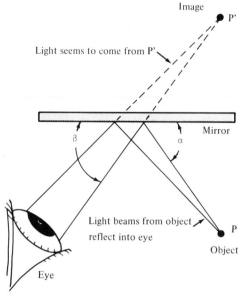

Fig. 1-6 The angle of incidence is equal to the angle of reflection.

at the same speed, both before and after reflection. This speed is about 186,270 miles/sec. However, the speed of light through glass or water is less. This change in speed causes light rays to be refracted when they travel from air into water, as shown in Fig. 1-7. In this classroom experiment, the penny becomes visible when water is poured into the cup, because light rays from A are refracted at C.

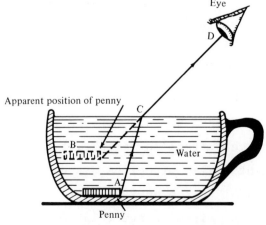

Fig. 1-7 Light rays are refracted at point C.

Next consider how light rays are focused by lenses.　A
prism refracts　light as depicted　in Fig. 1-8, because　the

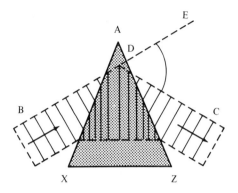

Fig. 1-8　Refraction of light by a prism.

speed of　light in glass is　slower than in air.　Note that
the light rays are bent toward the thicker part of the prism,
and that the light is bent where it enters the prism and
where it emerges.　Angle CDE is called the deviation of the
prism and is a measure of the total change in direction of
the light rays.　The deviation depends upon the kind of glass
or plastic that is used in the prism.　Note that the angle
XAZ between the two refracting surfaces is called the angle
of the prism.

Various types　of lenses　are diagrammed　in Fig. 1-9.

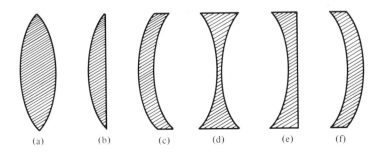

Fig. 1-9　Types of lenses:　(a) double convex,
(b) plano-convex, (c) meniscus, (d) double concave,
(e) plano-concave, (f) convexo-concave.

The first three types are termed convergent lenses, and the last three types are termed divergent lenses. Figure 1-10

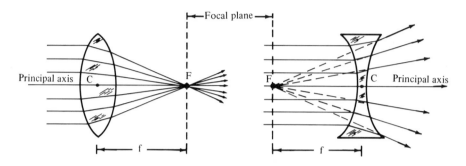

Fig. 1-10   Refraction of light by converging and diverging lenses.

depicts the refraction of light by converging and diverging lenses. Observe that the principal axis is a straight line passing through the center of the lens, perpendicular to the two faces at the points of intersection. Point F, the principal focus, falls on the principal axis. For a converging lens, the principal focus is the point where parallel light rays are refracted together. For a diverging lens, the principal focus is the point from which parallel light rays appear to originate. The distance from the focal point to the lens, f, is termed the focal length. An image is formed by a convex lens as shown in Fig. 1-11. Observe that the image is upside down, with respect to the object.

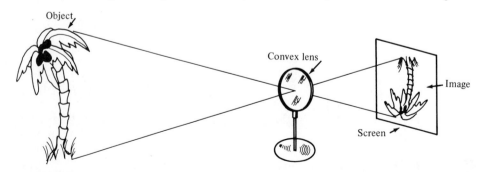

Fig. 1-11   An image is upside down with respect to its object.

1.2 Plan of the Black and White Television System

A black and white television system comprises a transmitter and a receiver, as shown in Fig. 1-12. The transmit-

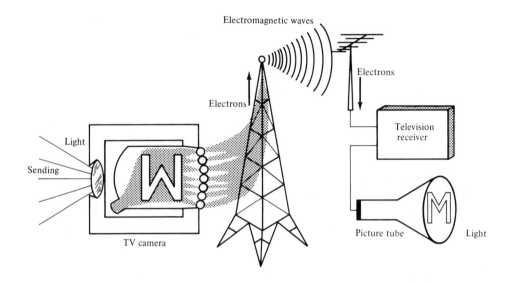

Fig. 1-12 The television system is comprised of a transmitter and a receiver.

ter utilizes a television camera, which breaks the image up into tiny picture elements. These picture elements are changed into electron (electric) currents, which are suitably processed and fed to a transmitting antenna. From the antenna, the television signal is radiated in the form of electromagnetic waves. At the receiving location, the incoming electromagnetic waves strike the receiving antenna. In turn, the waves are changed into signal currents which are fed to the television receiver. These signal currents are suitably processed and finally produce a visible image on the screen of a picture tube.

As shown in Fig. 1-13, a television station employs both an AM picture transmitter and an FM sound transmitter. Simi-

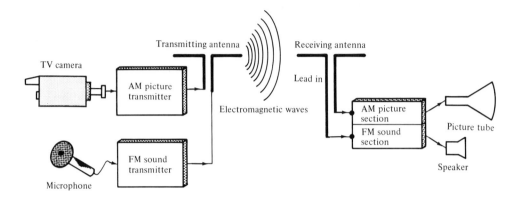

Fig. 1-13 A television station has two transmitters, and a television receiver has two receivers.

larly, a television receiver comprises an AM picture section and an FM sound section. The picture and sound signals are transmitted on different frequencies, so that they do not interfere with each other. Note that the picture and sound signals are transmitted by a single antenna, and the two signals are also received by a single antenna. The picture signal originates in a television camera and terminates in a picture tube. Similarly, the sound signal originates in a microphone and terminates in a loudspeaker.

1.3 Principles of Scanning and Picture Information Transfer

It is not technically feasible to transmit all parts of an image simultaneously. Therefore, the image must be broken down into picture elements, so that the elements can be transmitted sequentially. This principle is depicted in Fig. 1-14. Television picture tubes will be considered in some detail subsequently. However, it is helpful at this point to present a brief overview of the basic cathode-ray tube (CRT), diagrammed in Fig. 1-15. Cathode rays are beams of electrons. Electrons are emitted from the heated cathode and are attracted toward the positive anode. This electron

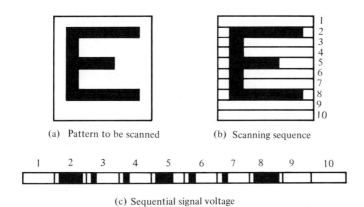

(a) Pattern to be scanned   (b) Scanning sequence

(c) Sequential signal voltage

Fig. 1-14 Video-signal voltages produced by the scanning process.

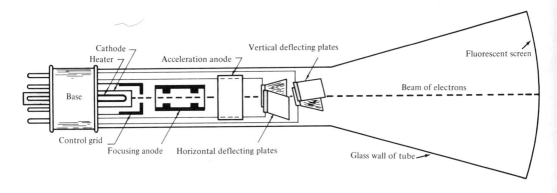

Fig. 1-15 Layout of the CRT.

beam is directed by means of two sets of deflecting plates. This movable electron beam strikes the screen at the end of the CRT. The screen fluoresces, or glows, where it is struck.

If no voltage is applied to the deflecting plates in a CRT, the electron beam is unchanged in direction, and it produces a dot of light in the center of the screen. However, if an alternating voltage is applied to the horizontal deflecting plates, the beam is swept back and forth from left to right on the screen. In turn, a horizontal glowing line is displayed. Similarly, if an alternating voltage is applied to the vertical deflecting plates, the beam is swept

up and down on the screen.   Thus, a vertical glowing line is
displayed.   If suitable voltages are applied to both the
horizontal and vertical deflecting plates, the electron beam
can be caused to strike the screen at any desired point.

   A simple form of television camera that scans transparencies employs a CRT and a photoelectric cell, as
shown in Fig. 1-16.   The basic scanning sequence depicted

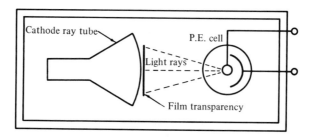

Fig. 1-16 Arrangement for scanning transparencies.

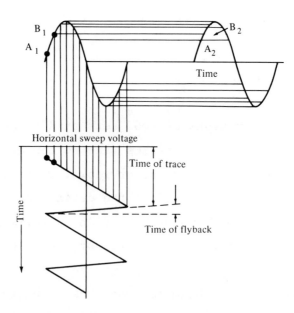

Fig. 1-17 Sawtooth voltage applied to horizontal
deflection plates, and sinusoidal voltage applied to
vertical deflection plates.

in Fig. 1-14 is produced by applying sawtooth deflection voltages to the horizontal and vertical deflecting plates in the CRT. This process is shown in Fig. 1-17. In this example, a sawtooth deflection voltage is being applied to the horizontal deflecting plates, and a sinusoidal deflection voltage is being applied to the vertical deflecting plates. In turn, a sine waveform is displayed on the CRT screen.

Now observe the effect of applying sawtooth deflection voltages to both the horizontal and the vertical deflecting plates. In the example of Fig. 1-18, the horizontal sawtooth

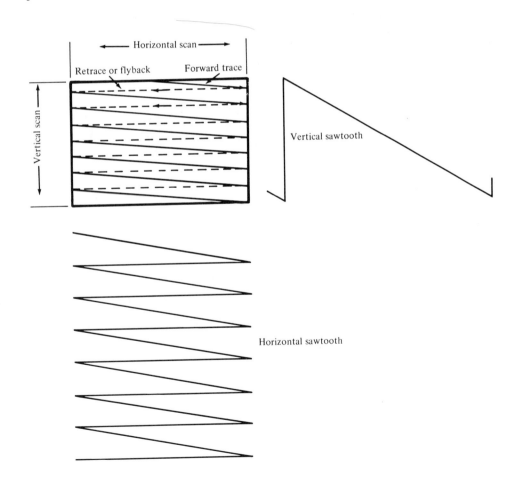

Fig. 1-18 Low-frequency sawtooth voltage applied to vertical deflection plates, and high-frequency sawtooth voltage applied to horizontal deflecting plates.

frequency is several times faster than the vertical sawtooth
frequency. Therefore, the electron beam sweeps more rapidly
from left to right than up to down.   Note that the retrace
(flyback) interval is very short, compared with the forward
trace interval.   When the beam reaches the lower right-hand
corner of the screen, it quickly returns to the top of the
screen. Then, the scanning pattern is repeated. This pattern
of glowing lines is called a raster. Of course, many more
scanning lines are used in practice than are depicted in the
simplified example of Fig. 1-18.

    It is helpful at this point to observe the operation of
the flying-spot scanner diagrammed in Fig. 1-19.   A raster

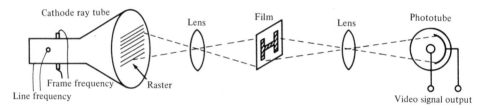

Fig. 1-19 Plan of the flying-spot scanner.

on the screen of a CRT is the light source.   Because a short
persistence type of screen is used, the phototube effectively
responds to a moving spot of light, instead of a complete
raster.   Short persistence means that the glowing point on
the screen decays rapidly. Sharp focusing of the image is
provided by optical lenses.   Thus, this arrangement produces a
clearer reproduction than the simple method shown in Fig. 1-16.
In a practical scanner, a 525-line pattern is used. The sawtooth voltage for horizontal deflection is said to operate
at line frequency, whereas the sawtooth voltage for vertical
deflection is said to operate at frame frequency.   These
frequencies are explained in the following discussion.

A picture element is the smallest area in an image
that can be reproduced by the video signal. The size of a
picture element depends upon the size of the scanning spot,
the number of scanning lines, and the highest frequency
utilized in the video signal. FCC standards stipulate that
the basic or ideal television image shall contain 211,000
picture elements.[*] This standard entails the use of 525
scanning lines, a maximum video frequency of 4 MHz, and a
well-focused electron beam in the picture tube. However,
the actual television image is less than ideal, in that only
495 lines are effective in picture information transfer. That
is, flyback time reduces the number of active picture
elements, as depicted in Fig. 1-20. The horizontal flyback

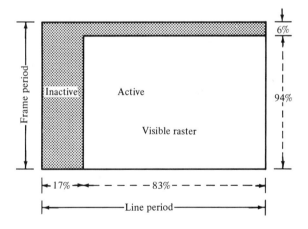

Fig. 1-20 Active and inactive scanning periods.

interval occupies 17% of the line period, and the vertical
flyback interval occupies 6% of the frame period. This means
that the actual number of picture elements that can be reproduced in the visible area is reduced from 211,000 to about
160,000 elements.

---

[*]Federal Communications Commission.

Note the proportion of height to length of the visible
raster in Fig. 1-20.   This ratio is normally 3 to 4 and is
called the aspect ratio of the raster.   It is not a technical
consideration but an artistic judgment--a picture is regarded
as most pleasing to the eye when framed in a 3-to-4 aspect
ratio.   To minimize flicker, the basic frame of 525 lines is
broken down into two fields, each of which contains $262\frac{1}{2}$ lines.
This is called the interlaced scanning method, as specified
by the FCC.   The basic or ideal interlaced scanning system is
depicted in Fig. 1-21.   Because of the half-line relations in
the two fields, the lines of the second field fall in
between the lines of the first field.

Because only 495 lines are active, the actual visible
raster includes   fields with $247\frac{1}{2}$ lines each.   The   line
frequency   is 15,750 Hz,   the field frequency   is 60 Hz,   and
the frame   frequency is 30 Hz.   This means that   the   time
from   the beginning of one scanning   line to   the next   is
63.5 μsec; the time from the   beginning of one   field to   the
next is 16,667 μsec; the active scanning time along each line
is 52.5 μsec; and the active scanning time over each field is
15,500 μsec.   Each scanning line is said to be blanked for
11 μsec, and there are 1167 μsec of blanking time between
consecutive fields.

1.4 Synchronization Requirements

It is necessary to keep the scanning spot in the picture
tube exactly in step with the scanning beam in the television
camera.   If the two scanning sequences fall out of step,
the reproduced picture becomes "torn up."   Correct timing
is controlled by means of synchronizing pulses, as depicted
in Fig. 1-22.   A sync pulse is transmitted at the start of
each forward scan.   The pulse triggers the scanning genera-

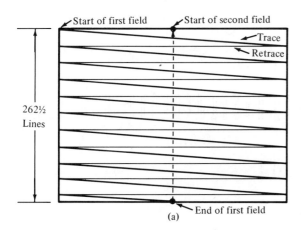

(a)

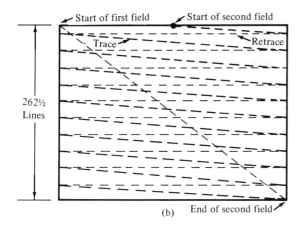

(b)

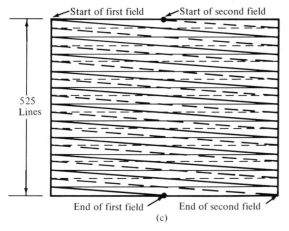

(c)

Fig. 1-21 Interlaced scanning process for the basic or ideal raster: (a) structure of the first field, (b) structure of the second field, (c) structure of the complete frame.

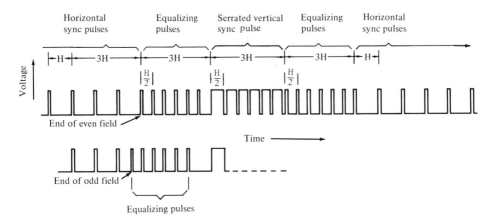

Fig. 1-22 Synchronizing waveform specified by the FCC.

tor in the television receiver, so that the electron beam in
the picture tube starts a new scanning line at exactly the
same time that a new scanning line is started in the television
camera.

Note in Fig. 1-22 that the last horizontal sync pulse
at the end of a field is followed by six or seven equalizing
pulses, spaced at half-line intervals. These equalizing pulses
serve to stabilize the operation of the vertical scanning
generator in the television receiver, as explained subsequently.
The equalizing pulses are followed by a wide vertical sync
pulse, which triggers the vertical scanning generator. Serrations ("slots") are placed in the vertical sync pulse to
stabilize the operation of the horizontal scanning generator
during vertical retrace time. Each horizontal sync pulse
follows its predecessor by 63.5 μsec. The duration of a horizontal sync pulse (pulse width) is 5.1 μsec.

Interlaced scanning is provided in the sync waveform
(Fig. 1-22) by provision of six equalizing pulses at the
end of both even and odd fields, but with the last equalizing
pulse at changed spacing from the vertical sync pulse. Note

also that the sync pulses extend upward (above the video signal). This is called the "blacker-than-black region," as explained in greater detail later. Other sync waveform arrangements are also employed. For example, Fig. 1-23 shows the sync waveform specified by the BBC.* In this system, the

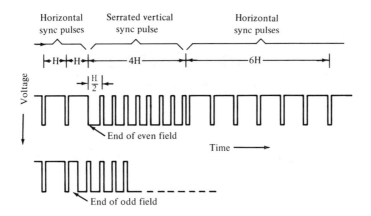

Fig. 1-23 Synchronizing waveform specified by the BBC in Great Britain.

sync pulses extend downward (below the video signal), into the "whiter-than-white" region. Different numbers of horizontal sync pulses are also utilized; whereas 525 lines are specified by the FCC, the BBC has a VHF (very high-frequency) standard of 405 lines, and a UHF (ultrahigh-frequency) standard of 625 lines.

The sync pulses extend above the blanking pedestals, as depicted in Fig. 1-24. Each blanking pedestal extends from the white signal level to the black signal level. Thus, the sync pulses are above the black level. A sync pulse has 25% of the total height of the waveform. The width of a horizontal blanking pedestal is 10 μsec. Observe that the verti-

---

*British Broadcasting Corporation.

cal sync waveform extends from a very broad blanking pedestal,
often called the vertical blanking pulse. The vertical sync
pulse has six component pulses, each of which has a width of
190 μsec. These component pulses are separated by five serration pulses, each of which has the same width as an equalizing
pulse, or about 2.5 μsec.

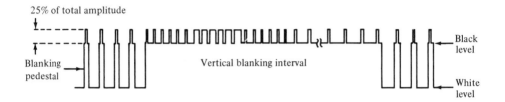

Fig. 1-24 Sync pulses extended above the blanking pulse.

1.5 The Composite Video Signal

When a blanked picture (camera) signal is combined
with the sync signal, the composite video signal is obtained.
Note that the complete television signal consists of the
composite video signal and the sound signal. A video signal
is produced as shown in Fig. 1-25. This is the line waveform;
that is, it is the waveform that appears between consecutive
horizontal sync pulses. To determine the narrowest pulse
(smallest picture element) that can be reproduced by the
video signal, note that the highest video frequency in the
U.S. system is 4 MHz. This corresponds to a period of
0.25 μsec, which includes a white "dot" followed by a black
"dot."   In turn, there are approximately 21,000 white and
black "dots" that can be reproduced along an active scanning
line. Thus, if an active scanning line is 16 in. in length,
each of the "dots" is about 0.035 in. long.

As depicted in Fig. 1-26, the composite video signal
is processed through an amplitude modulation system. Sync

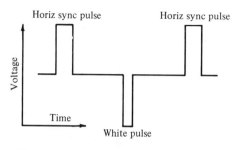

(a) Video waveform repeated on each horizontal line　(b) Resulting vertical white line screen display

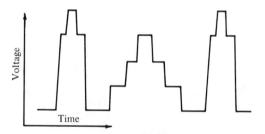

(c) Video waveform for light-grey,
grey and black vertical bars

(d) Scale of tones as image

Fig. 1-25 Formation of the video signal: (a) waveform for a white vertical line, (b) waveform for three shades of gray.

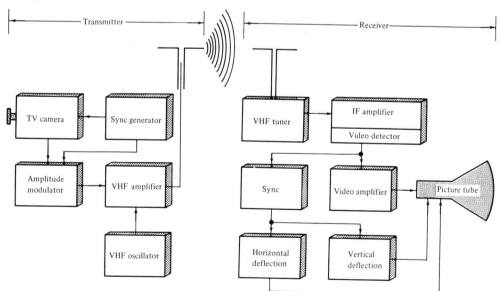

Fig. 1-26 The composite video signal is processed through an amplitude modulation system.

pulses are added to the camera signal and fed to an amplitude modulator. In turn, the composite video signal is encoded into the VHF (or UHF) signal and radiated from the transmitting antenna. At the receiver, the intercepted signal is amplified through a superheterodyne arrangement. The receiver-IF waveform appears as shown in Fig. 1-27. This is a waveform that characterizes negative transmission, as speci-

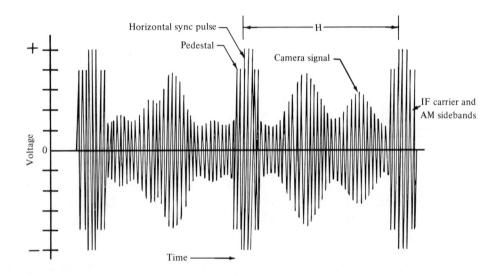

Fig. 1-27 IF waveform in the television receiver system.

fied by the FCC. The BBC, on the other hand, specifies positive transmission, as shown in Fig. 1-28. Note that the white and black levels are reversed in these two systems.

1.6 FM Sound Channel

A sound section is associated with the picture section in a television receiver, as depicted in Fig. 1-29. This sound section is basically a radio receiver. In accordance with FCC standards, the audio signal is frequency modulated on a carrier 4.5 MHz above the picture carrier. Figure 1-30 shows how a frequency-modulated signal is formed. Note that

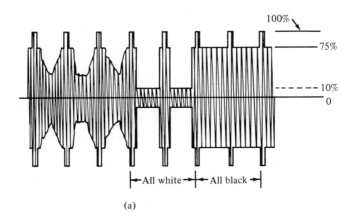

(a)

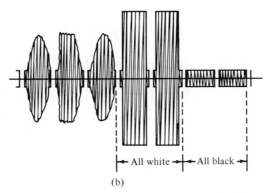

(b)

Fig. 1-28 Comparison of the same signal in positive and negative transmission system: (a) negative transmission, (b) positive transmission.

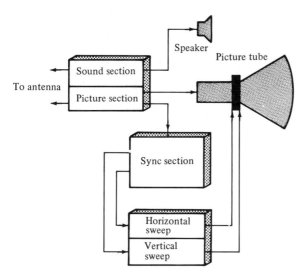

Fig. 1-29 A sound section is associated with the picture section in the television receiver.

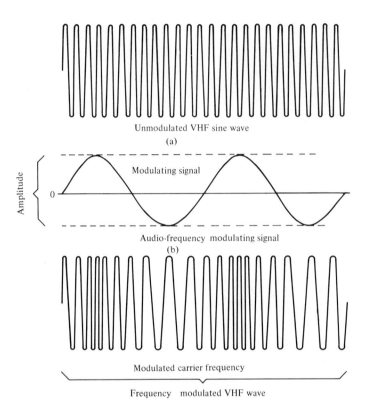

Fig. 1-30 Development of FM waveform.

the amplitude of the carrier remains unchanged, whereas the instantaneous carrier frequency is varied in accordance with the variation of the audio modulating signal. FM sound was standardized by the FCC in broadcast television systems to minimize interference from the AM video signal. That is, an FM receiver is unresponsive to AM signals, and vice versa. Note that the BBC specifies the use of amplitude modulation for both picture and sound in the VHF band.

The maximum frequency swing (deviation) of the television FM sound signal is ±25 kHz. By way of comparison, the maximum deviation of broadcast FM sound signals is ±75 kHz. Note also that whereas broadcast FM systems provide high-fidelity reproduction, television FM sound systems provide little more fidelity than AM broadcast systems. An elaborate television receiver can provide sound reproduction over a substantially greater frequency range than an AM radio receiver, although not as great as a broadcast FM radio receiver. Table 1-1 lists the picture and sound carrier frequencies for television VHF and UHF bands.

1.7 Basic Television Antennas

An antenna has the function of coupling a receiver or transmitter to space. When an antenna is energized by a transmitter, it radiates electromagnetic waves into space. Conversely, when an antenna intercepts electromagnetic waves, a signal voltage is induced which may be utilized by a receiver. Although there are many forms of antennas, the basic dipole and its derivatives are commonly employed in television systems.

Horizontally and vertically polarized dipole antennas are depicted in Fig. 1-31. A horizontally polarized antenna radiates horizontally polarized electromagnetic waves. It will not intercept vertically polarized waves and has maximum response to horizontally polarized waves. Conversely, a vertically polarized antenna radiates vertically polarized waves. It will not intercept horizontally polarized waves and has maximum response to vertically polarized waves. Horizontal polarization is standardized for television systems in the United States. On the other hand, both horizontal and vertical polarization are utilized in England. Note that a wave that is transmitted with horizontal polarization often undergoes various reflections during propagation so that it has become elliptically or circularly polarized upon arrival at a receiving antenna. In such a case, either a horizontally or a vertically polarized antenna will provide

P Carrier	S Carrier	Channel No.	Freq. Limits
			54
55.25	59.75	2	60
61.25	65.75	3	66
67.25	71.75	4	72
			76
77.25	81.75	5	82
83.25	87.75	6	88
			174
175.25	179.75	7	180
181.25	185.75	8	186
187.25	191.75	9	192
193.25	197.75	10	198
199.25	203.75	11	204
205.25	209.75	12	210
211.25	215.75	13	216
			470
471.25	475.75	14	476
477.25	481.75	15	482
483.25	487.75	16	488
489.25	493.75	17	494
495.25	499.75	18	500
501.25	505.75	19	506
507.25	511.75	20	512
513.25	517.75	21	518
519.25	523.75	22	524
525.25	529.75	23	530
531.25	535.75	24	536
537.25	541.75	25	542
			542
543.25	547.75	26	548
549.25	553.75	27	554
555.25	559.75	28	560
561.25	565.75	29	566
567.25	571.75	30	572
573.25	577.75	31	578
579.25	583.75	32	584
585.25	589.75	33	590
591.25	595.75	34	596
597.25	601.75	35	602
603.25	607.75	36	608
609.25	613.75	37	614
615.25	619.75	38	620
621.25	625.75	39	626
627.25	631.75	40	632
633.25	637.75	41	638
639.25	643.75	42	644
645.25	649.75	43	650
651.25	655.75	44	656
657.25	661.75	45	662
663.25	667.75	46	668
669.25	673.75	47	674
675.25	679.75	48	680
681.25	685.75	49	686
687.25	691.75	50	692
693.25	697.75	51	698
699.25	703.75	52	704
705.25	709.75	53	710
711.25	715.75	54	716
			716
717.25	721.75	55	722
723.25	727.75	56	728
729.25	733.75	57	734
735.25	739.75	58	740
741.25	745.75	59	746
747.25	751.75	60	752
753.25	757.75	61	758
759.25	763.75	62	764
765.25	769.75	63	770
771.25	775.75	64	776
777.25	781.75	65	782
783.25	787.75	66	788
789.25	793.75	67	794
795.25	799.75	68	800
801.25	805.75	69	806
807.25	811.75	70	812
813.25	817.75	71	818
819.25	823.75	72	824
825.25	829.75	73	830
831.25	835.75	74	836
837.25	841.75	75	842
843.25	847.75	76	848
849.25	853.75	77	854
855.25	859.75	78	860
861.25	865.75	79	866
867.25	871.75	80	872
873.25	877.75	81	878
879.25	883.75	82	884
885.25	889.75	83	890

P = Picture Carrier Freq.   S = Sound Carrier Freq.   All frequencies in MHz
VHF Channels 2-13   UHF Channels 14-83

TV VHF and VHF Frequency Allocations

Table 1-1

approximately the same response.

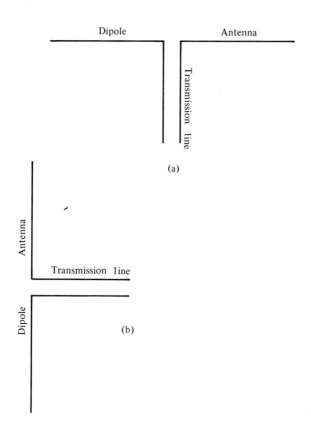

(a)

(b)

Fig. 1-31 Basic dipole antennas: (a) horizontally polarized antenna, (b) vertically polarized antenna.

A transmission line serves to conduct signal currents to or from an antenna to a transmitter or receiver. Dipole antenna characteristics are independent of the transmission line in normal operation. We will find that a dipole antenna is a resonant structure, whereas a transmission line (also called television twin lead) is normally non-resonant. The resonant frequency of a dipole antenna depends primarily upon its length, and to some extent upon the diameter of antenna conductors. Electromagnetic waves travel approximately 186,000 miles, or 3×10^{10} cm/sec. In turn, it follows that wavelength and frequency are related as follows:

$$\text{wavelength} = \frac{\text{speed of light}}{\text{frequency}} \qquad (1.1)$$

or,
$$\lambda = \frac{186,000}{f} \text{ miles} \qquad (1.2)$$

or
$$= \frac{30,000,000,000}{f} \text{ cm} \qquad (1.3)$$

where f is measured in Hz.

A dipole is resonant to a given wavelength of electromagnetic radiation when each arm is one quarter-wave in
electrical length, as depicted in Fig. 1-32. The antenna

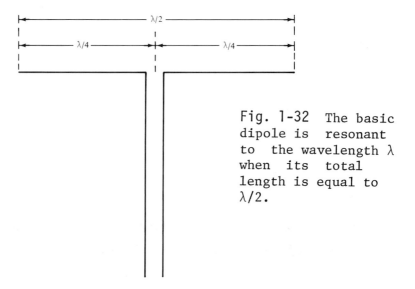

Fig. 1-32 The basic
dipole is resonant
to the wavelength λ
when its total
length is equal to
$\lambda/2$.

terminal impedance is equal to approximately 75 Ω at its
resonant frequency. If the dipoles are constructed of thin
wires, the bandwidth of the antenna is comparatively small.
On the other hand, if the dipoles are constructed of large-
diameter rods or tubing, the bandwidth of the antenna is
comparatively great. A conical antenna, such as depicted in
Fig. 1-33, also has a comparatively great bandwidth. Note

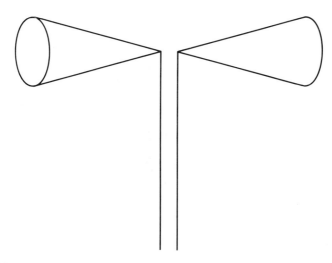

Fig. 1-33 The conical form of antenna has a comparatively
great bandwidth.

that the physical length of an antenna becomes less than its
electrical length, as the diameter of the conductors is
increased. This is a result of the greater capacitance
between the dipole elements.

A derived conical type of antenna is used to a considerable extent in television reception, in order to obtain
sufficient bandwidth for coverage of the VHF band. A
derived form, commonly called the V antenna, is generally
used, as depicted in Fig. 1-34. The dipole members are
metal rodes or tubes, and their length is designed to resonate the antenna structure at about the center of the VHF
band. Another variation of the basic dipole antenna is
called the folded-dipole arrangement. The plan of a
folded-dipole antenna is shown in Fig. 1-35. Its advantage is a terminal impedance of 300 Ω at its resonant
frequency, which provides an optimum impedance match to
standard twin-lead line. If a folded dipole is constructed
from thick metal tubing, its bandwidth is thereby increased.

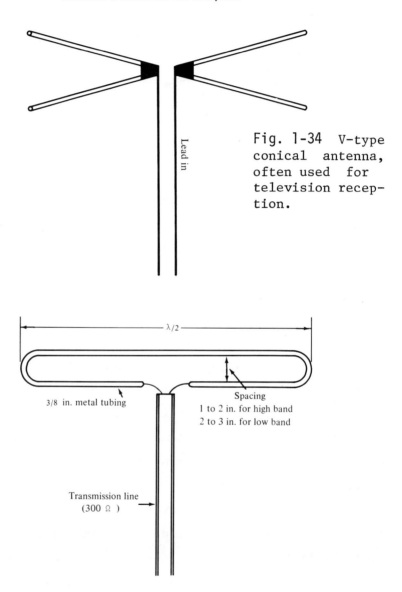

Fig. 1-34 V-type conical antenna, often used for television reception.

Fig. 1-35 Folded-dipole antenna construction.

Dipole antennas are bidirectional. That is, their maximum response is in a broadside direction; equal response is obtained in the forward and rear directions. On the other hand, a dipole has practically zero response in the direction of its elements. Therefore, a rotor may be required to orient the antenna suitably for reception from various directions.

The more elaborate types of television antennas are provided with director and reflector elements, as shown in Fig. 1-36.

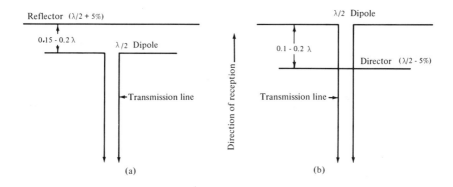

Fig. 1-36 Reflector and director elements: (a) reflector is longer than the dipole, (b) director is shorter than the dipole.

A reflector element can be compared with a mirror; it is called a parasitic element, and it increases the antenna response in the forward direction, while reducing the response in the backward direction. Note that a reflector element is cut somewhat longer than a dipole element.

A director element can be compared with a lens that focuses the incoming waves on to the dipoles; it is also called a parasitic element. Like a reflector, a director increases the antenna response in the forward direction, while reducing the response in the backward direction. Not only do reflectors and directors make a dipole antenna uni-directional, but they also increase its gain. Unidirectional response is often useful to eliminate interference from the rear, and high gain is useful in fringe areas to reduce "snow" in the picture. Directors and reflectors also narrow the "beam" of the antenna; this is often a useful feature to reduce interference, and it also tends to reduce ghosts due to multipath reflections. Figure 1-37 shows an elaborate type

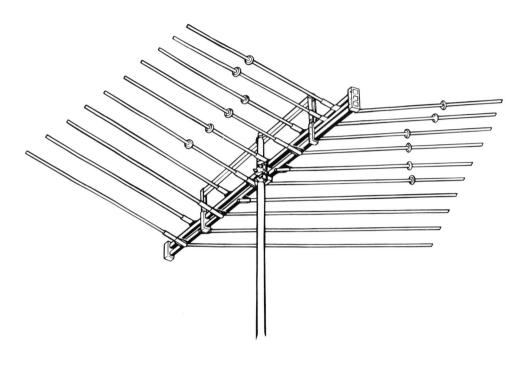

MODEL	NO. OF ELEMENTS	DESCRIPTION	DIMENSIONS
LPV-TV100	10	COLOR LOG PERIODIC FOR VHF & FM STEREO	Boom Length - 112 3/4" 1 pc. crossarm, boom braced
(Supersedes LPV-TV10)		VHF-up to 125 miles FM-up to 40 miles	Carton - 113 x 6 x 6 Turning Radius - 78 1/2" Tip to Tip - 92" Shipping Wt. 14 1/2 lbs. app.

Fig. 1-37   An elaborate type of television receiving antenna.   (Courtesy of JFD Electronics Corp.)

of commercial television receiving antenna.

Television transmitting antennas must meet somewhat different requirements. A transmitting antenna is usually omnidirectional. That is, it radiates in all directions of the compass, as depicted in Fig. 1-38. In this example, the omnidirectional characteristic is obtained by using a turnstile antenna. A turnstile antenna consists of a pair of dipole antennas mounted at right angles to each other. The

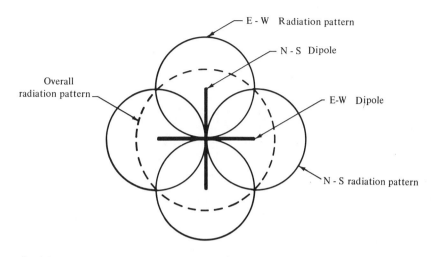

Fig. 1-38 A turnstile antenna radiates in all directions of the compass.

dipole elements are comparatively large in diameter for transmitter applications. Some turnstile antennas utilize elements in the form of heavy metal tubes, and others have elliptically shaped elements, as shown in Fig. 1-39. Quite

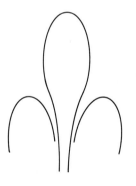

Fig. 1-39 Ellipti-cally shaped dipole element for a turn-stile antenna.

a few installations use turnstiles made up of batwing dipoles, as depicted in Fig. 1-40.

As noted previously, television antennas are generally connected to a receiver or transmitter by means of a trans-mission line. As seen in Fig. 1-41, a television line consists of a pair of parallel conductors, with fairly close

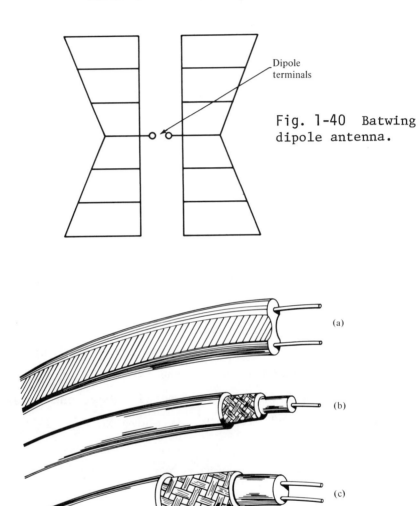

Fig. 1-40 Batwing dipole antenna.

Fig. 1-41 Typical television transmission lines: (a) twin leads, (b) coaxial cable, (c) shielded twin lead.

and uniform spacing between them. The advantage of a transmission line is that it provides electrical connection
without acting as a part of the antenna radiation system.
That is, a transmitting antenna can be erected high above
the ground clear of buildings, trees, and other objects, with

all the electrical energy radiated from the antenna, and no energy radiated from the line. Conversely, a receiving antenna can be erected high above the ground, where electrical noise from ignition, neon signs, and other sources is at a minimum, with no noise interference introduced by the lead-in from the antenna to the receiver location.

Note that standard television twin lead has a characteristic impedance of 300 Ω. Coaxial cable is commonly manufactured with 52 Ω or 75 Ω of characteristic impedance. Shielded twin lead is usually supplied with a characteristic impedance of 150 Ω. It is desirable to match impedances in an antenna system in order to obtain maximum power transfer and to eliminate line reflections that can sometimes cause poor picture definition due to production of close-in ghosts. When different impedances are to be contended with in an antenna system, an antenna matching transformer such as illustrated in Fig. 1-42 may be utilized. This type of

Fig. 1-42 A wide-band VHF antenna-matching transformer. (Courtesy of Windguard Antenna Systems)

transformer is designed for wide-band VHF operation.

In areas where both UHF and VHF television stations are in range, a receiving antenna of the type shown in Fig. 1-43 is generally installed. This design combines both long and short dipole elements in order to obtain reasonably uniform response over the frequency range from Channel 2 to

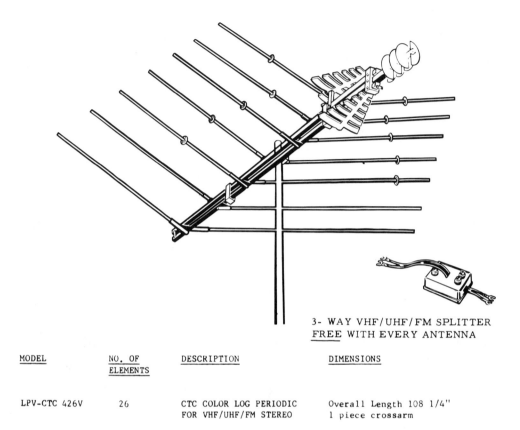

3- WAY VHF/UHF/FM SPLITTER
FREE WITH EVERY ANTENNA

MODEL	NO. OF ELEMENTS	DESCRIPTION	DIMENSIONS
LPV-CTC 426V	26	CTC COLOR LOG PERIODIC FOR VHF/UHF/FM STEREO	Overall Length 108 1/4" 1 piece crossarm Overall Width 90" Turning Radius 58" Shipping Wt. 12 lbs. app.

Fig. 1-43 Typical VHF-UHF antenna with high-gain directivity.
(Courtesy JFD Electronics Corp.)

Channel 83.   Built-in matching and coupling sections are
provided in the antenna structure to obtain a good impedance
match to a 300-Ω line. As noted previously, an antenna rotor
is usually required to obtain optimum reception from the
various television stations within range of the antenna.
Details of television receiving antennas are discussed in
greater detail in later chapters.

Questions

Short Answer

1. What is the number of frames/sec of a television picture?
2. Why are light rays bent as they pass through a glass of water?
3. Explain in basic terms the operation of a television system.
4. Explain the basic operation of a CRT.
5. What is a picture element?
6. Why does flyback time reduce the number of picture elements?
7. What is the aspect ratio of a television picture?
8. What is the purpose of interlace scanning?
9. What is the purpose of the horizontal sync pulse?
10. Of what signals does a complete television signal consist?
11. What are the characteristics of the sound signal of a television signal transmission?
12. Why was FM sound standardized in broadcast television systems?
13. What is the maximum frequency deviation of the sound in a television signal, and how does this compare to that of the FM broadcast system?
14. What is the purpose of an antenna?
15. What will occur if a vertically polarized antenna is used at a television receiver?
16. What is the purpose of a transmission line?
17. What is the approximate impedance of a center-coupled half-wave antenna?

18. Why is the V antenna used to a considerable extent in television reception?
19. What is the function of the director on an antenna?
20. What is the purpose of the reflector on an antenna?
21. What are the impedance values for twin lead, coaxial cable, and shielded twin lead?

True-False

1. Television pictures are transmitted at a rate of 30 frames/sec.
2. The amount of detail in a television picture depends upon the number of picture elements used.
3. Magnetic waves picked up by the television receiver antenna are converted to electromagnetic waves.
4. A television station employs both an FM picture transmitter and an AM sound transmitter.
5. The electron beam in the CRT used in a television receiver uses coils to deflect the electron beam.
6. A picture element is the smallest area in an image that can be reproduced by the video signal.
7. The television picture is made up of 450 lines/frame.

8. The scanning rate for the electron beam on the face of the CRT is 15,750 lines/sec.
9. The ratio of height to length of the visible raster on a television screen (3 to 4) is chosen for engineering purposes.
10. Each visible raster includes only $247\frac{1}{2}$ lines.
11. Loss of synchronization between the transmitter scanning beam and the receiver scanning beam results in picture tear.

12. The sync pulses extend above the blanking pedestal into the blacker-than-black area.

13. The maximum deviation of the television FM sound signal is ±75 kHz.

14. An antenna has the function of coupling a receiver or transmitter to space.

15. The length of an antenna is very important for the reception of a given band of frequencies.

16. The bandwidth of an antenna is not affected by the diameter of the dipoles.

17. Both the reflector and the director elements affect the directivity of an antenna.

18. Dipole antennas are omnidirectional.

19. Television transmitting antennas are usually bidirectional.

20. Standard twin-lead transmission lines have a characteristic impedance of 300 Ω.

Multiple Choice

1. The aspect ratio of a television screen is:
   (a) 3 to 3.
   (b) 4 to 3.
   (c) 4 to 4.
   (d) 3 to 4.

2. The line frequency of the television raster is _____ Hz.
   (a) 60
   (b) 15,750
   (c) 525
   (d) 495

3. The scanning spot in the television camera must be kept

in exact step with the scanning spot in the picture tube
to prevent the reproduced picture from

(a) having a "torn up" effect.

(b) being out of focus.

(c) decreasing in size.

(d) being blanked out.

4. A _____ is used to make sure that the electron
beam in the picture tube starts a scanning line at exactly
the same time that a new scanning line is started in the
television camera.

(a) sync pulse

(b) code pulse

(c) line counter

(d) power line lock generator

5. The area at which the sync pulses extend upward above the
video signals is called the:

(a) white region.

(b) black region.

(c) blacker-than-black region.

(d) whiter-than-white region.

6. The complete television signal consists of the:

(a) video signal.

(b) composite video signal and the sound signal.

(c) sound signal and sync pulses.

(d) sync pulses and video signal.

7. A device with the function of coupling a receiver or
transmitter to space is called a/an:

(a) antenna.

(b) transmission line.

(c) coupler.

(d) reflector.

8. The maximum allowable frequency swing (deviation) of the

television FM sound signal is:

(a) ±50 kHz.

(b) ±50 MHz.

(c) ±25 kHz.

(d) ±75 kHz.

9. In the United States, the standard polarization for transmitted waveforms for television is:

(a) horizontal for sound and vertical for video.

(b) horizontal.

(c) vertical for sound and horizontal for video.

(d) vertical.

10. To conduct signals from the antenna to the television
receiver, we use a:

(a) coupler.

(b) transmission line.

(c) matching stub.

(d) matching transformer.

11. The wavelength of a 150 MHz signal is:

(a) 3000 cm.

(b) 150 cm.

(c) 200 cm.

(d) 30 cm.

12. A reflector element for a dipole antenna is called a/an:

(a) parastic element.

(b) mirror element.

(c) antenna loop.

(d) transmission line.

13. A director element on an antenna is called a/an:

(a) parasitic element.

(b) mirror element.

(c) antenna loop.

(d) transmission line.

14. Television transmitting antennas are:

   (a) directional.

   (b) bidirectional.

   (c) unidirectional.

   (d) omnidirectional.

15. The impedance of standard television twin lead is _____ Ω.

   (a) 300

   (b) 150

   (c) 72

   (d) 50

16. The field rate of a television picture is_____ fields/sec.

   (a) 60

   (b) 30

   (c) 16

   (d) 32

17. A television station employs an _____ signal for the picture and an _____ signal for the sound.

   (a) FM, FM.   (c) AM, FM.

   (b) AM, AM.   (d) FM, AM.

18. A picture element is:

   (a) one frame of a television picture.

   (b) one scene in a television picture.

   (c) the largest area that can be reproduced in an image.

   (d) the smallest area that can be reproduced in an image.

19. The number of active picture elements in a television scene are:

   (a) increased by flyback time.

   (b) not affected by flyback time.

   (c) decreased by flyback time.

   (d) decreased as the number of scan lines increase.

Chapter 2

CAMERA TUBES
AND
PICTURE TUBES

2.1 Television Cameras

Three basic types of television cameras are used in programming operations. The most familiar of these is the live pickup studio camera, such as illustrated in Fig. 2-1. Another important type of television camera is used to televise motion-picture film and is called a film camera. Another type of camera is used to televise still pictures, such as test patterns and slides for special effects. This is termed a flying-spot camera. Although many types of camera pickup tubes have been developed in the past, two principal designs are in use at present. These are the image-orthicon and the vidicon camera pickup tubes.

Fig. 2-1 A black and white television camera. (Courtesy, Ampex Corp.)

2.2 Image-Orthicon Camera Tube

The appearance of an image-orthicon camera tube is seen in Fig. 2-2. Its internal structure is depicted in Fig. 2-3.

Fig. 2-2 An image orthicon tube.

Note that the image is processed in the forward part of the tube (image section). This is accomplished by an electron

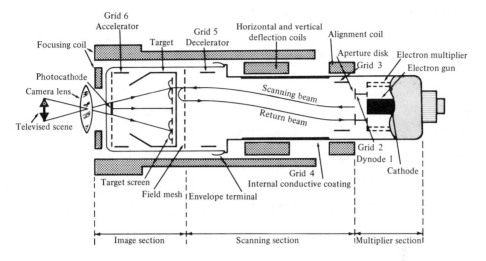

Fig. 2-3 Internal structure of an image orthicon tube.

scanning beam which is focused and deflected in the scanning section of the tube. The rear portion of the tube contains an electron gun and a five-stage electron multiplier for stepping up the level of the output video signal.

Observe that the image section of an image-orthicon tube consists basically of a photocathode, an accelerator assembly, and a target surface. The photocathode operates in the same manner as the cathode in a phototube. It is a semitransparent, conductive coating of cesium, or similar photoemissive substance, deposited on the inner surface of the glass faceplate. When light strikes the photocathode, electrons are emitted into the image section. These electrons are attracted to the positively charged target screen and are focused by the magnetic field of the focusing coil and by the electrostatic field between the accelerator and target screen. Thereby, the televised screen is focused as an electron image on the target screen.

This target screen is formed of a very fine metallic mesh with 1000 wires/in. The screen provides for 750,000 picture elements, of which 211,000 can be utilized by the television system. Some of the electrons emitted by the photocathode strike the screen and are conducted out of the tube. Others speed through the holes in the screen and strike the target, which consists of a sheet of conductive glass only 0.0002 in. thick. When an electron strikes the target surface, several secondary electrons are ejected and collected by the target screen. This process leaves a positive charge image on the surface of the target glass.

Observe that the electron scanning beam starts at the cathode on the electron gun. It is reduced to 0.0015 in. in diameter in passage through the aperture disk. Because the internal conductive coating of the tube is positively charged, the electron beam is attracted toward the target surface. Focusing action is provided by the magnetic field of the focusing coil, and the scanning pattern is produced by means of horizontal and vertical deflection coils. As the scanning beam approaches the target, it is slowed down by a decelerating ring so that the electrons have nearly zero velocity as they arrive at the target surface.

As noted previously, the target glass is sufficiently thin so that its positive charge distribution can be conducted from the forward surface to the rear surface. The positive charge image on the rear surface is neutralized by the electrons in the scanning beam. In the absence of a positive charge, all of the arriving electrons turn back in the form of a return beam, due to attraction of the internal conductive coating. A small positive charge collects some of the arriving electrons, and the remainder form a return beam. A large positive charge collects most of the arriving electrons, so that very few remain to form a return beam.

The end result is a return beam that varies in intensity in accordance with the charge image on the target during the scanning process.

This return beam strikes the aperture disk due to its positive potential. Each speeding return electron ejects several secondary electrons from the aperture disk. Secondary electrons are collected by the electron multiplier section, which consists of five dynode elements. The electron multiplier operates on the principle of secondary emission and steps up the strength of the return electron beam approximately 500 times. When a secondary electron from the aperture disk strikes the second dynode, it ejects additional secondary electrons. Each dynode has a progressively higher positive potential, and the secondary electrons are finally collected by the anode, which serves as the video-signal output electrode. An exploded view of an image-orthicon tube is shown in Fig. 2-4.

2.3 Vidicon Camera Tube

The appearance of a vidicon camera tube is illustrated in Fig. 2-5. Its internal structure is depicted in Fig. 2-6. One of its features is small size, which makes the tube suitable for use in outer-space vehicles where both size and weight must be minimized. The inner surface of the glass faceplate is coated with a transparent conducting film, which forms the video-signal electrode. A thin photosensitive layer is deposited on the film; it is basically a very large number of tiny resistive globules, which form the picture elements. Each globule can be compared with a small capacitor shunted by a resistor that decreases in value when struck by light rays. The forward surface of a globule is exposed to the electron scanning beam, and the rear surface of the

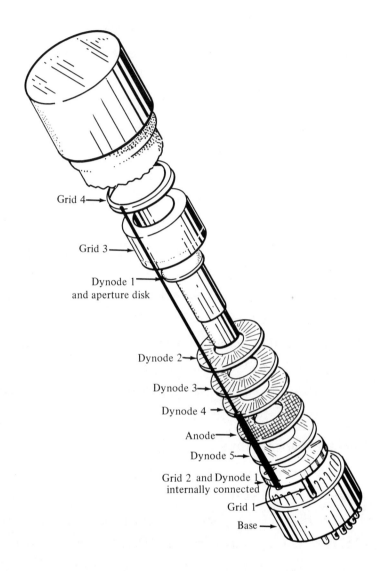

Grid 4

Grid 3

Dynode 1
and aperture disk

Dynode 2

Dynode 3

Dynode 4

Anode

Dynode 5

Grid 2 and Dynode 1
internally connected

Grid 1

Base

Fig. 2-4   Exploded view of an image orthicon tube.

Fig. 2-5   Appearance of a vidicon camera tube.

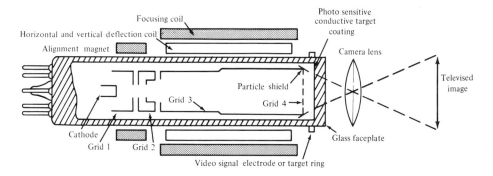

Fig. 2-6 Internal structure of a vidicon camera tube.

globule connects to the video-signal electrode.

When light strikes a globule in the photosensitive layer, its resistance decreases and the globule starts to charge up to a positive potential determined by the operating voltage applied to the video-signal electrode. Thus, a charge image is formed on the photosensitive layer. This entails storage action, because each illuminated globule will continue to charge until it is suddenly discharged by the electron scanning beam. This is a low-velocity scanning beam, and as the charged globules are suddenly discharged in turn, a capacitive current flow is produced which appears at the video-signal electrode as the camera signal voltage.

Note that the electron scanning beam starts at the cathode of the electron gun in the rear section of the tube. Its intensity is set by the bias on grid 1. Grid 2 is positively charged and accelerates the beam of electrons that emerge through the aperture of the first grid. Focusing is provided by the magnetic field action of the focusing coil and also by the electrostatic lens set up between the second and third grid. Finally, grid 4 is operated at a lower positive potential so that the electron beam is slowed down before it strikes the target coating. The beam is deflected by means of horizontal and vertical deflection coils.

2.4 Cathode-Ray Tubes

Cathode-ray tubes (CRT's) used in television receivers are commonly called picture tubes and are magnetically deflected. Our physics courses teach us that a beam of cathode rays is bent or deflected in passing through a magnetic field, as depicted in Fig. 2-7.   It is evident that if an electron beam

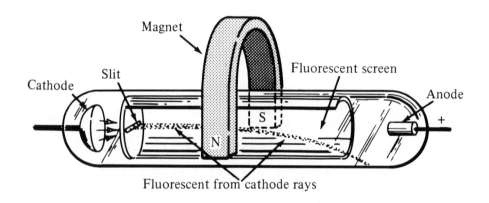

Fig. 2-7 A beam of cathode rays is deflected in passing through a magnetic field.

passes through a pair of horizontal and vertical magnetic fields, the screen of a CRT can be scanned by variation of the magnetic field strengths.   Figure 2-8 shows the principal features of a magnetically deflected picture tube.   It consists of a cathode for electron emission, a control grid for varying the intensity of the electron beam, and electrodes for accelerating and focusing the beam.   The electron beam finally strikes a fluorescent screen (not shown in the diagram).   A centering magnet is mounted on the neck of the CRT for "framing" the raster on the screen.   The deflecting yoke is also mounted on the tube neck.

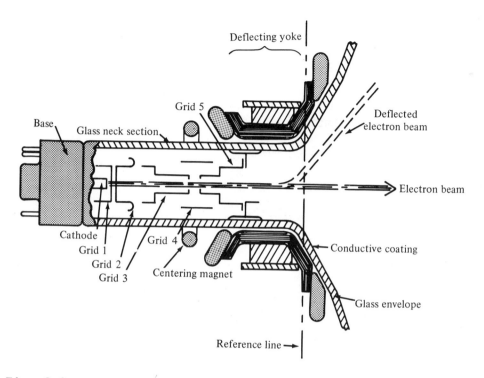

Fig. 2-8 Principle features of a magnetically deflected picture tube.

Note in Fig. 2-8 that the electron gun has its cathode surrounded by the first grid (control grid). A small aperture is provided in the center of the first grid, through which a narrow beam of electrons can pass. The number of electrons that pass through/sec is determined by the bias voltage on the first grid. Then the electron beam is speeded up by the attraction of accelerating anodes; these are grids 2 through 5. Thus, the second grid operates at a higher positive potential than the first grid; the fifth grid is at highest positive potential. The grids also are designed to provide electrostatic lens focusing action, as depicted in Fig. 2-9. In the example of Fig. 2-8, the adjustment of focus is optimized by variation of the potential on grid 4 to obtain the smallest spot size on the screen.

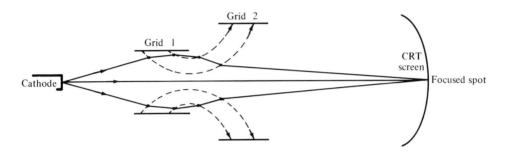

Fig. 2-9 Beam focusing action provided by the electron gun.

Note that the centering magnet in Fig. 2-8 is designed
so that its field strength can be adjusted; this centering
magnet can also be rotated on the neck of the tube.   Thereby,
the raster can be moved right and left and up and down as
required to frame the picture properly.   We will find that
the deflection yoke comprises a pair of horizontal deflection
coils and a pair of vertical deflection coils, as shown in
Fig. 2-10.   We know that the screen will be scanned in the
required manner if the fields of the deflection coils vary in
accordance with sawtooth waveforms.   Therefore, a 60-Hz sawtooth
current is passed through the vertical deflection coils, and a
15,750-Hz sawtooth current is passed through the horizontal
deflection coils.

As indicated in Fig. 2-8, the inner surface of the glass
envelope has a conductive coating; this is a deposit of col-
loidal graphite called aquadag, and it operates at a positive
potential on the order of 15 kV. This large accelerating
anode greatly increases the beam velocity, and it also serves
as part of the electrostatic lens system. The speeding electrons finally strike the fluorescent screen and cause it to
glow. Secondary electrons are ejected from the screen at the
point of beam impact, and these secondary electrons are

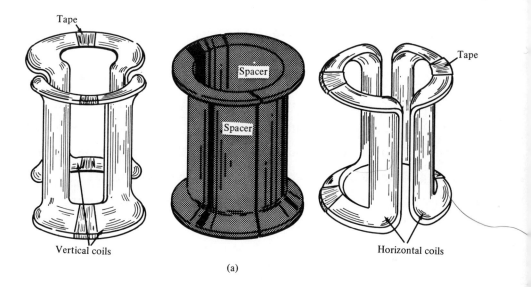

(a)

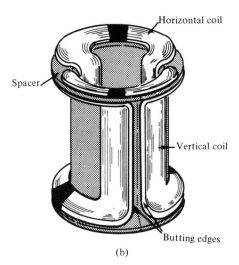

(b)

Fig. 2-10 Deflection yoke arrangement: (a) forms of the coil pairs, (b) placement of the coils on the yoke.

collected by the accelerating anode. Therefore, the high-voltage circuit is completed in the picture tube.

Modern picture tubes have aluminized screens. This means that an extremely thin film of aluminum is deposited on the rear surface of the fluorescent material. This very thin metal film serves two purposes; first, it acts as a mirror for light rays and causes a maximum amount of the fluorescent glow to radiate in the forward direction. It provides a brighter picture. Secondly, this aluminized layer rejects residual gas ions which would otherwise strike the fluorescent substance and damage it. This rejection is based on the difference in size between electrons and ions. That is, the pores of the aluminized film are sufficiently large to permit passage of electrons but are too small to permit passage of gas ions.

2.5 Image Display Requirements

Basic image display requirements are depicted in Fig. 2-11. Observe that low-voltage and high-voltage power supplies are provided for energizing the picture tube. Horizontal and vertical sweep sections apply current sawtooth waveforms to the deflection yoke. A video amplifier (as explained in detail subsequently) feeds a video (picture) signal to the first grid in the picture tube. Operating voltages for a typical large-screen picture tube are indicated in Fig. 2-12. Note that grid 1 is operated at a lower positive voltage than the cathode. In other words, the control grid is negative with respect to the cathode. All of the picture-tube supply voltages are dc, with the exception of the 6.3-V ac heater supply.

The picture-tube input section is supplemented by several image control devices and circuits which require occasional adjustment. Figure 2-13 shows the appearance of a centering magnet and adjustment lever. If the picture is not properly framed on the screen, rotate the magnet on the neck and adjust the lever as required. If the picture is

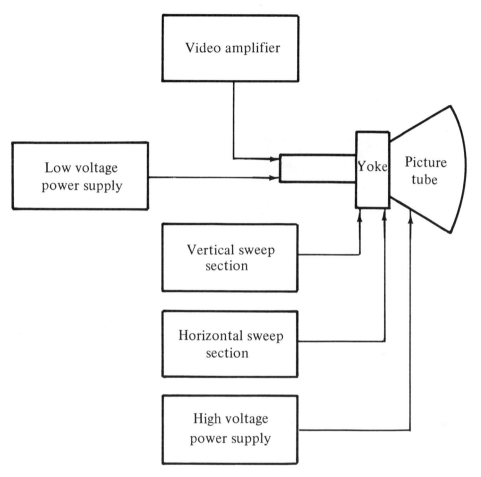

Fig. 2-11   Picture tube input section.

tilted on the screen, the deflection yoke is rotated on the
tube neck to bring the picture parallel with the top and
bottom edges of the screen.

Various types of horizontal width controls have been
used in television receivers. However, the most common
arrangement is a cylindrical brass collar, about 1 in.
long, which slides on the picture tube neck. This metal
collar can be slid under the deflection yoke to a point that
provides normal picture width. It is a "losser" device which
reduces the picture width by means of eddy currents. It

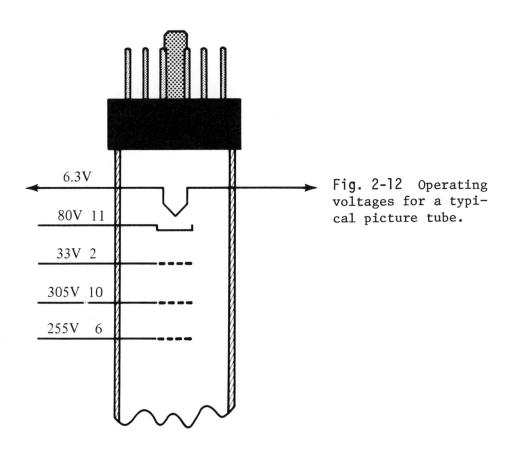

6.3V

80V 11

33V 2

305V 10

255V 6

Fig. 2-12 Operating voltages for a typical picture tube.

weakens the horizontal deflection field strength as it is slid under the yoke. Note that this type of horizontal width control has no practical effect on picture height because the vertical deflection frequency is 60 Hz, compared with a horizontal deflection frequency of 15,750 Hz. That is, eddy current losses increase rapidly with an increase in the operating frequency.

Vertical height of the picture is always adjusted by means of a potentiometer called the vertical height or vertical size control (see Fig. 2-14). It is turned as

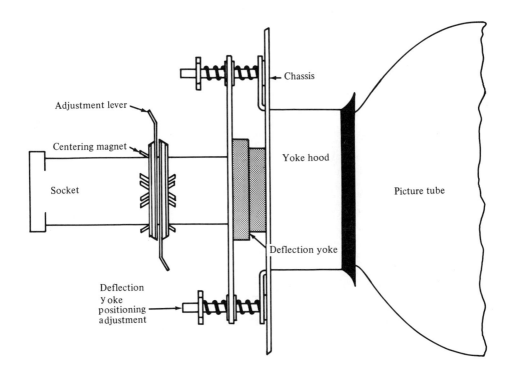

Fig. 2-13 Centering magnet and adjustment lever.

required to provide normal picture height. All receivers provide a vertical linearity control, and many provide a horizontal linearity control also. Examples of vertical nonlinearity are shown in Fig. 2-15. A line pattern can be displayed by driving the television receiver with the output from a modulated signal generator or from a linearity pattern generator. If the vertical linearity control is in correct adjustment, the horizontal lines will appear equally spaced from top to bottom on the screen. If the vertical linearity control is out of adjustment, the pattern will appear cramped at either the top or at the bottom of the screen.

Examples of horizontal nonlinearity are shown in Fig. 2-16. A vertical line pattern can be obtained by driving the television receiver with the output from a modulated

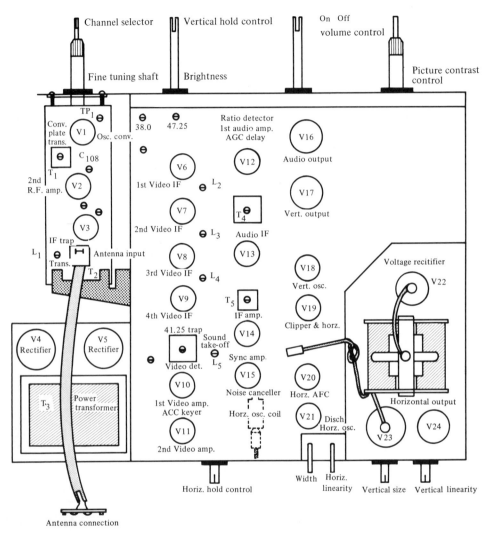

Fig. 2-14 A television receiver chassis layout, with control functions indicated.

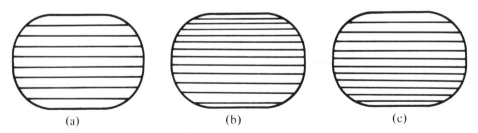

(a)　　　　　　　　　(b)　　　　　　　　　(c)

Fig. 2-15 Examples of vertical nonlinearity: (a) normal pattern, (b) raster cramped at the top, (c) raster cramped at the bottom.

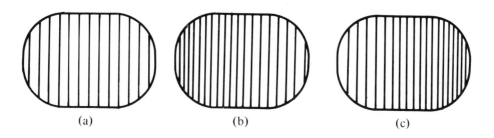

Fig. 2-16 Examples of vertical raster: (a) normal raster, (b) raster cramped at the left, (c) raster cramped at the right.

signal generator or from a linearity pattern generator. If a crosshatch or dot generator is used, both the vertical and the horizontal linearity can be checked simultaneously. Figure 2-17 shows normal crosshatch and dot patterns. These

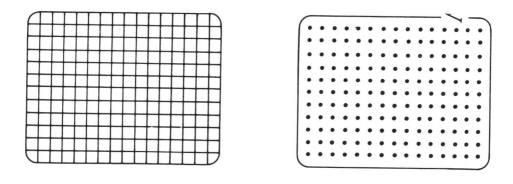

Fig. 2-17 Crosshatch and dot patterns.

patterns are also helpful when checking the adjustment of the focus control. As a practical consideration, in case scanning linearity cannot be brought into satisfactory adjustment by turning the service controls, assume that a component defect has occurred. In that case, troubleshooting procedures are required.

2.6 Receiver Operating Controls

Receiver operating controls are defined as controls that
are used by the viewer to tune in a television station signal
and to display the picture satisfactorily. With reference to
Fig. 2-14, the controls at the front of the chassis comprise
the operating controls, whereas the controls on the rear of
the chassis are called maintenance or service controls. Note
that the horizontal hold control is sometimes classed as a
service control, but it is also included with the operating
controls in other receivers. The function of the horizontal
hold control is to bring the horizontal sweep frequency within
range, so that the screen is scanned normally and the picture
does not break up into diagonal strips (out-of-sync condition).
Note also that if the horizontal hold control is out of range,
the slug in the horizontal oscillator coil will require
adjustment.

Again with reference to Fig. 2-14, the channel
selector control can be switched to any one of the 12 VHF
channels.   Exact tuning of the station signal is accomplished by adjustment of the fine-tuning control. Correct
setting of the fine-tuning control occurs just below the
point at which sound interference starts to appear in the
picture.   When adjusted in this way, the picture will
have maximum clarity of detail.   When switching from one
channel to another, it is sometimes desirable or necessary
to change the setting of the brightness and contrast controls.   If the brightness control is set too low, the screen
will have inadequate illumination. On the other hand, if
the brightness control is set too high, the excessive light
output will make the picture appear to be washed out.   The
contrast control is set for a normal display of the gray

range.

It is usually unnecessary to adjust the vertical hold control when switching channels. However, if the picture rolls up or down on the screen, the vertical hold control must be turned to stabilize the display. The function of the vertical hold control is to bring the vertical sweep frequency within range, so that the screen is scanned normally. It is seldom necessary to readjust the volume control, which operates in the same manner as a volume control of an FM radio receiver. All modern television receivers have a UHF tuning control, in addition to the VHF tuning control. Figure 2-18 depicts an example of a UHF

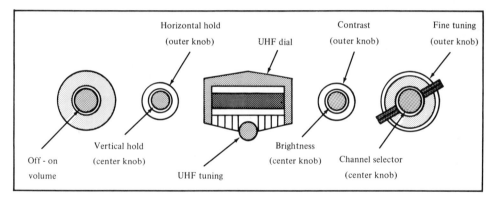

Fig. 2-18

tuning control and dial. To operate a receiver on the UHF range, the VHF channel selector is turned to its UHF position, and UHF station signals are then tuned in by rotating the UHF tuning control.

2.7 Symptoms of Control Misadjustment

One of the most common control misadjustment symptoms is a poorly defined or "smeary" image, or sound interference in the image. The first symptom is caused by rotation of the fine-tuning control too far in one direction, and the second symptom is caused by rotation of the fine-tuning control too far in the other direction. These symptoms should not be confused with somewhat similar image distortions that can be caused by incorrect orientation of the antenna. That is, if the fine-tuning control does not seem to operate normally, the antenna rotor setting should then be checked.

Another common control misadjustment symptom is an excessively bright raster, which tends to wash out the image. Note that the brightness control must be set higher for daytime viewing than for night viewing. That is, the ambient illumination is comparatively high in the daytime, and the brightness control may have to be set higher than normal. This situation is increased if the receiver has been installed facing a window toward the sun. It is preferable to install a receiver with the picture tube screen facing a wall across the room.

Inexperienced viewers may tend to confuse the brightness control with the contrast control. This confusion is often increased by a tendency of the controls to interact somewhat. The experienced viewer knows that a misadjustment of the brightness control cannot be corrected by adjustment of the contrast control, or vice versa. That is, he has learned the functions of these controls and notes whether the raster may be too bright or too dim, and whether the gray range in the image may be too light or too dark. In turn, he adjusts each control in accordance with its function.

Marginal misadjustments of the hold controls can be confusing to the beginner. For example, if the vertical hold control is set too far in one direction, the picture will tend to roll down at intervals, and then to move up again into frame. Or, if the vertical hold control is set too far in

the other direction, the picture will tend to break sync lock
at intervals, and to roll up one or more frames before it
locks in sync again. The correct setting for the vertical
hold control is midway between these two marginal extremes.
If a stable adjustment cannot be obtained, there is a component defect present in the receiver.

When the horizontal hold control is marginally adjusted
in either direction, the picture generally tends to "tear" at
intervals. That is, some portion of the image (usually along
the top) bends and wavers and may start to break up into
diagonal lines. When this occurs, the horizontal hold control
should be set midway between these two marginal extremes. In
some receivers, the horizontal hold control seems to act like
a horizontal centering control to some extent. However, the
centering function should not be confused with the hold
function. Any horizontal centering correction that may be
required should be made by means of the centering control.

Questions

Short Answer

1. What are the two principal types of camera pickup tubes,
   and what is the primary function of each?
2. What type of deflection does the CRT in a television
   receiver employ?
3. How is the brightness of the display on a picture tube
   usually controlled?
4. What is the purpose of the aquadag (graphite) coating on
   the inner surface of a CRT?

5. What are the two purposes of the aluminum screen in a picture tube?

6. Draw a diagram of a picture tube, and name each of its parts.

7. Why doesn't the brass collar, used for width control, affect the vertical picture size?

8. Explain the function of each of the following controls: (a) vertical size, (b) vertical linearity, (c) horizontal size, (d) horizontal linearity, (e) focus, and (f) brightness.

9. What is the difference between operating controls and service controls?

10. How is the correct linearity of a television receiver tested?

11. What is the function of the horizontal hold control?

12. What is the purpose of the contrast control?

13. What causes sound interference in the picture?

14. When is the vertical hold control correctly adjusted?

True-False

1. The two principal types of camera pickup tubes are the image-orthicon and the vidicon.

2. The aquadag coating is a metal shield that strengthens the picture tube.

3. The aluminized screen in a picture tube protects the fluorescent substance on the CRT screen.

4. The aluminized screen in a picture tube provides a brighter picture.

5. A brass collar is used on the neck of a CRT for control of both vertical and horizontal size.

6. When the vertical linearity is out of adjustment, the picture appears cramped at either the top or the bottom of the screen.

7. The controls at the rear of a television set are called operating controls.

8. The vertical linearity of a television receiver can be tested with a crosshatch generator.

9. Adjustment of the vertical hold control will usually correct a picture that is broken up into diagonal strips.

10. The contrast control is set for a normal display of the gray range.

11. Misadjustment of the fine-tuning can cause sound interference in the picture.

12. The brightness and the contrast controls usually interact slightly.

13. If the vertical hold control cannot be adjusted to correct the rolling of the picture, the problem is probably a defective component.

14. In some sets, the horizontal hold control seems to act like a horizontal centering control.

Multiple Choice

1. The _____ camera tube is made up of a photocathode, an accelerator assembly, and a target surface.
   (a) vidicon
   (b) flying-spot scanner
   (c) image-orthicon
   (d) cathode-ray

2. The number of electrons that strike the screen of the CRT are controlled for the most part by the:

   (a) distance that the screen is located from the cathode.

   (b) bias voltage on the first grid.

   (c) cathode voltage.

   (d) filament voltage.

3. The conductive coating inside a picture tube is called:

   (a) the filament.

   (b) aquadag.

   (c) the accelerating anode.

   (d) aluminum.

4. The _____ inside a picture tube blocks the residual gas ions that would damage the inner surface of the CRT.

   (a) aquadag coating

   (b) bias grid

   (c) ion bias grid

   (d) aluminized screen

5. Both the vertical and the horizontal linearity of a television receiver may be tested simultaneously with a/an:

   (a) line generator.

   (b) vertical linearity generator.

   (c) horizontal linearity generator.

   (d) crosshatch pattern.

6. If the picture is broken into diagonal strips (out-of-sync condition), a possible trouble could be a misadjusted:

   (a) focus control.   (c) vertical control.

   (b) horizontal control.   (d) width control.

7. If the picture is doing a slow roll, the most likely problem is a misadjusted _____ control.

   (a) focus   (c) vertical

   (b) horizontal   (d) width

8. A picture that rolls up or down on the screen can be corrected by adjusting the _____ control.
   (a) contrast
   (b) vertical hold
   (c) horizontal hold
   (d) fine-tuning

9. A smeary image or sound interference can be corrected by adjustment of the _____ control.
   (a) focus
   (b) fine-tuning
   (c) contrast
   (d) vertical hold

10. If the horizontal hold control changes the centering of the picture,
    (a) a component is bad.
    (b) the picture should be centered by the horizontal centering control.
    (c) the focus control must be readjusted.
    (d) the ion trap is misadjusted.

Section
TWO

TELEVISION RECEIVERS

Chapter 3

WAVE PROPAGATION
AND
RECEIVER INPUT SYSTEMS

3.1 Electromagnetic Waves and Propagation

Television wave energy differs from other forms of electromagnetic radiation in wavelength (frequency). For example, heat energy has a comparatively short wavelength, and light energy has still shorter wavelength. Table 3-1 shows the basic

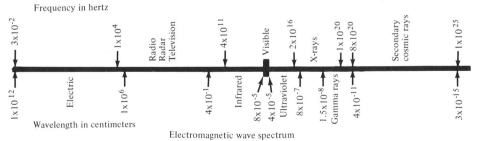

Table 3-1 Electromagnetic Wave Spectrum

relationships. All electromagnetic waves travel at the same

73

speed--about 300,000,000 m/sec. As its name indicates, an
electromagnetic wave has both an electrostatic field component
and a magnetic field component, as depicted in Fig. 3-1. Each

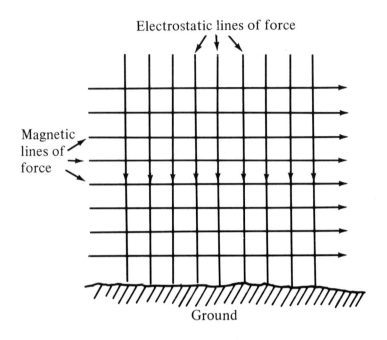

Fig. 3-1 Flux lines in an electromagnetic wave propagated
toward the reader.

of these component fields contains half of the wave energy,
and one field cannot exist without the other during wave propagation through space.

Polarization is defined as the direction of the electrostatic lines of force in an electromagnetic wave with respect
to the earth's surface. For example, the wave front depicted
in Fig. 3-1 is vertically polarized. Like light waves, television wave energy can be reflected from airplanes, mountains,
buildings, trees, or any solid, liquid, or gas that has a
dielectric constant different from air. Note in passing that
the dielectric constant of air is practically the same as that
of empty space. After television wave energy is reflected, as

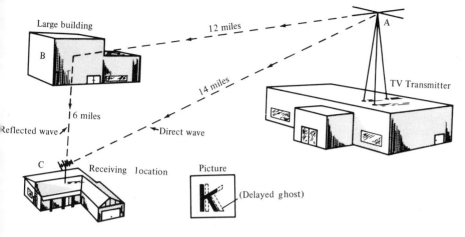

Fig. 3-2 An example of multipath reception.

from an airplane, its direction of travel is changed. When
electromagnetic waves arrive at a receiving antenna from both
the original wave and from one or more reflected waves, the
condition of multipath propagation occurs.

There is a time delay of the reflected signal with respect
to the direct signal in multipath reception, as shown in Fig.
3-2. Note that in this example the reflected wave travels a
total distance of 18 miles, or 4 miles more than the direct
wave. This means that the reflected wave arrives approximately
22 μsec after the direct wave. If the displayed image has a
width of 15 in., it is easy to show that the delayed signal, or
ghost image, is displayed more than 2 in. to the right of the
direct signal, or image. A ghost image is usually weaker than
the direct image; however, the reverse situation can occur if
the direct wave is partly blocked by objects in its path.

Television waves are considered to follow a line-of-sight
path in the first analysis. However, reception is also possible in various locations that cannot be "seen" from the
transmitting antenna. When an electromagnetic wave grazes the
edge of an intervening object, it becomes bent around the edge
to some extent. This process is called diffraction, and it
results in a change of direction of propagation for the portion

of wave energy that is diffracted.

3.2 Receiver Input Systems

The simplest receiver input system consists of a dipole antenna connected to a section of lead-in, which is connected in turn to the antenna input terminals of a television receiver. In a strong signal area, the dipole antenna might consist of a pair of "rabbit ears" placed on top of the receiver (see Fig. 3-3). In most locations, an outdoor ele-

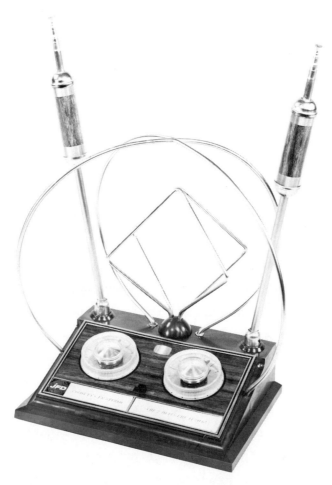

Fig. 3-3 A typical "rabbit ear" antenna unit. (Courtesy, JFD Electronics Corp.)

vated antenna must be used to obtain satisfactory reception. Although often overlooked in antenna installation procedures, a lightning arrester such as depicted in Fig. 3-4 should

Fig. 3-4 A lightning arrestor. (Courtesy, G. C. Electronics Inc.)

always be included. It makes connection to both conductors of a lead-in; a pair of close gaps is provided, across which a lightning surge easily jumps. In turn, the surge is conducted harmlessly to ground by means of a ground wire connected from the arrester to a cold water pipe or equivalent earth contact.

In many receiving locations, it is desirable to operate more than one receiver from the same antenna, as depicted in Fig. 3-5. One of the basic requirements is to provide receiver isolation, so that one receiver cannot interfere with another. That is, the local oscillator in a television or radio receiver generates a high-frequency voltage that tends to "back up" into the antenna input terminals. In turn,

Fig. 3-5 Operation of four receivers from a single antenna. (Courtesy, JFD Electronics Corp.)

other television receivers that are directly connected to the same lead-in are likely to display wavering patterns of interference on their screens. Mutual interference of this type is most troublesome when the incoming signal from the antenna is comparatively weak.

Although mutual interference can be reduced by coupling television receivers through resistive pads to a lead-in, this method is not always satisfactory. A resistive pad necessarily has an insertion loss and reduces the available signal strength accordingly. Picture contrast on some channels may become inadequate, and weak channels may be eliminated entirely. Therefore, it is desirable to employ either a low-loss type of coupler or a booster type of coupler that steps up the incoming antenna signal. Various high-frequency transformer networks are used to minimize coupler losses. The booster coupler shown in Fig. 3-5 utilizes high-frequency transistors, not only to provide unilateral (one-way) signal flow, but also to step up the signal level.

Signal-to-noise ratios are of primary concern in fringe area reception. A low signal-to-noise ratio results in a displayed image with excessive snow. The signal-to-noise ratio can be improved by use of a high-gain antenna with sharp directional characteristics. Note that the signal-to-noise ratio is always better at the antenna terminals. In other words, a lead-in picks up more or less noise voltage, and a long lead-in can deteriorate the signal-to-noise ratio considerably. The best approach to this problem is to install a booster amplifier on the antenna mast (see Fig. 3-6). Thereby,

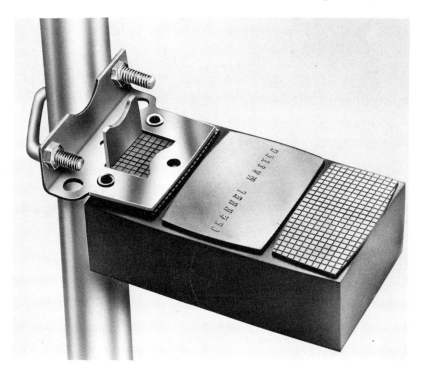

Fig. 3-6 A mast-mounted television booster. (Courtesy, Channel Master)

the signal voltage at the antenna terminals is stepped up so
that it effectively overrides the noise voltages contributed by
the lead-in.

All modern television receivers are provided with a pair
of VHF input terminals and a pair of UHF input terminals.
When separate antennas are used, the VHF lead-in is connected
to the VHF input terminals, and the UHF lead-in is connected
to the UHF input terminals. If a combination VHF-UHF antenna
is utilized, a band separator, such as illustrated in Fig.
3-7, is generally installed on the back of the receiver. A

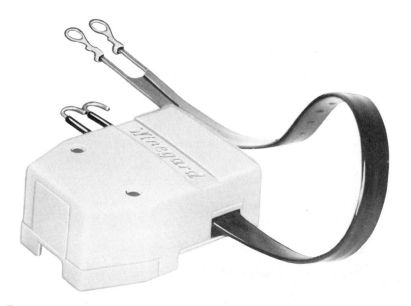

Fig. 3-7 A VHF-UHF band seperator. (Courtesy, Wingard
Antenna Systems)

band separator is basically a VHF-UHF bandpass network with
one pair of input terminals and two pairs of output terminals.
It accepts the combined VHF and UHF signals from the antenna
lead-in and feeds VHF signals to the VHF input terminals of
the receiver and feeds UHF signals to the UHF input terminals
of the receiver. The chief advantage of a band separator is
its maintenance of an impedance match throughout the antenna

input system.   Not only is maximum power transfer thereby
realized, but possible difficulties from lead-in reflections
are eliminated.   Reflected waves are most troublesome on long
runs of lead-in and are essentially close-in ghosts which tend
to reduce picture definition.

3.3 MATV and CATV

A master antenna television system (MATV) serves a number
of television receivers, such as in an apartment building,
motel, or hotel.   One or more antennas may be used, with sufficient booster amplification to provide satisfactory reception
by all the receivers connected into the distribution system.
Figure 3-8 depicts a typical MATV system for use by an apart-

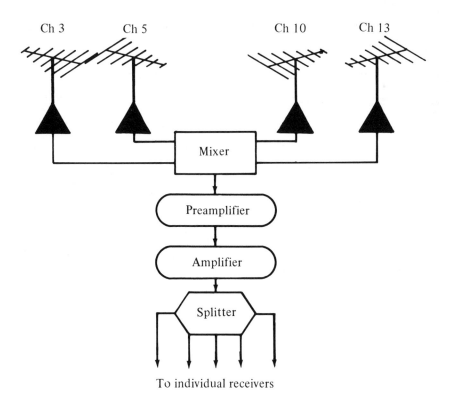

Fig. 3-8   An MATV system for an appartment building.

ment building with up to 100 television receivers. In this example, the active channels are 3, 5, 10, and 13. A separate high-gain and properly oriented antenna is used on each channel. The antenna output signals are mixed or combined in a resistive or equivalent network and then stepped up through a wide-band amplifier. In turn, the output signals from the amplifier are divided or split into separate cables for each television receiver.

Considerable signal amplification is required when an MATV system includes a large number of receivers. That is, each cable that is energized by the amplifier consumes a certain portion of the available output. Unless adequate amplification is provided, the reproduced pictures will be weak and lack normal contrast. Various system details are employed, depending upon local conditions. For example, a single all-channel antenna may be adequate where the field strength is high and all the active channels are received from the same general direction. Again, one of the active channels might be weak; in this case, a separate high-gain single-channel antenna would be installed to supplement the all-channel antenna. Or, if multipath reception and ghosts are a problem, the required number of highly directive antennas would be installed.

A community antenna television system (CATV) is used to provide good reception to an entire community situated in a fringe or far-fringe area. For example, a CATV system often serves an entire town in an isolated area. The antenna site is carefully chosen and is typically on top of a hill or mountain near the town. In most installations, separate high-gain and properly oriented antennas for each active channel are mounted on the antenna tower. Figure 3-9 shows the plan of a typical CATV system.

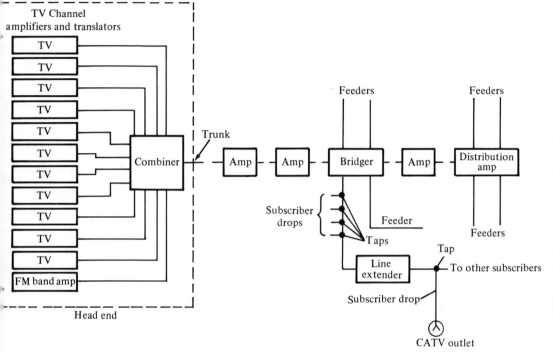

Fig. 3-9 Plan of a typical CATV system.

The head end in a CATV system includes booster amplifiers for the various antennas and a combiner or mixer for the output signals from the amplifiers. In case UHF reception is provided in addition to VHF reception, a translator is utilized for each UHF channel. A translator is a frequency converter that changes a UHF signal frequency into a VHF signal frequency. This process is required because a CATV system employs long runs of coaxial cable, and cable losses increase rapidly with an increase in frequency. Therefore, if an 800-MHz signal is "beat down" to 100 MHz, for example, it can be routed through coaxial cable with comparatively little attenuation.

As shown in Fig. 3-9, the FM radio band of frequencies is also commonly processed by a CATV system. From the combiner network, the various signal voltages are fed into a trunk

cable, or possibly several trunk cables. A trunk cable serves
to conduct the signal voltages from their point of origin,
such as atop a mountain, to the site of utilization, such as a
residential area several miles away. Because the signals are
progressively attenuated through a trunk line, amplifiers must
be inserted at intervals. A typical coaxial cable imposes an
attenuation of 1 dB/100 ft of cable at an operating frequency
of 150 MHz. Thus, an amplification of about 50 dB/mile is
required. Table 3-2 lists voltage and power ratios corresponding to various dB values.

Trunk lines are routed from the head end to the beginning of the distribution system on poles in most installations.
However, there is a trend toward running the cables under-
ground in ducts or simply in trenches.   When a line amplifier
is to be inserted, a buried cable is brought above ground and
routed through a pedestal that houses the amplifier.   It is
standard practice to use 75-Ω cables, and to maintain 75-Ω
input and output impedances throughout a CATV system.   The
distribution system starts with a bridger or bridging amplifier.   A simple bridger consists of a passive network comprising a VHF transformer, capacitors, and resistors.   It
divides the input signal into several portions for supplying
feeder lines.   A 75-Ω impedance is maintained at all terminals
of a bridger. Because a passive device introduces substantial
signal attenuation, a bridging amplifier is often employed
instead, so that no insertion loss occurs.

When the distribution system is extensive, feeder amplifiers (also called line extenders) may be installed at intervals to maintain an adequate signal level. These are wide-band
VHF amplifiers, similar to trunk amplifiers, which provide up
to 25-dB gain over the frequency range from 50 to 220 MHz. All
amplifiers or signal splitters in a CATV system are usually

Power Ratio	Voltage Ratio	dB − ←	dB + →	Voltage Ratio	Power Ratio
1.000	1.0000	0		1.000	1.000
.9772	.9886	.1		1.012	1.023
.9550	.9772	.2		1.023	1.047
.9333	.9661	.3		1.035	1.072
.9120	.9550	.4		1.047	1.096
.8913	.9441	.5		1.059	1.122
.8710	.9333	.6		1.072	1.148
.8511	.9226	.7		1.084	1.175
.8318	.9120	.8		1.096	1.202
.8128	.9016	.9		1.109	1.230
.7943	.8913	1.0		1.122	1.259
.6310	.7943	2.0		1.259	1.585
.5012	.7079	3.0		1.413	1.995
.3981	.6310	4.0		1.585	2.512
.3162	.5623	5.0		1.778	3.162
.2512	.5012	6.0		1.995	3.981
.1995	.4467	7.0		2.239	5.012
.1585	.3981	8.0		2.512	6.310
.1259	.3548	9.0		2.818	7.943
.10000	.3162	10.0		3.162	10.000
.07943	.2818	11.0		3.548	12.59
.06310	.2512	12.0		3.981	15.85
.05012	.2293	13.0		4.467	19.95
.03981	.1995	14.0		5.012	25.12
.03162	.1778	15.0		5.623	31.62
.02512	.1585	16.0		6.310	39.81
.01995	.1413	17.0		7.079	50.12
.01585	.1259	18.0		7.943	63.10
.01259	.1122	19.0		8.913	79.43
.01000	.1000	20.0		10.000	100.00
10^{-3}	3.162×10^{-2}	30.0		3.162×10	10^3
10^{-4}	10^{-2}	40.0		10^2	10^4
10^{-5}	3.162×10^{-3}	50.0		3.162×10^2	10^5
10^{-6}	10^{-3}	60.0		10^3	10^6
10^{-7}	3.162×10^{-4}	70.0		3.162×10^3	10^7
10^{-8}	10^{-4}	80.0		10^4	10^8
10^{-9}	3.162×10^{-5}	90.0		3.162×10^4	10^9
10^{-10}	10^{-5}	100.0		10^5	10^{10}

Table 3-2 Table of dB Expressed as Power and Voltage (or Current) Ratios

provided with a tilt control, or equalizer. This is a band-pass type of filter device that can be adjusted to attenuate the low end or the high end of the VHF band, as required. In most situations, the high end of the band will have become attenuated, so that the tilt control is adjusted to introduce a compensating attenuation at the low end of the band.

Feeder cables are also called distribution cables. The cable run inside a building is also called a distribution cable. In the strict sense of the term, distribution cables are tapped off from a feeder cable. A tap point is called a subscriber tap. A bridging amplifier always has at least one trunk output, in addition to the feeder outputs. Thus, a trunk line continues through a bridger. The last amplifier at the end of a trunk line is called a distribution amplifier. It is basically the same as a bridging amplifier, except that the trunk line terminates at the distribution amplifier. A feeder line can be run at distances up to 1000 ft from the bridger. Beyond 1000 ft a line extender is required to maintain an adequate signal level.

A subscriber drop is a cable that is tapped at some point along a feeder line. Coupling is provided by the tap in a manner that does not introduce objectionable disturbance into the feeder cable. The simplest form of tap coupler is an isolating resistor connected between the tap point and the cable to the television receiver. Another form of tap coupler is a small capacitor. Capacitive coupling is sometimes preferred because it introduces a tilt which tends to compensate for the frequency slope of the subscriber drop cable. The signal level applied to a television receiver from a CATV system is commonly 1500 μV.

3.4 Interference Filters

Under usual conditions, interference is not a problem in television reception. However, some locations have an unusually high interference level that produces annoying disturbances in the displayed image. For example, a television receiver located near a powerful FM broadcast station may be subject to interference in the picture, particularly on certain VHF channels. In such a case, it is ordinarily expedient to employ an FM interference filter at the antenna input terminals of the television receiver. This type of filter is simply a pair of series resonant circuits, as depicted in Fig. 3-10.

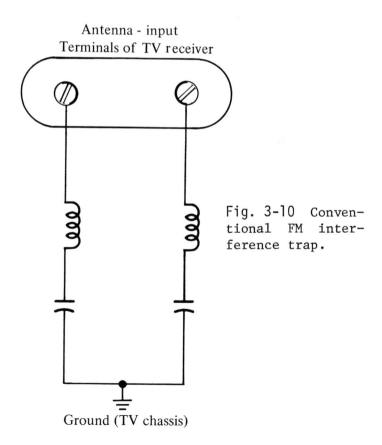

Antenna - input
Terminals of TV receiver

Fig. 3-10 Conventional FM interference trap.

Ground (TV chassis)

Variable inductors are usually employed, so that the resonant circuits can be tuned to any required frequency in the 88-to 108-MHz range. Because a series LC circuit is practically a short circuit at its resonant frequency, it provides great attenuation of an FM signal to which it is tuned.

Another common type of interference filter is the high-pass type, with a cutoff frequency of 50 MHz, as shown in Fig. 3-11. When suitable values of inductance and capacitance are

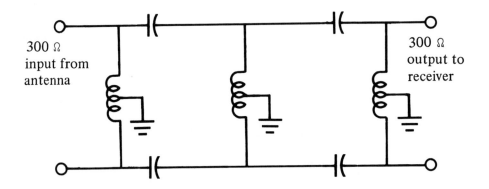

Fig. 3-11 A high-pass filter configuration.

utilized, the high-pass filter will permit VHF television signals to flow through with very little attenuation. On the other hand, all frequencies below Channel 2 are substantially attenuated. The basic difference between a trap (as exemplified in Fig. 3-10) and a filter is that a trap is sharply tuned to a certain frequency, whereas a filter rejects all frequencies on one side of its cutoff point and passes all frequencies on the other side of its cutoff point.

Note that there are some types of interference that cannot be trapped or filtered out. Cochannel interference is a basic example; in fringe areas, it sometimes happens that two television stations operating on the same channel are received with approximately the same strength. In such a case, severe cochannel interference, which is sometimes called "venetian blind" interference occurs. As one station signal cannot be filtered out without affecting the other station signal, other means must be sought to minimize or eliminate this cochannel interference. The most effective approach in most cases is to install a sharply beamed antenna with a rotor, in order to maximize one of the signals with respect to the other.

3.5 Television Signal Strength Measurement

Television signal magnitudes are measured in µV. When extensive systems are being installed and checked out, or when troubleshooting becomes necessary, a field-strength meter such as illustrated in Fig. 3-12 is commonly utilized.

Fig. 3-12 A professional type of field-strength meter. (Courtesy, Jerrold Electronics)

Basically, this instrument is a highly sensitive, tuned transistor voltmeter. It can be tuned to any television channel, and the strength of the applied signal is indicated by a meter calibrated in µV. Field-strength meters are customarily provided with an audio channel and speaker, so that the operator can verify the station to which the instrument is tuned. If substantial interference is present, it will often disturb the sound output so that the operator is made aware of the difficulty. Field-strength meters are always battery operated, so that they can be transported and used where power outlets are unavailable.

Questions

Short Answer

1. How does television wave energy differ from other forms of electromagnetic radiation?
2. What are the two component fields of electromagnetic radiation?
3. Define the term "polarization" as it is used with electromagnetic radiation.
4. How does a reflected wave cause a ghost on the television screen?
5. How does diffraction sometimes aid television reception?
6. Why should a lightning arrester always be included in an antenna installation?
7. Why is isolation usually necessary when more than one television is operated from the same antenna?
8. What is the disadvantage of using a resistive pad for isolation of two television receivers?
9. In fringe areas of television reception, what is the primary consideration for a good picture?
10. How does the type of antenna improve the signal-to-noise ratio?

11. How can we reduce the problem of noise picked up by the antenna lead?

12. What is the purpose of a band separator?

13. Draw a block diagram of a MATV system.

14. Draw a block diagram of a CATV system.

15. What is a translator?

16. What is the purpose of a trunk cable in reference to a CATV system?

17. What is the maximum length of the feeder line, without the use of an extender line?

18. What is the approximate signal level that is usually applied to a television in a CATV system?

19. What is the purpose of a high-pass type of filter when it is connected to a television receiver?

20. What is the most effective approach to the elimination of cochannel interference?

21. How and in what units would you measure television signal magnitudes?

True-False

1. Television wave energy differs from other forms of electromagnetic radiation in wavelength.

2. Polarization has to do with the type of modulation used in a transmitted signal.

3. Multiple-path propagation occurs when electromagnetic waves arrive at a receiving antenna from both a direct and a reflected wave.

4. A ghost image is usually stronger than the direct image.

5. Diffraction occurs when a television signal is bent as it grazes an object in its transmission path.

6. A pair of rabbit ears is a tool used by the technician

to determine the direction of a television transmission station.

7. All television antenna installations should include a lightning arrester.

8. When two receivers are connected to the same antenna, the local oscillator of one may interfere with the picture on the other.

9. A long transmission line will not harm the signal-to-noise ratio.

10. The best approach to overcome a low signal-to-noise ratio is by a booster amplifier at the antenna.

11. A band separator is usually connected at the antenna.

12. The purpose of the band separator is to maintain an impedance match over the bank.

13. A MATV system can be used to supply signals to a number of television receivers.

14. A CATV community system is good only in a strong signal area.

15. A translator is usually used to change a VHF signal frequency into a UHF signal frequency.

16. The last amplifier at the end of a trunk line is called a distribution amplifier.

17. Beyond 1000 ft a line extender is required to maintain an adequate signal level.

18. The signal level applied to a receiver from a CATV system is usually 100 μV.

19. A tap coupler is simply an isolating resistor.

20. Series resonant circuits are often used to eliminate interference from an FM broadcasting station.

Multiple Choice

1. Television wave energy differs from other forms of elec-
    tromagnetic radiation:
    (a) in wavelength.
    (b) in rate of travel.
    (c) in polarization.
    (d) in field alignment.
2. The direction of electrostatic lines of force in an
    electromagnetic wave with respect to the earth's surface
    is called:
    (a) ionization.
    (b) radiation.
    (c) polarization.
    (d) dielectric alignment.
3. The condition of multipath propagation occurs when
    electromagnetic waves:
    (a) are transmitted at low frequencies.
    (b) are transmitted at high frequencies.
    (c) arrive at a receiving antenna from both the original
         wave and one or more reflected waves.
    (d) are transmitted with phase modulation.
4. The effect of two images on a picture tube is called:
    (a) propagation delay.
    (b) a double signal.
    (c) snow.
    (d) a ghost.
5. In a strong signal area, the antenna used may be called a:
    (a) pair of dog ears.
    (b) pair of rabbit ears.
    (c) loop.
    (d) corkscrew.

6. The one important component that is often left off of an antenna installation is:

    (a)   the antenna.

    (b)   the transmission line.

    (c)   a wave trap.

    (d)   a lightning arrester.

7. The basic requirement for more than one receiver to operate from one antenna is:

    (a)   isolation.

    (b)   distortion.

    (c)   a double transmission line.

    (d)   proper polarization.

8. The primary concern in fringe area reception is the:

    (a)   type of antenna.

    (b)   type of transmission line.

    (c)   signal-to-noise ratio.

    (d)   propagation ratio.

9. When a combination UHF-VHF antenna is used, we need to employ:

    (a)   two transmission lines.

    (b)   a booster amplifier.

    (c)   no special connections.

    (d)   a band separator.

10. The purpose of a band separator on a receiver is to:

    (a)   amplify the signal at the antenna.

    (b)   maintain an impedance over the band.

    (c)   prevent a ghost image.

    (d)   make tuning easier.

11. A number of television receivers can be served by a _____ system.

    (a)   MATV   (c)   complex connected

    (b)   CATV   (d)   band separator

12. An entire community may be served by a _____ system.
    (a) CATV
    (b) MATV
    (c) CBS
    (d) RNTV

13. A unit that changes a UHF signal frequency into a VHF signal frequency is a:
    (a) translator.
    (b) recorder.
    (c) booster.
    (d) modulator.

14. Feeder cables are also called:
    (a) lead lines.
    (b) bridgers.
    (c) distribution cables.
    (d) line extenders.

15. A cable that is tapped at some point along the feeder line is called a:
    (a) bridging gap.
    (b) subscriber drop.
    (c) line extender.
    (d) tap coupler.

16. A feeder line can be run to distances of up to _____ ft from a bridger.
    (a) 100   (c) 10,000
    (b) 1000   (d) 100,000

17. The signal level applied to a television receiver from a CATV system is commonly:
    (a) 15 μV.   (c) 1500 μV.
    (b) 150 μV.   (d) 15,000 μV.

18. An FM interference filter should be connected at the:

(a) television receiver antenna.

(b) television transmitter antenna.

(c) television receiver terminals.

(d) receiver tuner.

19. A high-pass filter is used to:

(a) reject low frequencies.

(b) reject high frequencies.

(c) reject any interference.

(d) pass all frequencies.

20. The instrument used to measure the television signal magnitude in μV is called a/an:

(a) voltmeter.

(b) microvolt meter.

(c) ammeter.

(d) field-strength meter.

Chapter 4

RF TUNERS

4.1 RF Tuner Function

An RF tuner processes the incoming signal from the antenna, as depicted in Fig. 4-1. Note that the RF section is also called the front end or head end of the television receiver. The function of the RF section is to provide selectivity, thereby rejecting interference; the television signal to which the input circuits are tuned is then heterodyned to a lower frequency. Three subsections are included in an RF tuner, as shown in Fig. 4-2. Both the RF amplifier and mixer sections provide gain; however, the major portion of the total gain is contributed by the following intermediate frequency section. Note that the local oscillator merely provides a source of high-frequency voltage to beat against the incoming television signal in the mixer section.

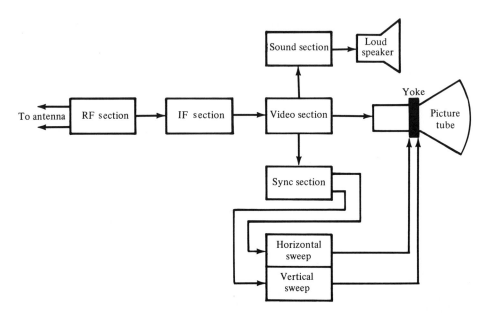

Fig. 4-1 The RF section processes the incoming signal from the antenna.

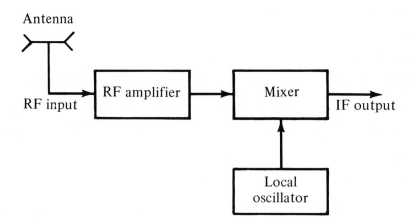

Fig. 4-2 An RF tuner comprises three subsections.

Several solid-state types of RF tuners are in wide use, and all provide the same signal-processing function. Figure

4-3 illustrates a typical solid-state RF tuner. The RF

Fig. 4-3 Appearance of a solid state RF tuner, with UHF tuning unit.

amplifier is aligned for a frequency response as shown in Fig. 4-4. Selectivity considerations are as follows:

1. Each television channel is 6 MHz in width. It is desirable that the RF amplifier have minimum response to adjacent channel signals.

2. A television transmission comprises a picture carrier and a sound carrier which are 4.5 MHz apart. An RF tuner should provide full amplification at both carrier frequencies.

3. All frequencies in the interval from the picture carrier to the sound carrier should have essentially full amplification.

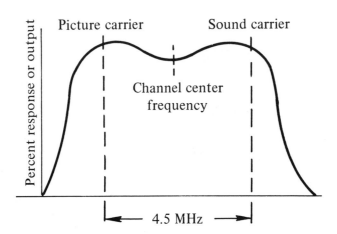

Fig. 4-4 Frequency response curve of an RF tuner.

Full amplification means a gain of 20 dB or more in the RF section and a gain of about 16 dB in the mixer section, as indicated in Fig. 4-5. The total gain of an RF tuner is

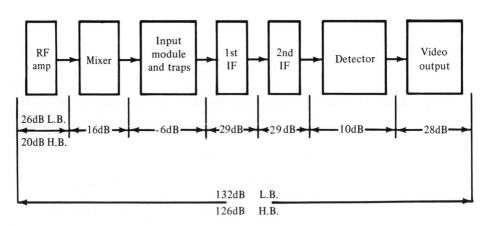

Fig. 4-5 Typical gain figures for the picture section of a television receiver.

thus in the order of 40 dB. Due to design limitations, RF tuners usually provide about 6 dB more gain on the low VHF channels than on the high VHF channels. Note that most of

the RF passband accommodates the picture signal, as depicted
in Fig. 4-6. That is, the picture signal sidebands extend

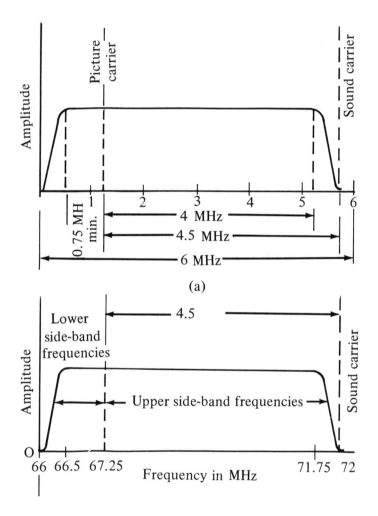

(a)

Fig. 4-6 Television channel frequency relations: (a) frequency intervals, (b) allocations for channel 4.

to the left and right of the picture carrier; the picture
signal has a bandwidth of approximately 4 MHz. On the other
hand, the sound signal occupies only a small "slice" in the
RF passband; the sound signal has a bandwidth of approximately
50 kHz.

With reference to Fig. 4-6, observe that the picture
signal contains comparatively few lower sideband frequencies,
and all of the higher picture frequencies are contained in
the upper sideband. That is, a television transmitter employs
vestigial sideband transmission, wherein most of the lower
sidebands are suppressed. This mode of transmission is specified by the FCC to conserve channel space. Vestigial sideband
transmission involves a trade-off, in that a small amount of
picture distortion is entailed. However, the quality of the
reproduced picture is quite acceptable. Note that if vestigial
sideband transmission were not used, each television channel
would be 12 MHz in width.

As noted previously, all modern RF tuners have provi-
sions for coverage of the UHF band. Because it is comparatively costly to manufacture a UHF section that has substantial
gain, it is customary to operate the UHF section simply as a
frequency converter, and to obtain the required gain through
the VHF section at intermediate frequency, as depicted in Fig.
4-7. This signal processing is accomplished as follows:

1. The UHF mixer section contains tuned circuits that
    provide the necessary selectivity.

2. A substantial insertion loss occurs in signal pro-
    cessing through the UHF mixer.

3. Incoming UHF signals are "beat down" in the mixer
    to the intermediate frequency range of the television
    receiver (approximately 44 MHz).

4. Tuned circuits in the VHF tuner are switched to
    operate in the 44-MHz range; thus the RF section
    and the mixer section provide two additional IF
    stages during UHF reception (see Fig. 4-8).

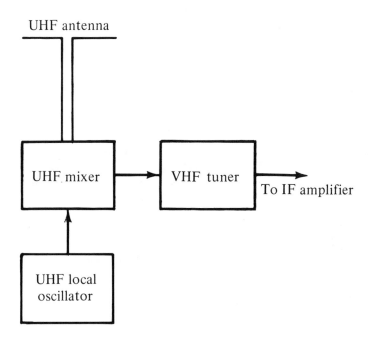

UHF antenna

UHF mixer

VHF tuner

To IF amplifier

UHF local oscillator

Fig. 4-7 After conversion to a lower frequency band, the output from the UHF mixer is amplified through the VHF tuner.

4.2 Basic RF Tuner Designs

More turret tuners are in use than any other type. A turret tuner employs a completely separate set of coils for each channel. When the tuner is set to various channels, three sets of coils are changed; these are the RF, mixer, and oscillator coils. Another type of tuner in fairly extensive use is called the switch tuner. This design utilizes tapped coils, or coils that are progressively connected in series with one another. When the tuner is switched to various channels, the inductances of the RF, mixer, and oscillator coils are increased or decreased as required. Still another type of tuner has certain features of both the turret and the switch types and is called a

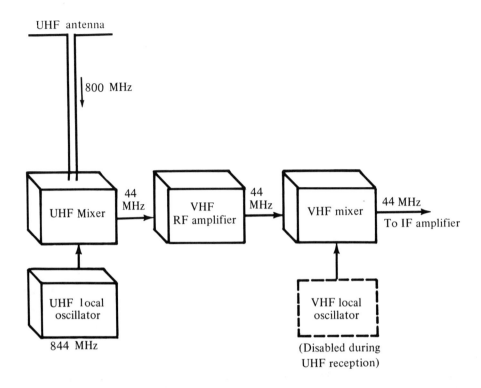

Fig. 4-8   The VHF sections operate in the 44 MHz band during
UHF reception and the VHF oscillator is disabled.

wafer tuner.   Although it is designed with coils mounted on
wafer switch forms, it has a separate set of coils for each
channel.

Figure 4-9 shows the configuration of a turret-type
tuner. This design provides either a 300-Ω input (for twin
lead) or 75-Ω input (for coaxial cable). The 300-Ω input
circuit consists of a balun, or VHF transformer arrangement,
that changes a 300-Ω balanced (push-pull) input into an
unbalanced (single-ended) 75-Ω output. This balun consists
of two pairs of coupled coils, $L_1 L_2$ and $L_3 L_4$. When a 75-Ω
input is employed, the balun is omitted.

Note in Fig. 4-9 that the antenna signal input passes
through a trap configuration before it is applied to the RF

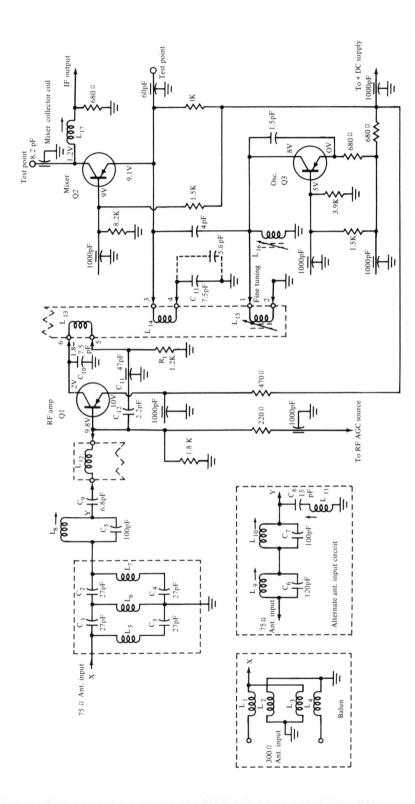

Fig. 4-9 Configuration of a turrent-type tuner.

amplifier.   These trap circuits   minimize two common forms
of television interference--FM broadcast signals and IF range
interference. L_5 and C_3 operate as a series trap; L_7 and
C_4 also operate as a series trap. L_6, C_1, and C_2 operate as
a T-type high-pass filter.   Interference signals in the
88- to 108-MHz range are greatly attenuated. L_8 and C_5
function as a parallel trap for interference in the 41- to
47-MHz range (intermediate frequency range).   That is, the IF
amplifier following the RF tuner operates in this range, and
the parallel trap prevents feedthrough interference into the
IF amplifier. L_8 has an adjustable slug, so that it can be
resonated to a desired frequency in the IF band.

When IF range interference is more troublesome than FM
interference, an alternate trap configuration can be utilized,
as depicted in Fig. 4-9.   This arrangement comprises two IF
traps and one FM trap.   The IF traps are parallel resonant
circuits, and the FM trap is a series resonant circuit.   All
three inductors are adjustable, in order to provide maximum
rejection at chosen frequencies.   If the alternate trap section is employed, L_8 is disconnected from C_9, and the output
lead from L_{10} is connected to C_9.   Transistor Q1 operates as
a common emitter RF amplifier.   Its input circuit is tuned
to a selected channel by C_9 and L_{12}.   This is a series-tuned
circuit.   Note that L_{12} is mounted on a turret with 11 additional coils to accommodate the VHF band.

The output circuit of the RF amplifier in Fig. 4-9
comprises a tank consisting basically of L_{13} and C_{10}.   Tuned
amplifiers often require neutralization to avoid positive
feedback and resulting oscillation.   The neutralization
network includes R_1, C_{11}, and C_{12}.   Note that the collector
output signal drops across R_1 and is capacitively coupled
back to the base of Q1.   Phase relations in this neutraliza-

tion network are such that the positive feedback voltage
through Q1 from collector to base is cancelled by the negative
feedback voltage through the neutralization network. Thereby,
operation of the RF amplifier is stabilized.

Forward automatic gain control (AGC) is used to control
the gain of Q1 in Fig. 4-9. That is, reduced gain is obtained
by increasing the forward-biased current and shifting the
operating point of the transistor toward the saturation region.
Unless AGC were provided for the RF stage, the transistor
would overload on strong input signals. Overload results in
nonlinear amplification, and cross-modulation with residual
interference signals that might be present. To minimize this
possibility of picture distortion, the AGC system is designed
to optimize the operating point of Q1 at any level of incoming
signal.

Note that L_{13} is coupled to L_{14} in Fig. 4-9. Thus, the
amplified signal in the collector circuit of Q1 is coupled
to the mixer section. The mixer transistor Q2 operates in a
common base configuration. However, its operating point is
different from that of Q1. Only 0.1-V bias is provided
between base and emitter, with the result that Q2 operates in
a highly nonlinear region. It is for this reason that the
mixer stage is sometimes called the first detector. This is
a superheterodyne process in which the incoming signal is
"beat" against a higher-frequency voltage from the local
oscillator Q3. Because Q2 operates in a nonlinear mode, its
collector output contains the difference frequency, also
termed the intermediate frequency.

Note that the television signal waveform is the same
throughout the RF tuner, as depicted in Fig. 4-10. In passage through the mixer, however, the frequency of the high-
frequency component is changed. For example, the input

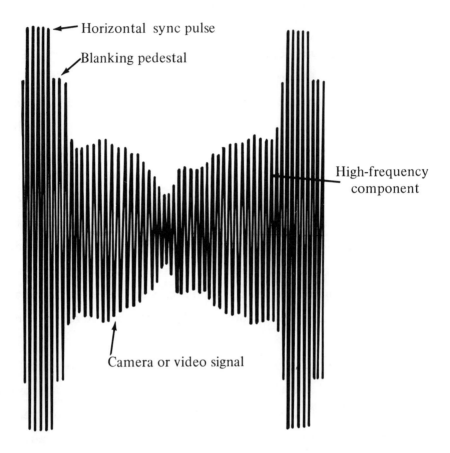

Fig. 4-10 Television signal waveform at the mixer.

signal at the mixer might have a high-frequency component of
200 MHz. On the other hand, the output signal from the mixer
will have a high-frequency component in the 45-MHz range.
As in standard superheterodyne processing, the mixer output
always has the same value of high-frequency component (IF
frequency), regardless of the input frequency.

It is standard practice to operate the local oscillator
on the "high side" of the picture carrier.   Thus, Q3 in
Fig. 4-9 is tuned to 221 MHz when the RF tuner is set to
Channel 7.   Consider the frequency relations that are

involved in this example:

> Channel 7 Picture Carrier Frequency = 175.25 MHz
> Channel 7 Sound Carrier Frequency = 179.75 MHz
> Local Oscillator Frequency = 221 MHz
> IF Picture Carrier Frequency = 45.75 MHz
> IF Sound Carrier Frequency = 41.25 MHz

Observe that these frequency relations involve difference frequencies:

$$221 \text{ MHz} - 175.25 \text{ MHz} = 45.75 \text{ MHz}$$
$$221 \text{ MHz} - 179.75 \text{ MHz} = 41.25 \text{ MHz}$$

Finally, note that whereas the VHF picture carrier frequency is lower than the VHF sound carrier frequency, the IF picture carrier frequency is higher than the IF sound carrier frequency, as a consequence of "high-side" local oscillator operation. However, the difference between the picture and sound carrier frequencies is the same (4.5 MHz) at both the input and output of the mixer. This 4.5-MHz difference is called the intercarrier frequency and will be treated in greater detail in Chapter 12.

The high-frequency voltage from the local oscillator is coupled from L_{15} to L_{14} in Fig. 4-9. This is called the oscillator injection voltage into the mixer circuit. Note that L_{15} is connected parallel to L_{16}. A tuning slug is provided as an operating control for L_{16}. This is called the fine-tuning function. After the RF tuner has been set to a selected channel, the fine-tuning control is adjusted for best picture and sound reproduction. This entails precise adjustment of the local oscillator frequency so that the heterodyne output signal from L_{17} "fits" the following IF passband properly.

The inductors and capacitors included in the RF amplifier and mixer circuits must resonate at suitable frequencies

to provide the standard frequency response curve that was
shown in Fig. 4-4.   This curve is called   a double-humped
response curve, and it is obtained by stagger-tuning the RF
and mixer resonant frequencies in an alignment procedure.
Special test equipment is required for alignment of an RF
tuner, as explained subsequently.   To obtain a standard frequency response curve for the configuration in Fig. 4-9, C_{10}
is adjusted to resonate with L_{13} near the VHF picture carrier
frequency; C_{11} is adjusted to resonate with L_{14} near the VHF
sound carrier frequency.   These two trimmer capacitors are
called the VHF alignment adjustments.

If the fine-tuning control happens to drift out of
normal range, the local oscillator section in Fig. 4-9 will
require alignment.   This is a very simple procedure, which
consists of adjusting the slug in L_{15} so that the slug in
L_{16} provides the normal fine-tuning range.   That is, best
sound and picture reproduction should be obtained when the
fine-tuning control is set to approximately the midpoint
of its range.   Note in passing that L_{17} is not included in
the VHF alignment procedure, because it operates in the
45-MHz range and is a portion of the IF section.   The test
points provided in the mixer section are utilized in alignment and troubleshooting procedures.

RF tuners often employ germanium transistors of the
microalloy diffused-base type (MADT).   However, dual-gate
MOS field-effect transistors (MOSFET) are also utilized.
They provide certain advantages over bipolar, junction field-
effect, and single-gate MOS field-effect transistors.   RF
amplification and mixing processes are improved by use of
this low-feedback transistor, which has a low-noise figure
and a large dynamic range.   A dual-gate MOSFET transistor
has a second gate electrode which can be used for AGC or

for local oscillator injection. A widely used type is an N channel, depletion mode, dual-gate MOS transistor with built-in back-to-back Zener diodes between both gates and the source electrode to eliminate handling problems in production or service.

A MOSFET transistor is similar to a triode electron tube in its basic characteristics, and a dual-gate MOSFET transistor is comparable to a double-grid electron tube. Figure 4-11 depicts a basic RF tuner configuration using MOSFET dual-gate transistors in the RF amplifier and mixer sections. Observe that the circuit arrangement is conventional except for the method of applying AGC voltage in the RF section and the method of establishing the operating point in the mixer section. That is, gate 2 of Q1 is connected to the AGC line. As the AGC voltage ranges from +8 to −6 V, the gain of the RF stage ranges from maximum to minimum. Next, note that the operating point of Q2 is determined by the bias on gate 2. This bias voltage is fixed by the associated voltage divider, at a value that provides optimum heterodyne action.

Now consider the switch-type tuner configuration shown in Fig. 4-12. Observe that the RF amplifier and mixer circuits are resonated by means of series-connected coils. These coils are mounted between successive terminals on the decks of wafer switches. Note that more inductance is inserted into the circuit each time that the switch arm is moved down to a lower position. On each VHF position, the ground return is made through L_3, a small inductor that provides resonance on Channel 13 by itself.

When the switch arm is set to the UHF position in Fig. 4-12, L_3 is disconnected from the circuit. Now, the resonant circuit consists of 11 VHF coils connected in series with L_1

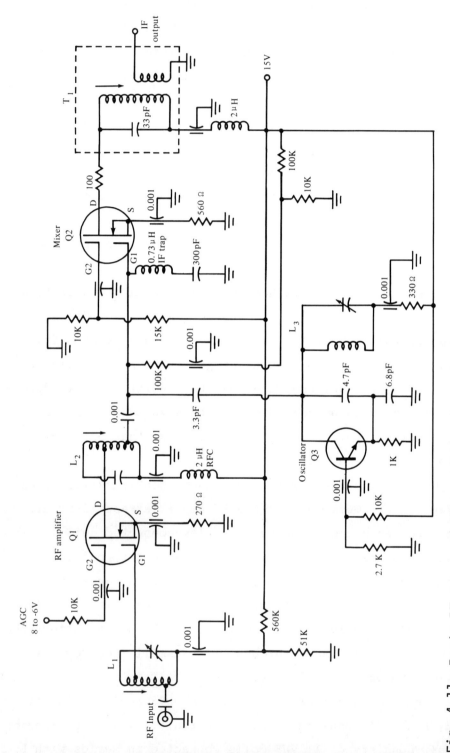

Fig. 4-11 Basic RF tuner configuration using MOSFET dual-gate transistors.

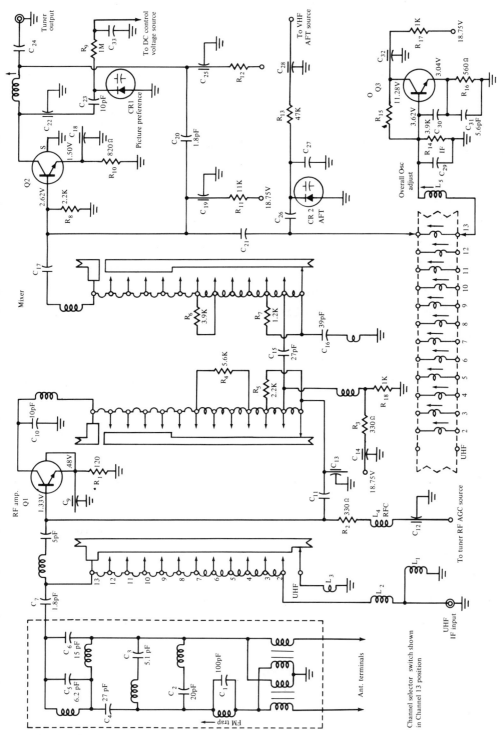

Fig. 4-12 A switch-type tuner configuration.

and L_2. This arrangement provides resonance at the IF frequency. In turn, the output signal from the UHF tuner is
applied across L_1, and Q1 operates as an IF amplifier stage.
A similar switching arrangement is provided in the RF output
and mixer input circuits, so that the mixer transistor Q2
also operates as an IF amplifier stage. Note that the oscillator transistor Q3 is disabled in the UHF position of the
channel selector switch. In other words, heterodyne action
does not take place in the RF tuner during UHF operation;
instead, straight IF amplifier operation is provided. As no
RF amplification is provided by a UHF tuner, two additional
stages of IF amplification are required to obtain normal
receiver gain when tuned to a UHF station.

The tuner configuration depicted in Fig. 4-12 employs
preset fine-tuning. This means that each oscillator coil
has a slug that can be engaged by the fine-tuning control.
In turn, each coil is individually tuned for optimum reception by the viewer, and subsequent adjustment of the fine-
tuning control is seldom required. By way of comparison,
the fine-tuning arrangement shown in Fig. 4-9 may require
readjustment each time the receiver is switched to a different channel. The overall oscillator adjustment, L_5, is a
maintenance control which is set to a point that brings all
of the individual oscillator coil slugs within adequate
operating range.

Now consider the automatic fine-tuning (AFT) diode CR2
in Fig. 4-12. This is a design refinement which further
decreases need for attention to the fine-tuning control.
AFT action serves to pull the oscillator on frequency,
provided that it does not drift excessively off frequency.
This is accomplished by means of the variable capacitance
shunted across the oscillator tank circuit by diode CR2.

That is, CR2 is a reverse-biased junction diode, often called a varicap or a varactor. Its junction capacitance depends upon the amount of reverse bias voltage that is applied. In an AFT system, the amount of reverse bias voltage is deterquadruple by the departure of the oscillator frequency from its normal value. That is, a sensing arrangement in the IF section (to be described subsequently) develops a corrective dc voltage as required to bring the oscillator back on frequency.

Finally, let us consider the function of the picture preference diode CR1 in Fig. 4-12. This is a reverse-biased junction diode shunted across the mixer output coil L_5. It serves to raise or lower the resonant frequency of L_5, thereby changing the shape of the IF frequency response curve. Note that the mixer output circuit is the beginning of the IF input circuit. As will be explained in Chapter 5, reproduction of picture detail, contrast, and snow (atmospheric noise) visibility depend upon the contour of the frequency response curve, and upon the prevailing signal level. Thus, when the RF tuner is switched from a strong station to a weak station, the viewer often prefers the picture reproduction that results from certain changes in the shape of the IF frequency response curve. Accordingly, an operating control is provided in this arrangement whereby the amount of reverse bias voltage across CR1 can be varied.

4.3 UHF Tuner Design

A UHF tuner provides a heterodyne function, in the same basic manner as a VHF tuner. However, design techniques in the 470- to 890-MHz range are somewhat different from those employed in the 54- to 216-MHz range. The most prominent difference is the use of resonant lines as tuned circuits, instead of coils. Figure 4-13 depicts the con-

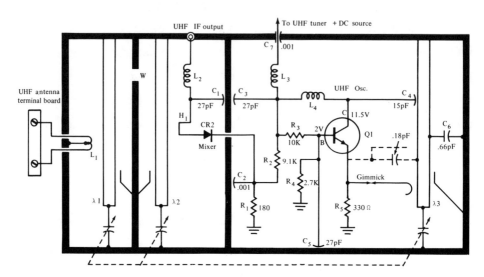

Fig. 4-13 A typical UHF tuner arrangement.

figuration of a UHF tuner.   A resonant line can be defined
as a line that operates with standing waves of voltage and
current.   It is not terminated in its characteristic impedance, and reflections of voltage and current take place as
depicted in Fig. 4-14. Observe that the voltage and current
waves are 90° out of phase with each other.

A resonant line is said to be resonant at some particular frequency.   This means that it is operating at some
multiple of a quarter-wavelength.   To change the resonant
frequency, the length of the line can be varied or a small
variable capacitor can be connected at the end of the line,
as seen in Fig. 4-13.   Note in Fig. 4-14 that a resonant
line "looks like" a parallel resonant circuit at even multiples of a quarter-wavelength, and "looks like" a series
resonant circuit at odd multiples of a quarter-wavelength.

In the arrangement of Fig. 4-13, the incoming UHF signal is heterodyned to the IF range through the diode mixer
CR2. Transistor Q1 operates as a local oscillator. No RF

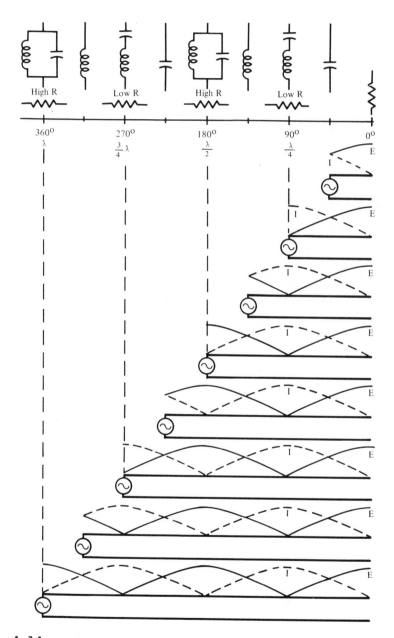

Fig. 4-14 Voltage and current relations on resonant lines of various lengths.

amplification is provided because the efficiency would be low in the UHF range, and it is more practical to obtain amplification at the IF frequency through the VHF tuner. Note in

Fig. 4-13 that the incoming UHF energy is coupled from L_1 to the first resonant line λ_1. This line operates as a tuned circuit and provides preselection. Field energy from the first resonant line is coupled through the "window," or port W, to the second resonant line λ_2. Increased selectivity is provided by this second resonant line.

From the second resonant line in Fig. 4-13, UHF energy is coupled to the hairpin loop H_1 and fed into the mixer diode CR2. This mixer diode is also supplied with a UHF voltage from the oscillator section. In turn, the IF difference frequency is produced and becomes available at the UHF IF output terminal. Observe that the oscillator-tuned circuit is also a resonant line, λ_3. As in a VHF tuner, the oscillator circuit is tuned to a frequency that is higher than the incoming signal frequency by a difference equal to the IF frequency. The oscillator transistor operates in the common base mode, and the amplitude of oscillation is determined by the effective capacitance from collector to emitter. This capacitance is commonly adjusted by means of a wire "gimmick" as seen in Fig. 4-13.

4.4 Typical Troubles in RF Tuners

When a no-picture symptom occurs, the fault may or may not be localized to the RF tuner. Note that a no-picture symptom should not be confused with a dark screen symptom. That is, a no-picture symptom is accompanied by a visible raster, although no image is reproduced. Figure 4-15 depicts a visible raster with no picture. The sound signal is often audible when a no-picture symptom is present; however, there are certain types of tuner trouble that produce a no-sound symptom also.

It is good practice to check the antenna and make sure

Fig. 4-15 Visible raster, but no picture, sound may or
may not be audible.

that it is not defective.   In case of doubt, a portable
receiver can be connected to the lead-in. Then, the following
checks and tests should be made:

1. If an old style of receiver is being serviced, test
    or replace the tubes in the RF tuner.

2. Observe the raster to see if snow is visible when
    the contrast control is turned up. Figure 4-16
    shows the appearance of snow. This test is based
    on the fact that the RF tuner normally generates
    noise voltages.

3. If snow is visible, the RF tuner is probably
    workable. The trouble is most likely to be located
    in a subsequent portion of the picture signal chan-
    nel.

Fig. 4-16   Appearance of snow on the picture tube screen.

4.   If little or no snow is visible, there is preliminary suspicion of RF tuner trouble.

Absence of snow in the raster does not necessarily mean
that there is a fault in the RF tuner itself.   For example,
excessive bias voltage from the AGC section could be cutting
off the RF amplifier stage.   Therefore, it is advisable to
check the AGC voltage at the outset.   An FET meter such as
illustrated in Fig. 4-17 is generally used in solid-state
servicing procedures.   If the AGC voltage is incorrect,
according to the value specified in the receiver-servicing
data, the RF tuner is cleared from suspicion, and attention
is turned to the AGC section of the receiver.

When there is a no-picture symptom with little or no
snow in the raster (with the contrast control advanced), it
is possible that the local oscillator is at fault.   To check
this possibility, couple the output from a signal generator

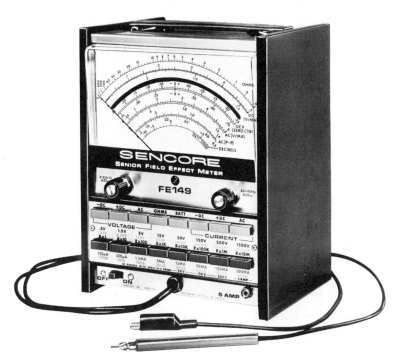

Fig. 4-17 An FET meter, suitable for use in solid state servicing procedures. (Courtesy, Sencore, Inc.)

to one of the antenna input terminals. Set the generator for unmodulated output and tune it through the proper local oscillator frequency. If a picture appears on an active television channel, the test indicates that the local oscillator is defective. That is, the signal generator substitutes for the local oscillator in this test.

Mechanical defects can occur in RF tuners. For example, contacts and contact springs can become corroded and require cleaning. Sometimes spring tension is inadequate to make good electrical contact. From a statistical viewpoint, capacitor failures are most likely to occur, aside from the possibility of mechanical defects. If a fixed capacitor short-circuits, an associated transistor may also be damaged due to excessive current flow. A capacitor can also become open-circuited, or leakage resistance may develop. Repairs to television tuners are comparatively difficult, because of the compact construction that is utilized. For this reason, defective tuners are often sent to specialized repair shops. If extensive repairs are required, it is sometimes more economical to replace a defective tuner.

Questions

Short Answer

1. What are the functions of an RF amplifier?

2. What is the function of the mixer?

3. What are the selectivity considerations of the RF tuner?

4. How is the reception of UHF stations usually handled in modern television receivers? List the four steps.

5. What is the impedance of each of the two inputs to a turret tuner?

6. What functions do the traps, shown in Fig. 4-9, serve?

7. What is the purpose of the fine-tuning control?

8. What adjustment would you make if the fine-tuning was out of range in the tuner shown in Fig. 4-9?

9. Explain the method of selecting a station with the RF tuner in Fig. 4-12.

10. What is the range of the AGC voltage in the RF amplifier shown in Fig. 4-11?

11. Where does the heterodyne action take place in the UHF section of Fig. 4-12?

12. Why are two additional RF stages necessary to obtain normal gain when the tuner shown in Fig. 4-12 is set to UHF?

13. What is preset fine-tuning?

14. How does the AFT in Fig. 4-12 operate to control frequency?

15. What is the purpose of diode CR2 in Fig. 4-12?

16. Where is the AFT voltage developed in the diagram in Fig. 4-12?

17. Upon what factor does the picture reproduction depend?

18. What is the purpose of a gimmick?

19. What is the difference between a no-picture problem and a dark screen?

20. Why are defective tuners often sent to specialized repair shops?

True-False

1. An RF tuner processes the incoming signal from the antenna.

2. The input signal to which the RF amplifier is tuned is processed at that frequency.

3. Each television channel is 4 MHz wide.

4. A television transmission provides the signal-processing function.

5. RF tuners usually provide more gain on the low VHF channels than on the high VHF channels.

6. The sound signal has a bandwidth of approximately 50 kHz.

7. Modern television receivers usually have a separate RF amplifier section for UHF reception.

8. Most television receivers use a turret tuner for the RF section.

9. The antenna signal passes through traps before it is applied to the RF amplfiers.

10. In the superheterodyne process, the incoming signal is

beat against the lower-frequency voltage from the local oscillator.

11. The mixer stage is sometimes called the first detector.

12. The intercarrier frequency of a television receiver is the difference between the local oscillator frequency and the RF station frequency.

13. The fine-tuning control is used to make precise adjustment of the local oscillator for best picture and sound reproduction.

14. If the fine-tuning control were out of range, you would adjust the RF coil.

15. In Fig. 4-12, the smallest value of inductance provides resonance for Channel 1.

16. The AGC voltage controls the gain of the RF amplifier in the circuit shown in Fig. 4-11.

17. Heterodyne action does not take place in the UHF model of the tuner shown in Fig. 4-12.

18. The tuner configuration shown in Fig. 4-12 employs preset fine-tuning.

19. The AFT action serves to pull the RF amplifier frequency.

20. Diode CR2 in Fig. 4-12 is a voltage-controlled capacitor.

21. In Fig. 4-12, a sensing arrangement in the RF amplifier develops a corrective dc voltage to bring the local oscillator back on frequency.

22. Reproduction of picture detail depends upon the contour of the frequency response curve and the prevailing signal level.

23. The shape of the IF frequency response curve can be varied in the circuit in Fig. 4-12 to compensate for signal level changes.

24. Design techniques are the same for UHF and VHF tuners.

25. To change the resonant frequency of a resonant line, we

can change the length of the line.

26. A resonant line can be made to look like a parallel resonant circuit, but not like a series resonant circuit.

27. A gimmick is a tuning screwdriver.

28. A no-picture symptom is recognized as a dark screen.

29. Snow can be caused by noise in the tuner.

30. Absence of snow in the raster when the contrast is full means that the RF tuner is faulty.

31. Repairs to tuners are often difficult because of their compact construction.

Multiple Choice

1. The signal from the antenna is processed by the:
   (a) transmission line.
   (b) RF amplifier.
   (c) RF oscillator.
   (d) demodulator.

2. Selectivity is provided and interference is rejected by the:
   (a) RF oscillator.
   (b) transmission line.
   (c) RF amplifier.
   (d) mixer stage.

3. The sound signal has a bandwidth of approximately:
   (a) 4 MHz.　　　　(c) 175 kHz.
   (b) 1.5 MHz.　　　(d) 50 kHz.

4. Television transmission employs _____ transmission.
   (a) single-sideband　　(c) vestigial sideband
   (b) phase-modulated　　(d) dual-sideband

5. The most common type of tuner employed in television
    receivers is the _____ tuner.
    (a) turret   (c) double
    (b) phase   (d) switch

6. The mixer stage is sometimes called the:
    (a) RF amplifier.
    (b) RF oscillator.
    (c) first detector.
    (d) divider stage.

7. The intercarrier frequency of a television receiver is:
    (a) 455 kHz.   (c) 22.5 MHz.
    (b) 4.5 MHz.   (d) 75 kHz.

8. The fine-tuning control is used to adjust the _____
    frequency.
    (a) intercarrier   (c) sound
    (b) RF   (d) carrier

9. If the fine-tuning control is out of range, you should:
    (a) adjust the local oscillator.
    (b) add capacitance to the fine-tuning control.
    (c) adjust the RF trap.
    (d) check the transmission line.

10. When each oscillator coil in a tuner has a slug that can
    be varied by the fine-tuning control, it is said to have:
    (a) automatic tuning.   (c) preset tuning.
    (b) controlled tuning.   (d) mode tuning.

11. The purpose of the AGC voltage in Fig. 4-11 is to con-
    trol the:
    (a) gain of the local oscillator.
    (b) frequency of the local oscillator.
    (c) gain of the RF amplifier.
    (d) frequency of the RF amplifier.

12. The purpose of the AFT diode shown in Fig. 4-12 is to:

   (a) pull the local oscillator on frequency.

   (b) pull the RF amplifier on frequency.

   (c) adjust the gain of the RF amplifier.

   (d) automatically turn the fine-tuning control.

13. AFT circuit action in Fig. 4-12 is due to a:

   (a) fixed capacitor.

   (b) variable capacitor.

   (c) diode that acts like a variable capacitor.

   (d) variable coil.

14. In Fig. 4-12, the AFT correction voltage is developed as:

   (a) an ac voltage in the RF amplifier.

   (b) a dc voltage in the RF amplifier.

   (c) an ac voltage in the IF amplifier.

   (d) a dc voltage in the IF amplifier.

15. Reproduction of picture detail, contrast, and snow depends upon the:

   (a) contour of the frequency response curve.

   (b) prevailing signal level.

   (c) antenna.

   (d) signal level and the contour of the frequency response curve.

16. In UHF tuners, resonant circuits are _____ to reduce losses.

   (a) silver-plated

   (b) inductors with copper slugs

   (c) shielded

   (d) resonant lines with copper slugs

17. A trouble that may be caused by a faulty tuner is:

   (a) a dark screen.   (c) no sound.

   (b) no picture.   (d) no raster.

Chapter 5

VIDEO-IF AMPLIFIERS
AND DETECTORS

5.1 Video-IF Section

An IF amplifier contributes the greater portion of the
gain and selectivity in a television receiver. Most designs
employ three IF stages, although some use only two stages,
and a few receivers have four stages. Figure 5-1 illustrates
a typical printed circuit-IF strip; the term "strip" denotes
the complete IF amplifier assembly, including the video detector, but lacking the tuned input-IF transformer or coil. This
first IF circuit is located in the RF tuner unit. When tuned
to a weak television signal, the IF input voltage is about
$\frac{1}{4}$ mV, and the IF output voltage is approximately 1 V. Thus,
the maximum available gain of an IF strip is on the order of
4000 times. Amplification takes place at a center frequency
of about 43 MHz.

Fig. 5-1   A printed circuit IF strip for a television receiver.

5.2   Basic IF Amplifier Principles

As depicted in Fig. 5-2, IF amplifier stages operate in

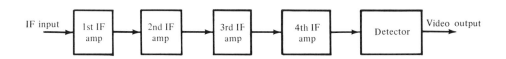

Fig. 5-2   IF amplifier stages operate in cascade.

cascade. Thus, the output signal voltage from one stage is multiplied by the gain of the following stage. All stages do not necessarily operate at the same gain, and the gain of a stage may be changed automatically over a wide range when the input signal level changes. This is the function of the AGC section, as indicated in Fig. 5-3. Note that the gain of the

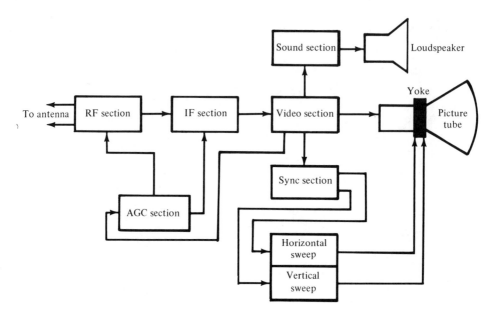

Fig. 5-3 Receiver gain is automatically controlled by the AGC section.

RF tuner is also controlled by the AGC section. The RF gain is varied at a different rate from the IF gain.

As shown in Fig. 5-4, the frequency spectrum at the

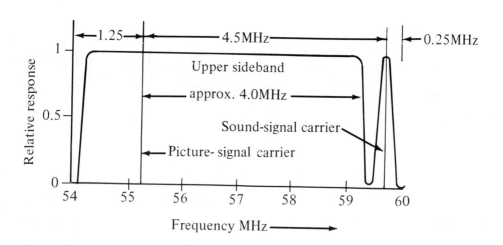

Fig. 5-4 Frequency spectrum at the output of the RF amplifier.

output of the RF amplifier comprises a vestigial sideband picture (video) signal and an RM sound signal. The lower sideband of the video signal extends 1.25 MHz below the picture carrier frequency. Alignment of the IF amplifier is made to compensate for the incomplete lower sideband, insofar as practical considerations permit. As noted previously, the local oscillator in the RF tuner generally operates on the "high side" of the incoming signal. Therefore, the frequency progression depicted in Fig. 5-4 becomes reversed through the mixer, and a typical IF response curve exhibits the picture carrier at a higher frequency than the sound carrier, as seen in Fig. 5-5.

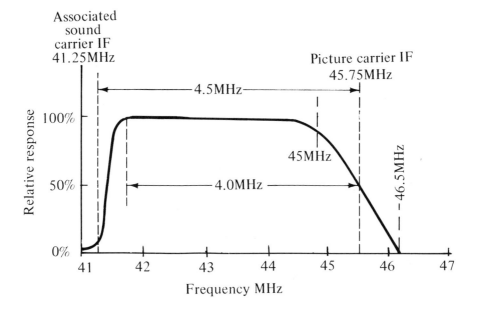

Fig. 5-5 A picture IF response curve.

Observe in Fig. 5-5 that the picture carrier frequency falls halfway up the side of the frequency response curve.

The slope of the curve is such that it falls to zero over a
0.75-MHz interval and rises to maximum over a 0.75-MHz interval, on either side of the picture carrier.   This form of IF
frequency response (alignment) provides optimum reproduction
of the picture signal in a vestigial sideband system.   Note
that the sound carrier is passed at 10% of maximum response
on the IF curve, at 41.25 MHz.   Thus, both the picture and
sound signals are processed through the IF amplifier.   However, the sound signal must be kept at a comparatively low
level to avoid visible beat interference in the image.   This
topic is considered in greater detail below.

5.3 Basic IF Amplifier Circuitry

Most television receivers utilize three IF amplifier
stages in the common emitter mode.   A typical configuration
is shown in Fig. 5-6.   Note that the necessary wide-band
response is obtained by stagger-tuning.   The first IF-tuned
circuit is the mixer tank, of which L_1 is a part.   Its
impedance is in the order of 1000 Ω, which assists in
obtaining wide-band response.   The second, third, and fourth
IF-tuned circuits are provided by T_1, T_2, and T_3.   Figure
5-7 depicts the result of stagger-tuning two successive
stages; the top of the overall response curve is broadened,
and the overall bandwidth is increased.   Of course, there
is a trade-off involved with respect to gain, and stagger-
tuning results in reduced overall gain.

Two traps are provided in the base input circuit of Q1
in Fig. 5-6.   The basic requirement for IF traps is depicted
in Fig. 5-8. T_1 is a series resonant, inductively coupled
trap for the accompanying sound signal in Fig. 5-6.   Note
that a tuned secondary operates as a series resonant circuit,
because each turn of the secondary is cut by the primary flux

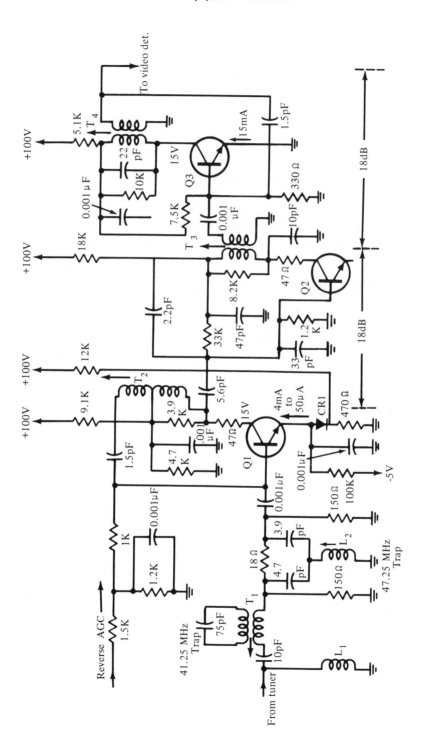

Fig. 5-6 A three-stage video–IF amplifier configuration.

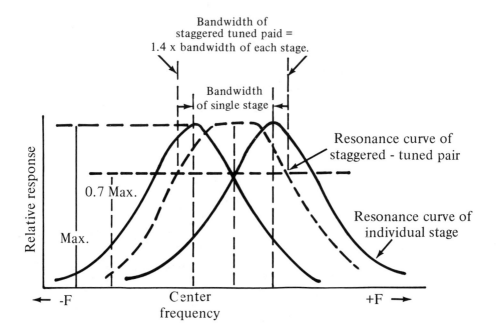

Fig. 5-7   Principles of stagger tuning.

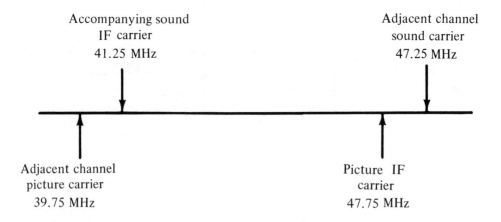

Fig. 5-8   Adjacent-channel picture and sound carrier frequencies can cause interence unless trapped out.

lines. In turn, these individual induced voltages operate in
series. Trap T_1 normally reduces the IF response to approximately 10% of maximum at 41.25 MHz. No adjacent channel
picture carrier trap is provided in this example. L_2 operates
as a bridged-T trap in combination with the 18-Ω resistor,
the 4.7-pF capacitor, and the 3.9-pF capacitor. This is the
adjacent channel sound carrier trap.

Observe in Fig. 5-6 that the collector load circuit T_2
is center-tapped and feeds out-of-phase signal voltage back
to the base of Q1 via a 1.5-pF capacitor. This is a neutralizing circuit for stabilization of the first IF stage.
Q1 operates with approximately 15-V collector potential, and
normally draws about 4 mA of emitter current. However, under
strong signal conditions, AGC bias action can cause the collector current to fall as low as 50 μA. The dynamic range of
Q1 is approximately 40 dB. Clamp diode CR1 prevents the
collector current from reaching zero so that Q1 cannot be
completely cut off. That is CR1 becomes reverse-biased under
strong signal conditions. Note that T_2 is shunted by resistance to lower the stage Q value and thereby obtain adequate
bandwidth.

The output from T_2 is capacitively coupled to the base
of Q2 in Fig. 5-6. This stage operates at fixed bias and is
not AGC controlled; a gain of approximately 18 dB is provided.
Note that the RC network between the base and collector of Q2
comprises both a bias source and a negative feedback path.
This negative feedback signal assists in obtaining wide-band
response; the 8.2-kΩ resistor shunted across the primary of
T_3 lowers the Q value of the load circuit and also contributes
to increased bandwidth. This is a bifilar transformer in which
the primary and secondary conductors are wound side by side.

It operates much the same as a single tuned coil, except that electrical isolation is provided between primary and secondary.

A higher power level is employed in the third stage of Fig. 5-6, because the video detector requires appreciable power input. The emitter of Q3 draws about 15 mA; this stage operates at fixed bias and is not AGC controlled. A gain of approximately 18 dB is developed. Note that the RC network between the base and collector of Q3 is a dc bias arrangement. That is, no IF signal can feed back from collector to base because of the bypassing action of the 0.005-μF capacitor. However, negative feedback occurs from the secondary of T_4 to the base of Q3 through a 1.5-pF capacitor. This feedback operates to neutralize the stage. Because a detector is inefficient at low-input levels, T_4 is designed to provide some step-up voltage transformation.

In deluxe receivers, a four-stage video-IF section may be utilized, as depicted in Fig. 5-9. Observe that comparatively extensive trap circuitry is employed. L_1 operates as an adjacent channel sound trap, L_2 is an accompanying sound trap, and L_3 is an adjacent channel picture carrier trap. Interstage coupling is provided by stagger-tuned bifilar transformers; nominal peaking frequencies for these transformers are noted in the diagram. Note that T_3 has no specified peaking frequency; it is adjusted during the IF alignment procedure to compensate for tolerances in the other stages, thereby optimizing the frequency response curve insofar as practical.

Shunt resistance is connected across the primary windings of the first three IF transformers in Fig. 5-9 to obtain necessary bandwidth. Thus, the primary of T_1 is shunted by the input cable impedance of approximately 75 Ω. The primary of T_2 is shunted by R_4, and the primary of T_3 is shunted by

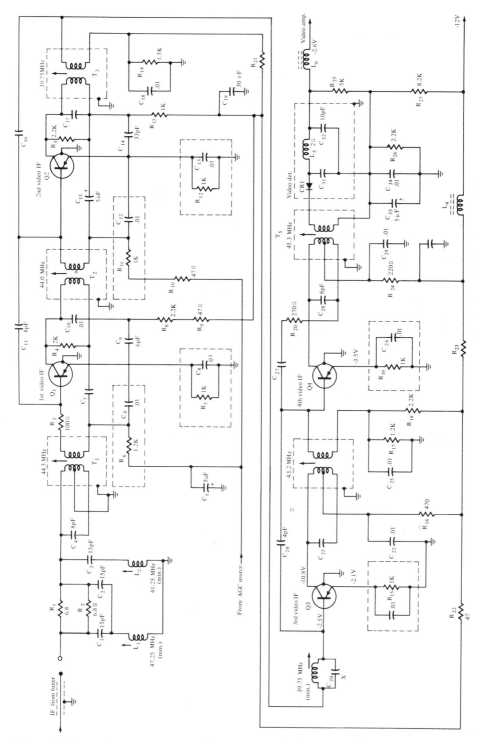

Fig. 5-9 A four-stage video-IF amplifier configuration.

R_5. The practical effect of resistance loading is shown in Fig. 5-10. Each stage is neutralized in this example; the

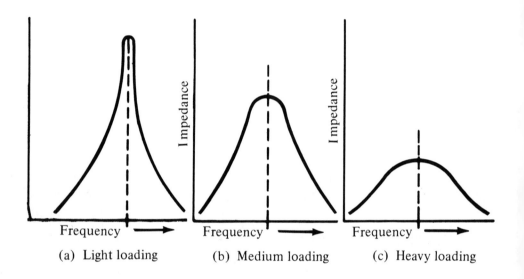

(a) Light loading   (b) Medium loading   (c) Heavy loading

Fig. 5-10 Resistive loading increases the bandwidth and reduces the output of the tuned circuit.

neutralizing capacitors are C_{11}, C_{16}, C_{24}, and C_{27}. Note that the primary of T_1 is tapped to provide an impedance match to the coaxial cable from the RF tuner.

Because a diode detector requires appreciable signal power input, Q4 is operated at a comparatively high level. These conditions produce impedance relations that are matched by tapping the primaries of T_5 and T_4. Bias stabilization is provided in each stage by 1000-Ω emitter resistors. The emitter resistors are bypassed to avoid loss of gain. The first and second stages are AGC controlled, whereas the third and fourth stages operate with fixed bias at maximum gain.

Because transistor junction capacitances change appreciably
with variation of base emitter bias, AGC action would lead to
objectionable stage detuning if it were not for the low L/C
ratio employed in the controlled stages. This low L/C ratio
is provided by C_{10} and C_{17}.

Extensive decoupling is employed in the −12−V supply
line (Fig. 5-9) to avoid interstage coupling. These decoupling
networks are comprised of L_4 and C_{30}, R_{27} and C_{33}, and similar
networks through the system. Note that C_{33} is shunted by C_{34}.
This dual arrangement is required because electrolytic capacitors often have appreciable impedance in the 40−MHz range,
although they have very low impedance at lower frequencies.
Conversely, a 0.01−µF capacitor has low impedance in the 40−MHz
range, although it has substantial impedance at lower frequencies. Note that the AGC line is decoupled in much the same way
as the −12−V supply line.

Figure 5-11 depicts the development of an overall IF
response curve obtained by stagger-tuning of individual stages.
The response drops off rapidly to 10% of maximum at 4.25 MHz.
This steep response is produced by the high Q sound trap L_2C_3
in Fig. 5-9. The curve rises slightly below 41.25 MHz, and
then drops to practically zero at 39.75 MHz (Fig. 5-11). This
drop is caused by the adjacent channel picture carrier trap
L_3C_{20} (Fig. 5-9). At the right-hand end of the curve in Fig.
5-11, the response is practically zero at 47.25 MHz, due to
the adjacent channel sound carrier trap $L_1C_1C_2R_1R_2$ (Fig. 5-9).

Note in Fig. 5-11 that the overall response is the product
of individual stage responses at any frequency. The output of
each IF stage is multiplied by the gain of the following stage.
This leads to the perhaps unexpected fact that if any one
transistor becomes weak, the shape of the overall curve does

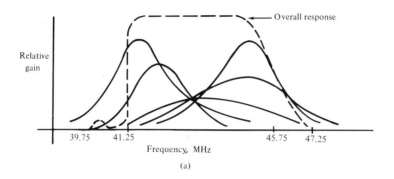

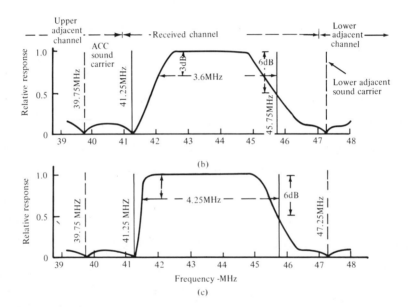

Fig. 5-11 Development and contours of IF response curves: (a) ideal response from five stagger-tuned circuits and three traps, (b) over-all IF response of a typical economy-type receiver, (c) over-all IF response of a typical de-lux receiver.

not change. Instead, only the amplitude of the curve is reduced. As a practical note, it should be recognized that the foregoing mode of system operation does not hold true if any significant degree of regeneration exists in the IF configuration. As it is difficult to neutralize an IF stage completely, the result is that transistor degradation usually causes an appreciable change in overall IF curve shape.

5.4 Integrated Circuitry

As noted previously, integrated circuits (IC's) are monolithic or integral solid-state devices comprising transistors, resistors, diodes, and capacitors. Typical IC packages are depicted in Fig. 5-12. An IC suitable for use in an IF

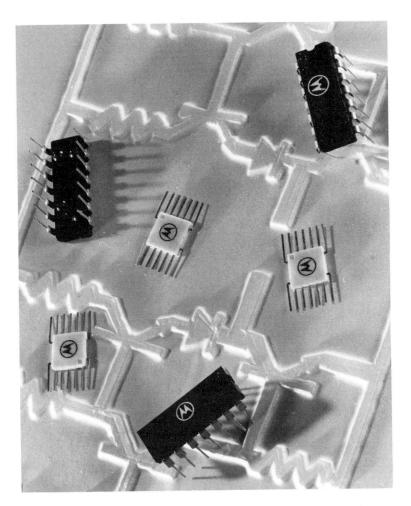

Fig. 5-12 Typical integrated circuit packages. (Courtesy, Motorola Communications & Electronics, Inc.)

amplifier has the configuration shown in Fig. 5-13. It comprises three transistors, four resistors, and a diode. The

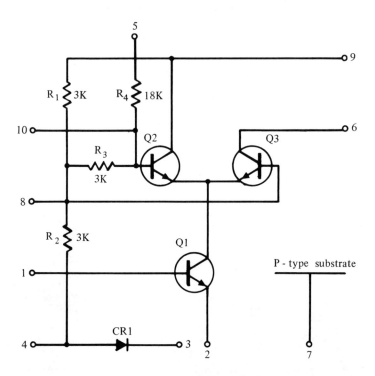

Fig. 5-13 Circuitry in an IC chip used in an IF amplifier strip.

substrate is the wafer substance upon which the foregoing components are formed simultaneously during manufacture. Transistors and diodes in an IC are basically the same as individual devices; however, there is more stray capacitance to be contended with because of the miniaturized arrangement.

Integral resistors in an IC (Fig. 5-13) are formed from semiconductor substance. An IC resistor is more responsive to temperature than a conventional composition resistor. For this reason, IC configurations are designed on the basis of resistance ratios, instead of absolute ohmic values. Two or three transistors are utilized in an IC to perform the function of a single individual transistor. Although the active and passive subunits in an IC are temperature-responsive, the amount of drift in absolute values will be virtually the same

for a pair of resistors, or for a pair of transistors. This
fact makes resistance-ratio design practical.

Figure 5-14 shows the plan of a basic IC. It is formed

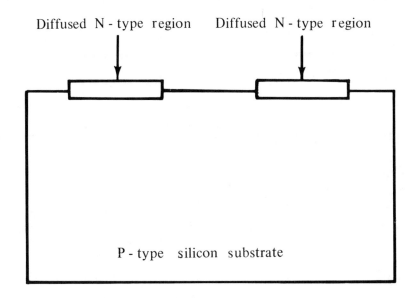

Fig. 5-14 Two N-type regions diffused into a P-type
silicon substrate.

on a P-type silicon wafer called the substrate.   An N-type
region may be diffused into the substrate to form a junction
diode. When two N-type regions are diffused into the wafer,
or chip, the substrate isolates the two N-type regions electrically. In other words, an electrical circuit cannot be
completed from one N-type region to the other, because these
regions are equivalent to a pair of diodes connected back
to back. Therefore, subunits formed on the substrate operate
as if they were formed on an insulating substance.

     When a P-type region is diffused into each of the
foregoing N-type regions, the P-type region can operate as
the base of a transistor.   Then, when another N-type region
is diffused into each of the P-type regions, as depicted in

Fig. 5-15, a pair of transistors is formed on the substrate.

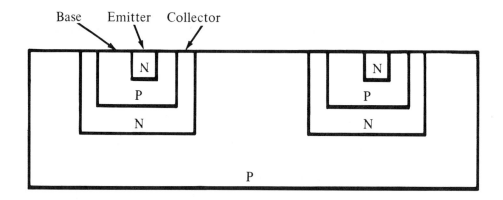

Fig. 5-15 A pair of NPN transistors formed on a P-type substrate.

Metalized contacts are fabricated to the three electrodes of each transistor. Note that each transistor is electrically isolated from the other transistor through the P-type substrate. Because the construction is miniaturized, the heat-dissipation ability of an IC is limited, and operation is limited to low-power applications.

To form a resistor in an IC substrate, a P-type region is diffused into an N-type region as shown in Fig. 5-16. Metalized contacts are made to the P-type region, which operates as the resistor. The value of resistance depends on the depth, length, and width of the P-type region. Note that an oxide layer is deposited on top of the P-type substrate; this oxide layer provides insulation between the metalized leads and the substrate.

The plan of an integrated capacitor is shown in Fig. 5-17. An N-type region is diffused into the substrate. A metalized contact is made to the N-type region, and both the substrate and N-type surface are coated with an oxide layer. This layer forms the dielectric of the capacitor; the N-type

Metalized contact

R   R¹

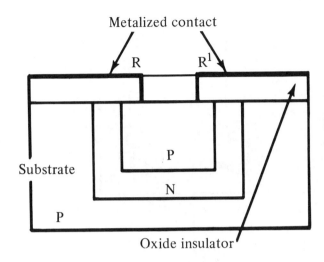

Substrate

Fig. 5-16 Formation of an IC resistor.

Oxide insulator

Metalized contact   Metalized plate

C   C¹

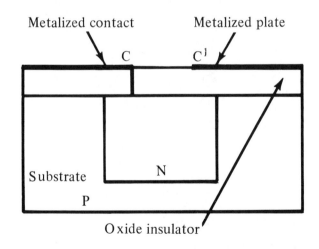

Fig. 5-17 Formation of an IC capacitor.

Oxide insulator

region serves as one electrode, and a metalized layer over the oxide coating forms the other electrode.

Figure 5-18 shows how the IC of Fig. 5-13 is connected into an IF amplifier arrangement. A pair of external tuned transformers, two external resistors, and one external capacitor are employed. It is instructive to observe the operation of this configuration. The IF signal input is

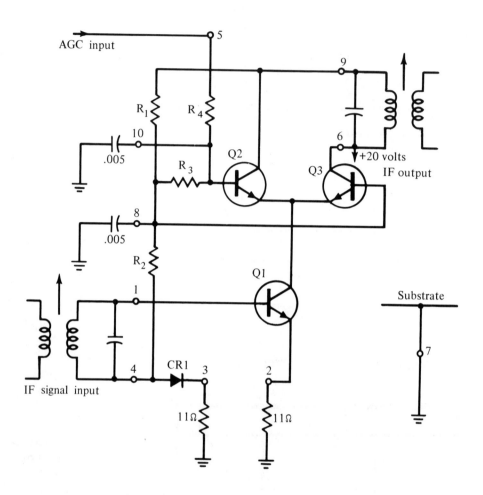

Fig. 5-18 Configuration of an IC IF stage.

applied to the base of transistor Q1, which operates in the
common emitter mode. In turn the collector output from Q1
drives the emitters of Q2 and Q3, which operate in the
common base mode. Note that output is taken from the collector of Q2, and that the collector is grounded with respect
to the IF signal. When two transistors are operated in
series, they are called a cascade pair. Thus, Q1 and Q2
form a CE–CB cascade pair, and Q1 and Q3 also form a CE–CB
cascade pair. This configuration assists in stabilizing

stage operation.

It should be noted that Q1 and Q2 are operative and that Q3 is cut off in the configuration of Fig. 5-18, unless the incoming signal is quite strong. A very strong signal produces sufficient AGC voltage so that Q1 and Q3 are operative, whereas Q2 is then cut off. Under this condition, it is evident that very little signal can be impressed across the primary of the IF output transformer. Delayed AGC action is provided by diode CR1. Resistors R_1 and R_2 form a voltage divider for base bias, and also bias CR1. The AGC voltage is applied at terminal 5. Resistors R_3 and R_4 are inserted to increase the dynamic range of AGC voltage; this minimizes the effect of noise voltages in the IF system. The range of AGC voltage is somewhat less than 1 V in this configuration.

The dc emitter current entering Q1 flows into the collector of Q1 and is then applied to the emitters of Q2 and Q3 in Fig. 5-18. The branch that is taken by this dc current depends upon the AGC voltage. For example, if the AGC voltage raises the reference base voltage on Q2 by 57 mV, Q2 will be cut off, and all of the collector current from Q1 will flow into the emitter of Q3. Because Q2 is cut off, very little signal can feed through into the output circuit. On the other hand, in case the AGC voltage lowers the reference base voltage on Q2 by 57 mV, all of the collector current from Q1 will flow into the emitter of Q2. That is, Q3 is cut off by this shift in AGC voltage. Q2 now amplifies the IF signal by an amount determined by the value of AGC voltage.

In the example of Fig. 5-18, a supply voltage of 20 V is applied between terminal 6 and ground. The substrate is connected to the ground system at terminal 7. Bypassing of the bases in the Q2 and Q3 circuits is provided by 0.005-μF

capacitors.   Q1 operates with an unbypassed 11-Ω emitter
resistor, which provides a small amount of negative feedback
and assists in stabilizing stage operation. Note that when
the incoming signal voltage is minimum, Q3 is cut off because
the AGC voltage makes the base of Q2 more positive than the
base of Q3.   When the incoming signal voltage is maximum, the
AGC voltage cuts off Q2 and also cuts off CR1. This rise of
positive voltage on the base of Q3 shifts the transistor into
conduction.

Figure 5-19 depicts   the conventional   symbol for an

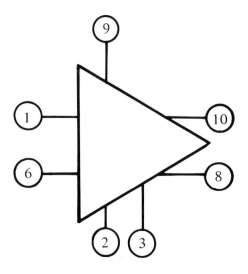

Fig. 5-19 Conventional symbol for an IC.

integrated circuit. This is a generalized symbol that identifies only the terminals.   That is, the IC may contain a
wide variety of monolithic circuitry.   As the integral
components are inaccessible, troubleshooting is restricted to
electrical measurements at the IC terminals. The dc voltages
are often changed when internal trouble occurs.   Sometimes,
dc current measurements will provide clues to internal faults.

Input-output relations are checked with a signal generator and a sensitive TVM, or with an oscilloscope that has adequate frequency response.

5.5 Video Detectors

The input circuit of a video detector is part of the IF system, whereas the output circuit of the detector is part of the video-amplifier system. These functions are apparent from the block diagram in Fig. 5-20; note that the video

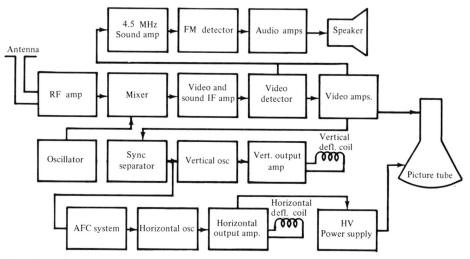

Fig. 5-20 Block diagram of the television receiver system.

detector is driven by the IF amplifier, and that the video detector drives the video amplifier. Semiconductor diodes are commonly employed as detection devices. Diode detection is preferred because of its comparatively low distortion (good detection linearity). However, diode detection entails an insertion loss which must be compensated for by additional gain in the IF or the video-amplifier section.

Two principal detector arrangements are utilized, as depicted in Fig. 5-21. The series circuit is shown in (a), and the shunt circuit is shown in (b). In each case, the last IF-tuned coil is L_1. This coil is grounded in the series

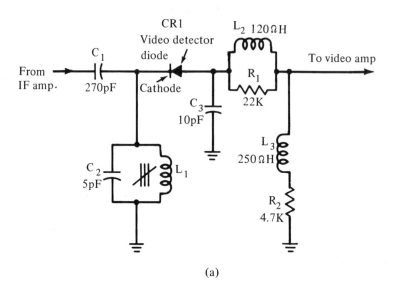

(a)

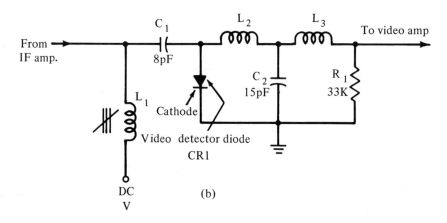

(b)

Fig. 5-21 Two basic diode detector configurations.

configuration but is connected to the dc supply source in the
shunt configuration. Most television receivers employ the
series detector circuit. The shunt arrangement has a comparatively high–output impedance. Both detectors are basically
peak detection configurations. That is, the series detector
tends to charge C_3 to the negative peak of the applied IF

signal. In between negative peaks, C_3 discharges to ground through R_2. Similarly, the shunt detector tends to charge C_2 to the negative peak of the applied IF signal. In between negative peaks, C_2 discharges to ground through R_1.

The detector diodes can be polarized oppositely in Fig. 5-21, if desired. In such a case a positive-going signal output will result. The diode polarity that is employed depends upon the signal polarity that is required at the pic-ture tube. If an error is made and a detector diode is replaced with incorrect polarity, a negative picture is dis-played on the picture tube screen. In a negative picture, black areas appear as white, and white areas appear as black. The effect is the same as viewing the negative film from a camera.

Figure 5-22 shows the basic action of a video detector.

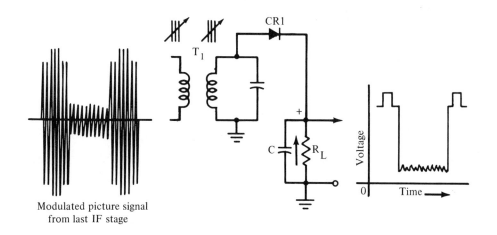

Modulated picture signal
from last IF stage

Fig. 5-22 Basic video-detector action.

This is an envelope detection process. That is, one of the IF waveform envelopes is reproduced at the detector output (the positive envelope is developed in this example). The diode operates as a rectifier; electrons flow from the ground into load resistor R_L, through diode CR1, and thence back to ground via T_1. A voltage drop appears across R_L; the instantaneous value of this voltage is proportional to the amplitude of the applied IF signal. This voltage drop charges C, which also serves to filter (bypass) the feedthrough IF signal to ground. It is desirable to eliminate residual IF signal to avoid possible overload of the following video amplifier.

R_L and C provide partial filtering action in Fig. 5-22. In other words, the value of C is sufficiently large so that 40-MHz frequencies are bypassed to ground. On the other hand, C has substantial reactance at frequencies of 4.5 MHz and less, so that the video and sound signals are not appreciably bypassed. Another characteristic of this partial filtering action is suitable choice of the load time constant (RC product), so that the charge on C can drain off fast enough through R_L to follow the comparatively rapid changes in amplitude of the video-frequency waveform.

Because the reactance of the load capacitor decreases as the frequency increases, the simple load circuit depicted in Fig. 5-22 does not have uniform impedance from 60 Hz to 4.5 MHz. For example, a 15-pF capacitor is practically an open circuit at 60 Hz, but it has approximately 2000-Ω reactance at 4.5 MHz. Therefore, frequency distortion will be produced by the detector load circuit, unless high-frequency compensation is provided. With reference to Fig. 5-21(a), high-frequency compensation is provided by peaking coils L_2 and L_3. Suitable values of peaking-coil inductance provide uniform frequency response up to 4.5 MHz. Details of peaking-coil characteristics and circuit action are explained in Chapter 6.

5.6 Automatic Fine-Tuning System

An AFT system functions to keep the local oscillator on frequency, in case the oscillator frequency tends to drift. Thereby, the viewer is not required to reset the fine-tuning control for optimum picture reproduction. An AFT system has a certain pull-in range, which is adequate to compensate for ordinary oscillator frequency drift. Of course, if a component defect occurs in the local oscillator section, the AFT action may be insufficient to keep the oscillator on frequency.

As seen in Fig. 5-23, an AFT system comprises a fre-

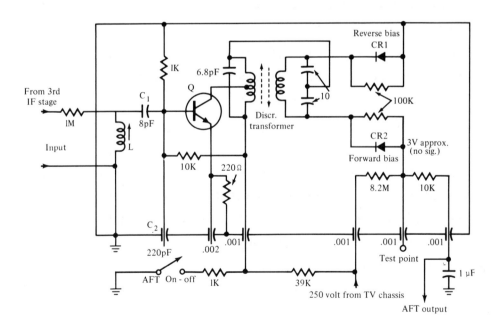

Fig. 5-23 A typical AFT discriminator configuration.

quency control arrangement. This frequency error sensor is

generally a discriminator configuration. In this example, the 45.75-MHz IF signal is coupled from the third IF stage through a 1-MΩ resistor to the discriminator input coil L. That is, the AFT discriminator operates at a center frequency equal to the IF picture carrier frequency. In practice, L is resonated at a slightly higher frequency than 45.75 MHz (such as 46.1 MHz) to compensate for the slope of the IF response curve through the picture carrier region. This ensures that the discriminator input signal will have practically a constant amplitude under conditions of local oscillator frequency drift. The capacitive divider circuit C_1-C_2 serves to couple the IF picture carrier signal at a suitable level to the base of transistor Q.

Observe in Fig. 5-23 that transistor Q operates in a CE configuration. It provides a voltage gain of approximately 10 times and a power gain of about 20 dB. In turn, output signal from the collector of Q drives the primary of the AFT discriminator transformer at a tap point that provides a suitable Q value. Note that the primary is coupled to the secondary both inductively and capacitively. Capacitive coupling is provided by two 10-pF capacitors. This coupling arrangement develops conventional in-phase and out-of-phase discriminator action. Matched diodes CR1 and CR2 rectify the secondary output signal, and the dc error signal appears at A. Filtering action and a suitable time constant are provided by the 1-μF capacitor.

Notice in Fig. 5-23 that diode CR1 is reverse-biased, and diode CR2 is forward-biased. In turn, under no-signal conditions, approximately 3 V will appear at test point A. On the other hand, with a normal signal present, the AFT control voltage varies between 1 and 8 V. Note that the forward and reverse bias voltage applied to CR1 and CR2 operate to modify the conventional discriminator S curve as depicted in Fig. 5-24. This modified frequency response

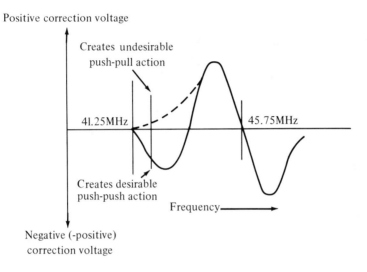

Fig. 5-24 Frequency response curve for an AFT discriminator. curve eliminates any push-pull circuit action with respect to the sound-IF (4.25 MHz) or the color subcarrier-IF (42.17 MHz), and the picture carrier-IF (45.75 MHz) frequencies, in case the oscillator drifts to a higher frequency.

It is evident that if push-push action were not provided by the AFT discriminator (instead of push-pull action), the sound-IF carrier would move up the S curve to produce a posi-tive-going correction voltage, whereas the picture-IF carrier would move down the S curve and produce a negative-going correction voltage. On the other hand, with push-push circuit action operative, both carriers will move in the same direction on the S curve and aid each other in producing a correction voltage. This correction or control voltage is applied in turn to a varactor diode, as seen in Fig. 5-25. This varactor

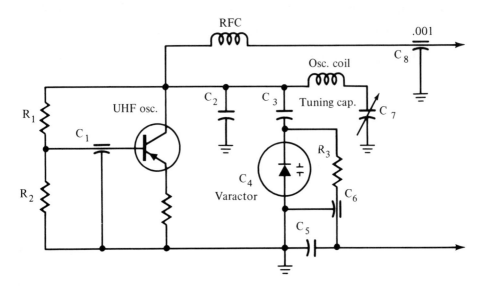

Fig. 5-25   Varactor control section for an AFT system.

diode operates as an electronic variable capacitor to maintain
correct local oscillator frequency in the UHF section.   In
this example, the varactor capacitance varies from 15 to 6 pF
as the control voltage varies from 1 to 8 V.

This AFT system provides a frequency pull-in range of
450 kHz and will hold the oscillating frequency within 50 kHz
of its design-center value.   AFT action is of considerable
advantage in UHF operation, because oscillator drift becomes
more of a problem at high frequencies.   Note that in VHF
operation, the pull-in range on high VHF channels is 300 kHz
in this example.   On low VHF channels, the pull-in range is
150 kHz.   Notice that the hold-in range of an AFT system is
considerably greater than its pull-in range.   That is, after a
station has been captured, the local oscillator must drift
considerably in frequency before AFT lock is broken.

An AFT on-off switch is customarily provided.   This
feature is desirable for facilitating the tuning in of com-

paratively weak stations. For example, suppose that a weak
UHF station is operating at a frequency in the vicinity of a
strong UHF station. Unless the AFT system is turned off when
the UHF tuner is being adjusted to receive the weak station,
it may be impossible to "find" the weak station. In other
words, if the AFT system is operative during the tuning-in
procedure, it will tend to capture the strong station and to
ignore the weak station. Therefore, turn the AFT system off
to tune in the weak station, and then turn the AFT system on
to obtain capture. Thereafter, the AFT system will continue
to lock in on the weak station.

5.7 IF Amplifier Troubleshooting

Symptoms of IF amplifier defects include weak picture,
no picture, poor definition, low contrast, sync buzz, smeared
picture, overload, and intermittent reception. Because many
of these symptoms can also be caused by RF tuner faults,
localization to the IF strip is required at the start of
troubleshooting procedures. A simple and effective approach
is to use a signal generator as a signal injector (Fig. 5-26).
Amplitude-modulated output at 43 MHz is used; a 250-pF capacitor is connected in series with the signal output lead of
the generator, to avoid dc bias drain-off. When the test
signal is injected at the base of an IF transistor, horizontal
bars are normally observed on the picture tube screen (Fig.
5-27). A typical AM signal generator is illustrated in Fig.
5-28.

As noted in Fig. 5-26, a VTVM or TVM can be connected
at the output of the video detector to measure the signal
voltage. A normal output level is 1 V peak to peak. The
generator signals is injected progressively at the bases of
the third, second, and first transistors. Approximate stage

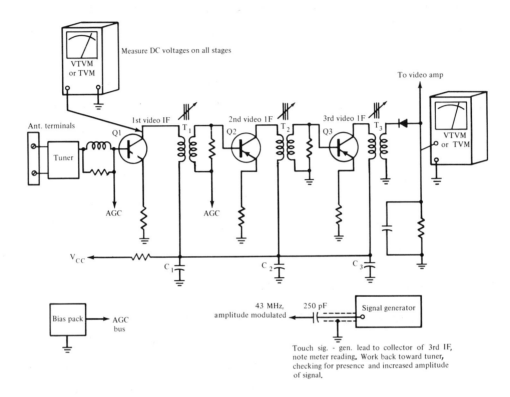

Fig. 5-26 Basic fault location procedures.

Fig. 5-27 Bar pattern produced on picture-tube screen by the signal from an AM generator.

Fig. 5-28 A typical AM generator. (Courtesy, Hewlett-Packard, Inc.)

gains may be observed. If the detector output falls to zero or is substantially attenuated in one of these steps, the fault is thereby localized to that particular IF stage. To close in on a defective component, dc voltage measurements are of greatest general utility. The measured values are compared with the values specified in the receiver service data.

Trouble in the AGC section can simulate trouble in the IF section. For example, the first and second stages in Fig. 5-26 are AGC controlled, whereas the third stage operates constantly at maximum gain. In case of a fault in the AGC system which cuts off the first and second transistors,

the first two stages will appear to be inoperative in the
signal injection test. Measurements of dc voltage will
point to the AGC section as the trouble source. If the AGC
line is clamped at a normal value with a bias pack, the
first two IF stages will then operate normally, thereby
confirming the preliminary conclusion.

IF oscillation can cause distorted picture reproduction,
or a no-picture symptom. Oscillation is usually caused by an
open capacitor, such as a bypass, decoupling, or neutralizing
capacitor. When the IF strip oscillates, a high-dc voltage
will be measured at the output of the video detector. That
is, oscillation generates a high-level IF voltage which is
rectified by the video detector. Overload in the IF section
is commonly caused by incorrect bias level(s).   This difficulty can be caused by capacitor leakage or by a fault in
the AGC section. Overload is often accompanied by sync buzz
in the sound, due to modulation of the intercarrier sound
signal by the vertical sync pulse.

When a tuned coil or transformer is replaced in the IF
section, alignment is required to obtain normal operation.
The purpose of alignment is to adjust the resonant frequencies
of the load and trap circuits in correspondence with the
specifications of the receiver service data.   In turn, the
overall IF response curve approximates the recommended bandwidth and contour, so that picture reproduction is optimized.
Two general methods of alignment are used in television
service shops. The simplest procedure is called the peak
alignment method; a somewhat more elaborate procedure is
called the sweep alignment method. The principles of peak
alignment follow (sweep alignment will be covered later):

1. With reference to Fig. 5-29, disconnect the UHF

cable from the VHF tuner and apply the output from a signal generator at the UHF input connector.

2. Clamp the AGC bus with a dc bias source to the voltage specified in the receiver service data.

3. Connect a VTVM or TVM at the output of the video detector.

4. Set the signal generator to the successive trap frequencies specified in the receiver service data. In each case, adjust the slug in the pertinent trap for minimum reading on the meter.

5. Set the signal generator to the successive peaking frequencies specified in the receiver service data. In each case, adjust the slug in the pertinent load circuit for maximum reading on the meter. (Reduce output from signal generator as required to avoid amplifier overload.) Overload results in an excessively broad and indefinite peak response.

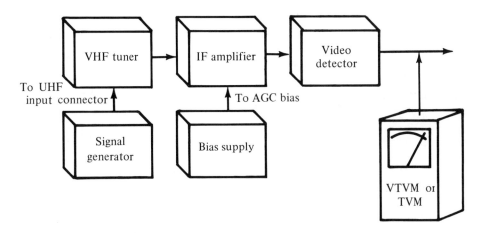

Fig. 5-29 Test setup for peak alignment of the IF section.

After the peak alignment procedure is completed, it is

good practice to obtain a plot of the IF response curve and to compare it with the curve specified in the receiver service data. Then, if necessary, compromise peaking adjustments can be made to improve the contour of the overall response curve. Because point-by-point plotting is tedious and time-consuming, experienced technicians prefer the sweep alignment method.

Questions

Short Answer

1. What is the function of an IF amplifier?
2. What is the function of the AGC circuit in the IF amplifier?
3. Why is the gain of the RF amplifier varied at a rate different from that of the IF amplifier by AGC circuit?
4. Why is the frequency progression reversed through the mixer stage so that the sound carrier is at a lower frequency than the picture carrier?
5. Explain how stagger-tuning can increase the bandwidth of a series of amplifier stages.
6. What is the function of the trap T_1 in the circuit shown in Fig. 5-6?
7. How does neutralization stabilize the operation of an IF amplifier?
8. Can you explain how a neutralizing capacitor can stabilize a transistor circuit?
9. How is the bandwidth extended in the IF amplifier circuitry in Fig. 5-9?
10. What is the advantage of a diode detector over a transistor detector?

11. What is the purpose of C_{10} and C_{17} in the circuit in Fig. 5-10?

12. In Fig. 5-9, which components make up the decoupling network for the -12-V supply?

13. In Fig. 5-9, why is capacitor C_{33} shunted by capacitor C_{34}?

14. What is the purpose of components L_2-C_3 in the circuit in Fig. 5-9?

15. What happens to the overall response curve in Fig. 5-11 if one of the amplifiers in Fig. 5-9 becomes weak?

16. What are the effects on the frequency response curve if any large amount of regeneration exists in the IF configuration?

17. Define an integrated circuit.

18. Why are integral resistors in an IC more temperature-sensitive than a conventional composition resistor is?

19. Why is the heat dissipation of an IC limited?

20. How would you troubleshoot an IC circuit?

21. What is the advantage of a transistor detector over a diode detector?

22. In Fig. 5-22, why is it desirable to eliminate the IF signal from the following video amplifier?

23. Why doesn't capacitor C bypass the video and sound signals in Fig. 5-22?

24. What are some of the symptoms of IF amplifier defects?

25. Explain the procedure for using a signal generator to troubleshoot an IF amplifier.

26. How are voltage measurements used to locate troubles in a television receiver?

27. What are some of the possible troubles that can cause oscillations in the IF section of a television receiver?

28. What are some of the troubles that can cause a sync buzz

in the sound section?

29. Discuss the peak alignment procedure for aligning an IF
     section.

30. Discuss the sweep alignment procedure for aligning the
     IF section.

True-False

1.   The maximum available gain of an IF amplifier is in the
     order of 4000 times.

2.   IF amplifiers operate in parallel.

3.   The gain of the RF stage and the IF stage are both con-
     trolled by the AGC voltage.

4.   The local oscillator in the RF tuner is usually made to
     operate on the low side of the RF signal.

5.   The sound carrier is passed at 10% of maximum response
     of the IF amplifier at a frequency of 22.5 MHz.

6.   One of the results of stagger-tuning is an increase in
     total overall circuit gain.

7.   The purpose of a neutralizing circuit is to stabilize
     the IF stage and to prevent oscillations.

8.   The 1.5-pF capacitor between the secondary of T_4 and
     the base of Q3 in Fig. 5-6 is a neutralizing capacitor.

9.   Resistors R_4 and R_5 in Fig. 5-9 are neutralizing
     resistors.

10. The purpose of capacitors C_{11}, C_{16}, C_{24}, and C_{27} in the
     circuit in Fig. 5-10 is neutralization.

11. A diode detector requires a relatively large signal
     level for proper operation.

12. The 1-kΩ emitter resistor in the circuit in Fig. 5-10
     extends the low-frequency response of the amplifiers.

13. Transistor junction capacitance changes appreciably
     with variation of base emitter bias.

14. In Fig. 5-9, capacitor C_{33} shunts capacitor C_{34} to increase its breakdown voltage.

15. Decoupling is used in the AGC line to prevent interstage coupling.

16. The response of the IF frequency curve in Fig. 5-11 drops to almost zero at 47.25 MHz, due to the effects of the picture carrier trap.

17. If any one transistor in the amplifier in Fig. 5-9 becomes weak, it causes little effect on the overall frequency response curve in Fig. 5-11.

18. An integrated circuit is a solid-state device comprised of transistors, diodes, resistors, and capacitors.

19. An integrated circuit has less stray capacitance than normal circuits, because of its small size.

20. External resistors must be used with an IC, because resistors cannot be formed in the IC.

21. External transformers are used with integrated circuits in IF amplifiers.

22. When two transistors are operated in series, they are called a cascade pair.

23. A diode detector has poor linearity and an insertion loss.

24. Most diode detectors use series detector circuits.

25. A diode detector operates as a rectifier.

26. When using a signal generator to troubleshoot an IF amplifier, a blocking capacitor should never be used between the generator and the IF input.

27. A TVM may be connected to the output of a video detector to measure the signal voltage.

28. Measurements of dc voltage are not of much help in troubleshooting the IF section of a television receiver.

29. Oscillation in the IF section can cause a distorted

picture or a no-picture symptom.

30. Oscillations are usually caused by a shorted capacitor, such as bypass, decoupling, or neutralizing.

31. An overload in the IF section can cause a sync buzz in the sound section.

32. After the peak alignment procedure is completed, it is good practice to plot the IF response curve.

33. Point-to-point plotting is most often used to check the IF response of a television receiver.

Multiple Choice

1. Most IF amplifiers use _____ stages.
   (a) 1   (c) 3
   (b) 2   (d) 4

2. The gain of a stage may be changed automatically over a wide range by the:
   (a) IF detector.
   (b) AGC voltage.
   (c) AFC section of the receiver.
   (d) remote control.

3. The sound carrier is passed at _____ of maximum response through the IF amplifier.
   (a) 5%   (c) 50%
   (b) 10%   (d) 90%

4. The sound level is kept low through the IF amplifier to prevent:
   (a) overdriving of the amplifier.
   (b) sound distortion.
   (c) distortion in the picture.
   (d) parallel lines.

5. Wide-band is obtained in the IF amplifier by:

    (a) peaking coils. (c) direct coupling.

    (b) RC coupling. (d) stagger-tuning.

6. Transistor Q_1 in the circuit in Fig. 5-6 cannot be completely cut off by the AGC voltage because of:

    (a) the clamp diode.

    (b) characteristics of the transistor.

    (c) leakage current.

    (d) temperature effect.

7. The purpose of a neutralizing capacitor is to:

    (a) prevent oscillation.

    (b) create temperature stability.

    (c) increase gain.

    (d) increase the frequency response.

8. The purpose of the shunt resistors across the primary windings of the circuit in Fig. 5-9 is:

    (a) to prevent oscillation.

    (b) for neutralization.

    (c) to increase the bandwidth.

    (d) for bias stability.

9. The primary of transformer T_1 in Fig. 5-10 is tapped to provide:

    (a) neutralization of Q3.

    (b) a sound trap.

    (c) a video trap.

    (d) an impedance match to the coaxial cable from the RF tuner.

10. The purpose of the 1-kΩ emitter resistor in the circuit in Fig. 5-10 is:

    (a) bias stability. (c) bandwidth.

    (b) neutralization. (d) filter action.

11. AGC is not used in the control stages of the circuit in
     Fig. 5-10 because:

     (a) AGC operates too slowly.

     (b) of the low-base emitter breakdown voltage.

     (c) transistor junction capacitance changes with a
          change of base emitter bias.

     (d) of the low L/C ratio of C_{10} and C_{17}.

12. Interstage coupling is prevented in the AGC line in the
     circuit in Fig. 5-9 by:

     (a) the diode detector.

     (b) a decoupling network.

     (c) the length of the wire.

     (d) bias on the transistors.

13. In Fig. 5-11, the frequency response drops off
     rapidly to 10% of maximum at 4.25 MHz. This is
     caused by:

     (a) sound trap L_2-C_3.

     (b) shunt capacitance of the transistors.

     (c) emitter resistors.

     (d) neutralization.

14. Two transistors operated in series such as Q1 and Q3 in
     Fig. 5-18 are called a/an _____ pair.

     (a) cascade

     (b) signal

     (c) differential

     (d) in-line

15. Troubleshooting an IC circuit is limited to:

     (a) feeling for excess heat.

     (b) external current and voltage measurements.

     (c) external voltage measurements.

     (d) external current measurements.

16. In Fig. 5-20, the video detector is driven by a/an:

    (a) IF amplifier.   (c) video amplifier.

    (b) RF amplifier.   (d) picture amplifier.

17. Most television receivers use _____ detector circuits.

    (a) series diode   (c) series transistor

    (b) parallel diode   (d) parallel transistor

18. In Fig. 5-22, capacitor C serves to:

    (a) bypass the sound signal to ground.

    (b) boost the dc voltage.

    (c) bypass the audio signal to ground.

    (d) bypass the IF signal to ground.

19. Symptoms such as weak picture, no picture, poor definition, low contrast, sync buzz, and overload and intermittent reception can all be caused by:

    (a) the tuner.   (c) the IF amplifier.

    (b) low-voltage power supply.   (d) the video amplifier.

20. To test an IF amplifier with a signal generator, use an _____ modulated signal at _____ MHz.

    (a) FM, 43   (c) FM, 39

    (b) AM, 43   (d) FM, 39

21. When an IF strip oscillates, we will measure a _____ voltage at the video detector output.

    (a) low-dc   (c) high-dc

    (b) low-ac   (d) high-ac

22. The sweep alignment method is used over the point-to-point system:

    (a) to save time.

    (b) for accuracy.

    (c) for safety.

    (d) because it takes less expensive equipment.

Chapter 6

VIDEO AMPLIFIERS

6.1 Video-Amplifier Section

The function of the video amplifier is to step up the
amplitude of the composite video signal from the picture
detector to a suitably high level for operation of the pic-.
ture tube.   It is more economical to amplify the picture
signal from 20 to 50 times after demodulation than to provide
final amplification prior to demodulation.   Picture quality
is also improved when the video detector is operated at a
moderate level. This response results because the forward
resistance of the diode decreases to a very low value on one
peak and increases to a very high value on the opposite peak.
In turn, excessive circuit-loading variation occurs if the
video detector is driven at a high level. With reference to
Fig. 6-1, a video-amplifier section is commonly composed of

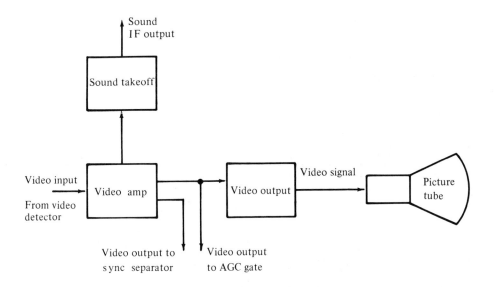

Fig. 6-1 Plan of the video amplifier section.

two stages. It amplifies the video-input signal from the
video detector from a level of approximately 1.5 V peak to
peak, to an output level at the picture tube of about 50 V
peak to peak.

Figure 6-2 depicts the waveform of a positive-going
composite video signal and the waveform of an FM sound
signal. Both signals are stepped up through the video-
amplifier section. However, the amplitude of the FM intercarrier sound signal is restricted to approximately 10% of
the composite video-signal amplitude. Unless the sound
signal is maintained at a comparatively low level in the
video-frequency channels, sound interference will become
visible in the picture. Note that the 4.5-MHz sound signal
is formed by heterodyning of the picture-IF carrier with
the sound-IF signal in the video-detector diode.

Observe in Fig. 6-1 that the sound takeoff circuit is
customarily located in the first video-amplifier stage.

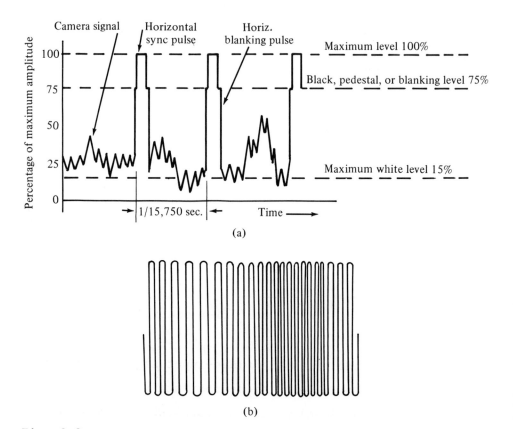

Fig. 6-2 Signal waveforms in the video amplifier channel:
(a) composite video signal (three lines), (b) frequency
modulated sound signal (4.5 MHz).

Another branch leads to the sync separator. As explained
in greater detail below, the sync separator functions to
strip the horizontal and vertical sync pulses from the composite video signal. In many receivers, still another branch
from the first video amplifier leads to the AGC section.
Note that the first video-amplifier, or driver, stage often
provides no voltage gain although it develops a current or
power gain. The signal voltage gain is generally contributed
by the video-output stage. The video-frequency channel provides a total gain of 28 dB in a typical example.

6.2 Basic Video-Amplifier Principles

It is instructive to observe the representative video-amplifier frequency response curve depicted in Fig. 6-3.

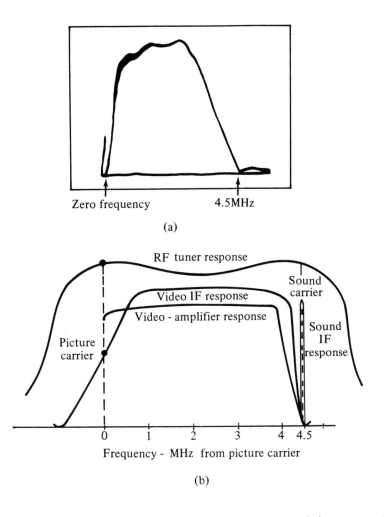

Zero frequency   4.5MHz

(a)

(b)

Fig. 6-3 Video amplifier frequency response: (a) typical video frequency response curve, (b) system relation of video amplifier response.

The response extends from almost zero frequency (dc) to 4.5 MHz; the sound takeoff circuit operates as a trap and produces the minimum overall response at 4.5 MHz. The bandwidth is measured between the 50%-of-maximum points on a television response curve, as shown in Fig. 6-4.   Thus,

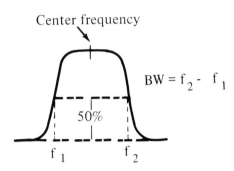

Center frequency

$BW = f_2 - f_1$

50%

f_1 f_2

Fig. 6-4 Definition of bandwidth for a television receiver
response curve.

the bandwidth of the response curve in Fig. 6-3 is approximately 3.5 MHz.   This bandwidth is typical of economy-type
receivers.   In deluxe receivers, the video-frequency bandwidth may range up to 4 MHz, or slightly more.   Extensive
bandwidth is desirable to maximize picture definition
(reproduction of fine detail).

A transistor video-amplifier configuration is shown
in Fig. 6-5.   Transistor Q1 operates in the emitter follower
mode to match the higher impedance of the video detector
to the lower impedance of transistor Q2.   In addition to
driving the video-output transistor, the emitter circuit of
Q1 also branches into the sound takeoff and sync takeoff
sections.   A 600-Ω potentiometer in the emitter circuit of
Q1 serves as a manual contrast control. L_1 is a peaking
coil that assists in obtaining uniform frequency response in
the video-detector output circuit. L_2 provides substantial
impedance at 4.5 MHz, so that most of the intercarrier sound
signal flows into the sound takeoff section.

The configuration in Fig. 6-5 is an ac-coupled ampli-

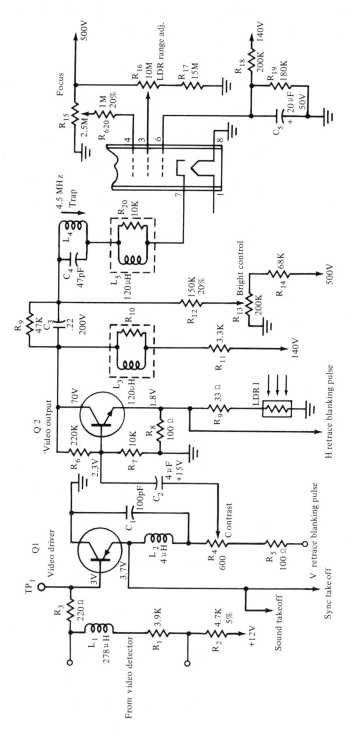

Fig. 6-5 An ac-coupled video amplifier configuration.

fier. The output signal from the contrast control is coupled
to Q2 via C_2. In turn, the dc component of the video signal
is lost; the technical significance of this ac coupling is
discussed at the end of this topic. Note that Q1 operates in
class A, with 0.7-V forward bias. Similarly, Q2 operates in
class A with a nominal forward bias of 0.5 V. The actual
emitter bias on Q2 is automatically controlled by the light-
dependent resistor LDR_1. This photoresistor changes in value
as the room illumination varies. In turn, when the ambient
lighting is high, the forward bias on Q2 increases, with
resulting increase in stage gain and image contrast. This
increase in forward bias also decreases the collector voltage
on Q2 and increases the raster brightness.

Peaking coil L_3 in Fig. 6-5 assists in maintaining full
response in the midband region.   This coil is shunted by
damping resistor R_{10} to lower the Q value of the load circuit
and minimize its tendency to ring transiently when a steep
wavefront is being processed.   The video-output stage operates at a   considerably higher level than the video-driver
stage.   Q2 is a power-type transistor and is supplied from
a 140-V source via L_3.   Q1 is a low-power transistor and is
supplied from a 12-V source via L_1. Basically, the collector
of Q2 is ac coupled to the cathode of the picture tube.
However, to permit automatic brightness control by LDR_1, C_3
is shunted by a 47-kΩ resistor.

In addition to the shunt peaking coil L_3 in the collector circuit of Q2 (Fig. 6-5), two series peaking coils are
employed to provide uniform frequency response and higher
gain. L_4 not only functions as a high-frequency peaking coil,
but also as a sound trap. That is, L_4 is resonated precisely
at 4.5 MHz. Thereby, visible dot interference (grain patterns)
are eliminated from the displayed picture. L_5 assists L_3 in

maintaining full response in the midband region. R_{15} varies the voltage on the focus grid in the picture tube and is set for maximum picture sharpness. Note that R_{16} varies the voltage on G_2 of the picture tube; it is provided to adjust the reference operating level of LDR_1.

Notice in Fig. 6-5 that vertical and horizontal blanking pulses are injected into the video-amplifier system. Blanking pulses function to cut off the picture tube during retrace, so that retrace lines are made invisible. In theory, blanking pulses are not required. That is, the blanking pedestals in the composite video signal are provided to cut off the picture tube during retrace. However, the blanking pedestals often fail to serve their intended purpose when ac-coupled video amplifiers are used. Therefore, unless the blanking pedestals are supplemented by blanking pulses, objectionable retrace lines may appear in the reproduced image. To anticipate subsequent discussion, the blanking pedestals will serve their intended purpose when dc-coupled video amplifiers are used.

Because a picture detector is basically a rectifier, the video signal has a certain polarity. The detector output signal is all negative, or all positive, depending on the polarity with which the diode is connected into the circuit. The detector output has an average value, which is called the dc component of the video signal. Figure 6-6 depicts two

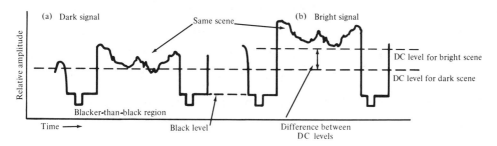

Fig. 6-6 How the dc component level shifts from a dark scene to a light scene.

basic examples of the dc component. The dc component has a
higher level when a bright picture is being reproduced.   In
other words, the dc component corresponds to the background
illumination of the televised scene.   The sync tips normally
remain in the blacker-than-black region, regardless of the
dc component level.

   A coupling capacitor cannot pass dc.   Therefore, the
dc component is lost from the video signal in an ac-coupled
circuit.   The result is that both light and dark scenes are
then reproduced by video signals that vary about the same
level (zero level), as shown in Fig. 6-7.   When the dc com-

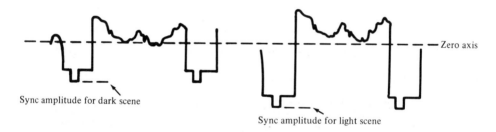

Fig. 6-7 Sync amplitude varies when the dc component is lost
from the composite video signal.

ponent is missing from the composite video signal, the sync
tips no longer remain in the blacker-than-black region.
Instead, the sync amplitude rises and falls in accordance
with the background illumination of the televised scene.
This variation is evident in Fig. 6-7.   In turn, the sync
tips have no fixed operating level at the picture tube, as
depicted in Fig. 6-8.   Consequently, the CRT beam current
is not cut off during retrace when dark scenes are being
reproduced and retrace lines become visible.   Hence, the
need for blanking pulses.

   It might be supposed that provision of blanking pulses
in an ac-coupled amplifier would be an insufficient solution

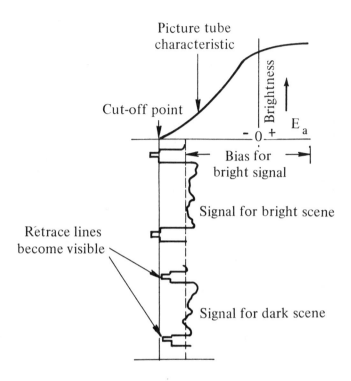

Fig. 6-8 Sync-tip level shifts at the picture tube when the dc component is lost.

to the problem of dc component loss. That is, blanking pulses merely eliminate visible retrace lines. Because the dc component is absent, night scenes tend to appear too light, and day scenes tend to appear too dark. However, this incorrect background illumination is actually less serious than it might seem. Basically, the viewer judges scenes on the basis of context to a considerable extent. For this reason, errors in background illumination are much less objectionable than are visible retrace lines. The majority of television receivers employ ac-coupled video amplifiers because of reduced production costs.

Blanking pulses are formed from deflection waveforms. A basic example is shown in Fig. 6-9. The vertical

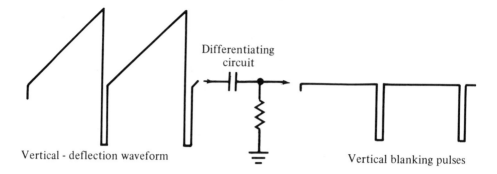

Vertical - deflection waveform   Vertical blanking pulses

Fig. 6-9 Formation of a vertical-blanking pulse from a vertical-deflection waveform.

deflection waveform is a peaked sawtooth. This waveform is passed through a differentiating circuit, and a blanking waveform is produced. This wave-shaping action occurs because the time constant of the differentiating circuit is chosen to reject the sawtooth component (low frequencies) and to pass the pulse component (high frequencies). The rapidly changing pulse component of the peaked sawtooth waveform is composed of higher frequencies than the slowly changing sawtooth component.

6.3 DC-Coupled Video Amplifiers

Many more dc-coupled video amplifiers are in use today than in past years. Figure 6-10 exemplifies a dc-coupled amplifier with modern design features. CR1 is the video-detector diode and is followed by a low-pass filter comprising C_3, L_1, L_2, and the base input capacitance of Q1. This network prevents passage of feedthrough-IF signal into Q1, thereby eliminating the possibility of overload and distortion from this source. Note that L_1 and L_2 are series and shunt peaking coils, respectively; they serve to maintain full response at midband and high-video frequencies. Q1 operates as an emitter follower with respect to Q2, thus providing

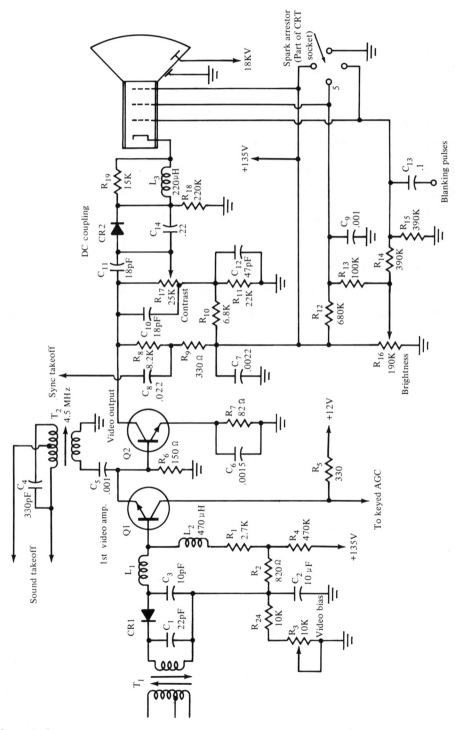

Fig. 6-10 A dc-coupled video amplifier configuration.

a practical impedance match between the video-detector and
the video-output stages.

Note that Q1 operates as a common emitter configuration
with respect to the keyed AGC takeoff branch in Fig. 6-10.
However, Q1 operates as an emitter follower with respect to
the sound takeoff branch. The operating point for this stage
is set by R_3, which is a maintenance control. Class-A
operation is utilized to avoid video-signal distortion.
Observe that the primary of T_2 provides 4.5-MHz trap action
in the emitter circuit of Q1. Thereby, most of the intercarrier sound signal branches into the sound takeoff channel,
and very little sound signal enters the base of Q2. If T_2
is not tuned precisely to 4.5 MHz, excessive intercarrier
sound signal will pass through to the picture tube, and
"sound grain" will appear in the image.

The video-output transistor Q2 operates in the CE configuration (Fig. 6-10). Its collector circuit drives the
picture tube input circuit, and also feeds the sync takeoff
branch circuit. Note that the contrast control R_{17} is
supplemented by the high-frequency compensating capacitors
C_{10} and C_{11}. These capacitors maintain normal passage of
the video frequencies when the control is set to attenuate
the signal considerably. Diode coupling is provided by CR2.
This form of dc coupling improves the gray range of the
reproduced image, because a picture tube is nonlinear, as
shown in Fig. 6-11. However, the semiconductor diode is also
nonlinear and tends to provide an overall linear characteristic. The diode is forward biased and does not operate
as a rectifier; it merely compensates for the picture tube
characteristic.

Picture brightness is varied by means of the brightness
control R_{16} in Fig. 6-10. Note that although dc coupling is

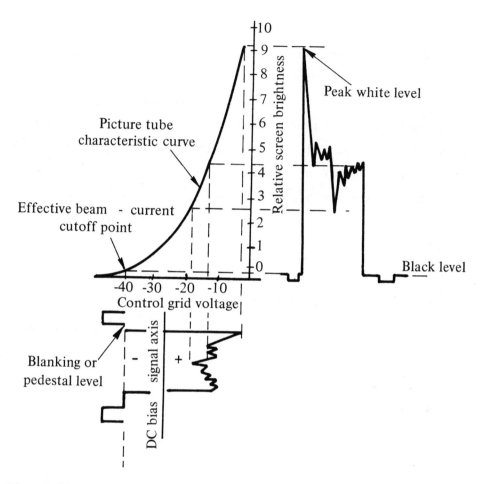

Fig. 6-11 A picture tube characteristic is nonlinear.

employed, blanking pulses are injected into the picture tube grid circuit via C_{13}. Although retrace blanking is not required when the picture tube is operating normally, set owners are generally reluctant to replace a failing picture tube. In compensation, the brightness control is turned up excessively to make up for the deteriorating screen phosphors. Under this abnormal condition of operation, retrace lines would be visible in the picture unless blanking pulses were provided. Uniform response at higher frequencies is maintained in the picture tube input circuit by the series peaking coil L_3.

Spark gap protection is provided for the video-output transistor Q2 in the configuration of Fig. 6-10. This precaution is required because picture tubes operate with a high-accelerating voltage (18 kV in this example), and an occasional spark discharge could occur. Because a transistor is instantly ruined if subjected to excessively high-collector voltage, a spark arrester device is commonly provided in the picture tube socket. This device consists of closely spaced points, so that a surge of excessive voltage will break down the air gap(s) and conduct the surge harmlessly to ground.

6.4 High-Frequency Compensation

High gain and wide-band response are contradictory characteristics in a video amplifier. In other words, if the bandwidth of an amplifier is doubled by increasing the load resistance, its gain will be approximately halved. Figure 6-12 shows the trade-off that is basically involved. As the

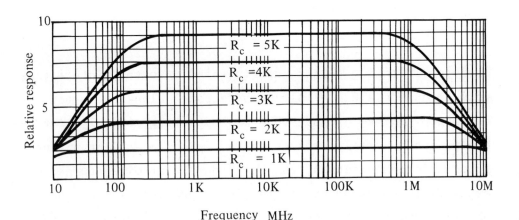

Fig. 6-12 Amplifier bandwidths for various values of load resistance.

load resistance value is reduced, the bandwidth is increased, and the gain is also reduced.   Simple resistive loads are impractical for video amplifiers that require uniform frequency response up to 4 MHz.   Therefore, peaking coils are generally used to supplement the load resistance and thereby provide high-frequency compensation.

Observe the principles of peaking action.   Figure 6-13

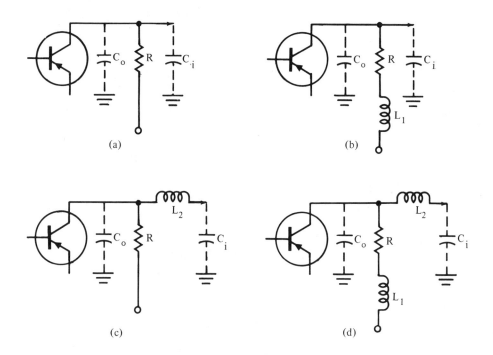

Fig. 6-13 Basic video amplifier load circuits: (a) resistive load, (b) with shunt peaking, (c) with series peaking, (d) with both series and shunt peaking.

shows three basic amplifier load configurations. In (a), the load is resistive; bandwidth is limited by the bypassing action of input and output capacitances C_o and C_i.   In (b), a shunt peaking coil L_1 is connected in series with the load resistor. This peaking coil has an inductance that will resonate with $C_o + C_i$ at a frequency in the region where the

response of (a) is falling off seriously.   The peaking coil
provides a parallel resonant, increasing load impedance with
increasing frequency, and the bandwidth of the stage is
thereby increased.

In Fig. 6-12(c), a series peaking coil is employed to
extend the high-frequency response.   However, instead of
operating as a parallel resonant circuit, note that L_2 operates as a series resonant circuit with respect to C_o and C_i.
A series resonant circuit provides a resonant rise of voltage
across the inductor and across the capacitor as the resonant
frequency is approached.   In turn, in the region where the
high-frequency response of (a) is falling off seriously, the
resonant frequency of L_2 is being approached in (c), and a
resonant rise of signal voltage appears across C_i.   Thus,
the bandwidth of the stage is effectively increased.

As might be anticipated, the maximum practical bandwidth
and gain in a video amplifier is obtained with a combination
of series and shunt peaking, as depicted in Fig. 6-12(d).   In
most designs, the inductance of L_1 is chosen to resonate in
the vicinity of midband, and L_2 is chosen to resonate in the
vicinity of high-frequency cutoff.   These peaking circuits
have performance characteristics that can be summarized in
various ways.   If all four loads are arranged to have the same
half-power bandwidth, the relative gain values are as follows:

1.   Resistive load: reference gain of 0.707 at cutoff
     point.

2.   With shunt peaking: gain of 1.

3.   With series peaking: gain of 1.5.

4.   With both shunt and series peaking: gain of 1.8.

In theory, it would be possible to obtain up to four

times the gain of an uncompensated stage by means of suitable peaking circuitry.   However, the   requirements are quite critical, and production engineers generally prefer compensating circuitry that provides somewhat more   than twice the gain of an uncompensated stage (1.8/0.707 = 2.54).

6.5 Integrated Video-Amplifier Units

Integrated circuits are used in the driver stages of some video amplifiers.   Figure 6-14 exemplifies an IC video-ampli-

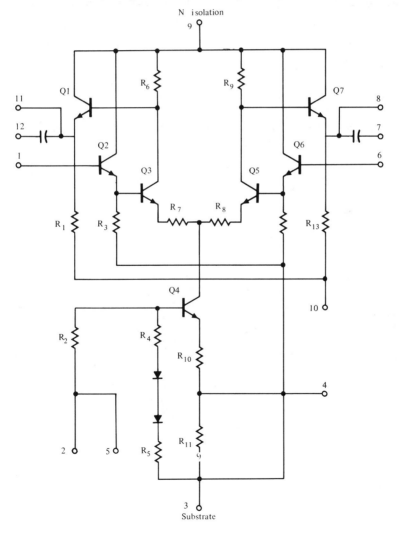

Fig. 6-14 A typical IC video amplifier package.

fier package. Terminal connections for operation from either
one or two dc supplies are shown in Fig. 6-15. Cascaded

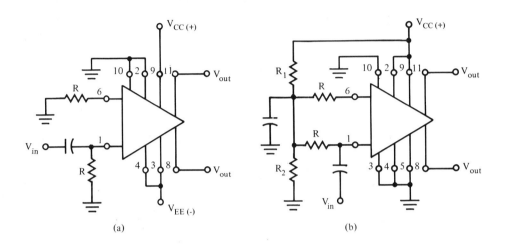

(a)   (b)

Fig. 6-15 Supply voltage arrangements: (a) connection of
IC to two dc supplies, (b) connection of IC to one dc supply.

arrangements such as depicted in Fig. 6-16 may also be utilized.

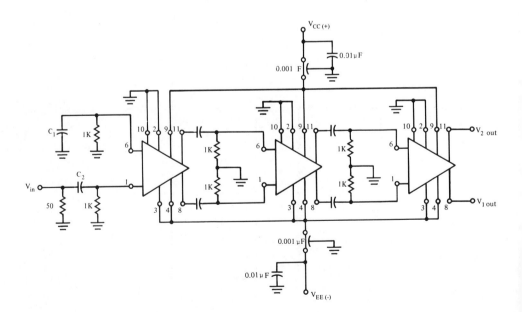

Fig. 6-16 Cascade operation of IC packages.

With reference to Fig. 6-14, transistors Q3 and Q5 operate in a differential amplifier configuration; this provides stability over a comparatively wide temperature range. Q4 is basically a common emitter load for Q3 and Q5; in addition, Q4 serves as a practical constant current source for Q3 and Q5, thereby contributing to operational stability.

The IC configuration in Fig. 6-14 provides high-input impedance and low-output impedance. These impedance relations result from connection of Q1, Q6, Q2, and Q7 in the emitter follower mode. Note that the IC package can be operated with push-pull input and push-pull output, or with push-pull input and single-ended output, or with single-ended input and push-pull output, or with single-ended input and single-ended output. Component values in the IC package are designed for provision of approximately uniform frequency response up to 4 MHz. Peaking coils are not used in any of the single or cascaded arrangements shown in Figs. 6-15 and 6-16.

With reference to Fig. 6-13, terminal 3 connects to a negative dc voltage source; terminal 9 connects to a positive dc voltage source. AGC voltage may be applied to terminal 2. When AGC is employed, increased dynamic range can be obtained by connecting terminal 10 to the negative dc voltage source. In most applications, however, terminals 2 and 10 are grounded. With reference to Fig. 6-15, the value of R is specified at 3300 Ω for optimum class-A operation. R_1 and R_2 have values that provide a current demand of 1.5 mA by the divider. When single-ended output is used, the IC package provides a gain of approximately 65 dB; double-ended output provides a gain of about 71 dB.

The maximum output signal voltage for the foregoing IC package is 6 V peak to peak in push-pull, or 3 V peak to peak in single-ended operation. This limitation is imposed by the

maximum rating of 6 V for each of the dc voltage supplies.
Accordingly, an IC driver must be followed by a special high-
voltage output transistor in order to operate the picture
tube.   The chief advantage of an IC driver stage is its simplicity from the standpoint of production.   Note that although
an IC is a unit, it has more parts than if discrete components
were used.

6.6   Transient Response of a Video Amplifier

Transient response is defined as the reproduction of a
steep wavefront, such as a sync pulse.   The transient response
of a video amplifier is usually checked with a square wave
generator, or a pulse generator (Fig. 6-17).   The reproduced

Fig. 6-17 A pulse generator suitable for testing video
amplifier transient response. (Courtesy, Simpson Electric
Co.)

square wave or pulse waveform is displayed on the screen of
a wide-band oscilloscope (Fig. 6-18). The vertical amplifier

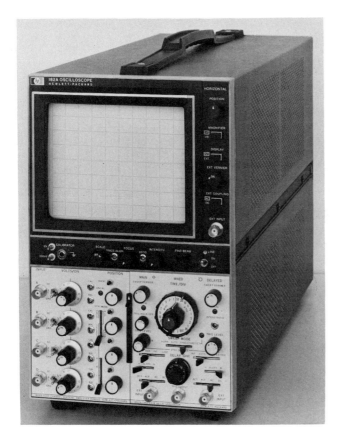

Fig. 6-18 A wide
band oscilloscope,
suitable for video
amplifier tests.
(Courtesy, Hewlett-
Packard, Inc.)

of the oscilloscope must have greater bandwidth than that of
the video amplifier under test. Note that a square wave is
different from a sine wave in that the square waveform can be
synthesized (built up) from a large number of sine waves, as
depicted in Fig. 6-19. This waveform is composed of a fundamental frequency, with a large number of harmonic frequencies.
All of the harmonics in a square waveform are odd harmonics--
that is, third, fifth, seventh, ninth, and so on. In theory
an infinite number of harmonics is required to synthesize a
perfect square wave. However, in practice, 20 harmonics
provide a reasonable reproduction of the waveform.

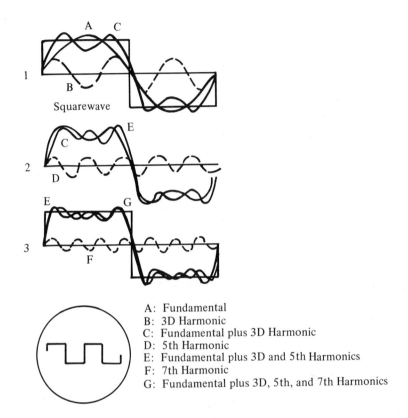

A: Fundamental
B: 3D Harmonic
C: Fundamental plus 3D Harmonic
D: 5th Harmonic
E: Fundamental plus 3D and 5th Harmonics
F: 7th Harmonic
G: Fundamental plus 3D, 5th, and 7th Harmonics

Fig. 6-19   How a squarewave is synthesized from a sinewave.

All of the harmonics depicted in Fig. 6-19 are in phase with the fundamental. In other words, the fundamental and all of the harmonics go through zero at the same instant at the start and end of the square wave. This is an important point, because if a video amplifier has phase distortion, the amplifier will shift the phases of some harmonics more than others.   In turn, the reproduced square wave will show this phase distortion in terms of sloping tops and bottoms in the reproduced square wave.   Phase distortion will also impair picture reproduction; that is, small image areas will undergo more or less phase shift (horizontal displacement) with respect to larger image areas. In turn, the edges of an image will appear smeared on the picture tube screen.

Figure 6-20 shows why an infinity of harmonics need not

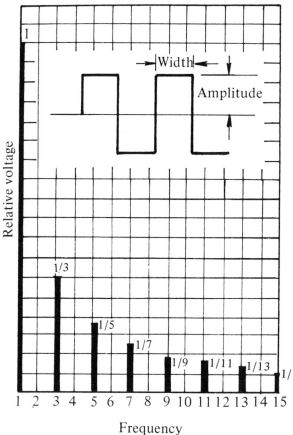

Fig. 6-20 Hormanic amplitude relations in a square waveform.

be included in a square waveform to obtain satisfactory reproduction of the waveform. Successive harmonics drop off rapidly in amplitude. Thus, the third harmonic has $\frac{1}{3}$ the amplitude of the fundamental, the fifth harmonic has $\frac{1}{5}$ the amplitude of the fundamental, and so on. Because the twentieth harmonic will have only $\frac{1}{20}$ the amplitude of the fundamental, its effect on the total waveform can often be neglected in practice. In exacting tests, however, as many as 40 harmonics might be taken into account. A video amplifier is often tested with a 100-kHz

square wave. The fortieth harmonic of the test signal has a
frequency of 4 MHz.

With reference to Fig. 6-21, square waves with different

Square - wave frequency	Time for ½ cycle	Percent of picture width	Relative length of continuous shade reproduced
1 MHz	0.5 µ sec.	1% (0.5/53.33 x 100)	▬
500 KHz	1 µ sec.	2% (1/53.3 x100)	▬▬
250 KHz	2 µ sec.	4% (2/53.3 x 100)	▬▬▬
100 KHz	5 µ sec.	10% (5/53.3 x 100)	▬▬▬▬▬▬

(a)

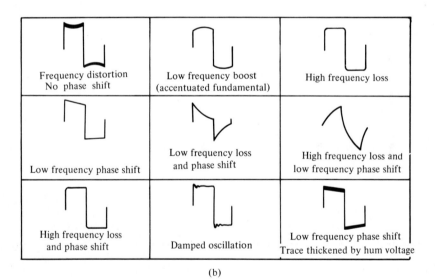

(b)

Fig. 6-21 Squarewave reproduction: (a) ideal reproduction
on picture tube screen, (b) oscilloscope presentations, with
various distortions.

repetition rates display black bars of various lengths on
the picture tube screen. An oscilloscope pattern affords
the best basis of distortion analysis. The more basic square

wave distortions and their causes are as follows:

1. Top and bottom of reproduced square wave are concave and level. Cause is low-frequency loss (chiefly fundamental) without accompanying phase shift.

2. Top and bottom of reproduced square wave are convex and level. Cause is low-frequency boost (chiefly fundamental) without accompanying phase shift.

3. Top and bottom of reproduced square wave are straight and level, but all corners are rounded. Cause is attenuation of the high-frequency harmonics without accompanying phase shift.

4. Top and bottom of reproduced square wave are tilted (top slopes downhill). Cause is leading low-frequency phase shift, with little or no frequency discrimination.

5. Top and bottom of reproduced square wave are tilted and concave (top slopes downhill). Cause is leading low-frequency phase shift with accompanying low-frequency attenuation.

6. Top and bottom of reproduced square wave are tilted and convex (top slopes uphill). Cause is lagging low-frequency phase shift with accompanying high-frequency attenuation.

7. Top and bottom of reproduced square wave are straight and level, but diagonal corners are rounded. Cause is high-frequency attenuation with accompanying phase shift.

8. Top and bottom of square wave are level but display
    transient ringing (damped oscillation).   Cause is
    a high-frequency peak in the frequency response of
    the video amplifier.

9. Top and bottom of the reproduced square wave are
    abnormally thickened (can be an accompanying symp-
    tom with any other form of distortion).   Cause is
    spurious hum voltage in the video amplifier.

Another basic characteristic of square wave or pulse
reproduction is the rise time of the waveform. Rise time is
depicted in Fig. 6-22; it is defined as the time that is
required for the leading edge of the reproduced square wave
to rise from 10% to 90% of its final amplitude. Rise time is
measured in μsec when the response of a video amplifier is
being checked. The rise time is indicated by the time base
calibration of a triggered sweep oscilloscope used in conjunction with the square wave or pulse generator. There is a
definite relation between the rise time of a video amplifier
and its bandwidth. This relation is formulated:

$$BW = \frac{1}{3T_r}$$

where: BW is measured in MHz,
         T_r is the measured rise time in μsec.

6.7 Video-Amplifier Troubleshooting

When a fault is suspected in the video-amplifier section,
it is necessary to first check the output signal from the picture detector. This is accomplished to best advantage with
an oscilloscope; the output waveform (if any) can be observed
and its peak-to-peak voltage measured. If the waveform has

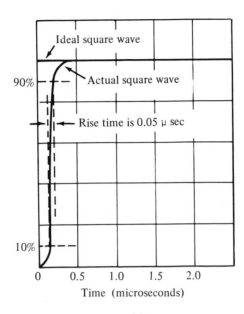

(a)

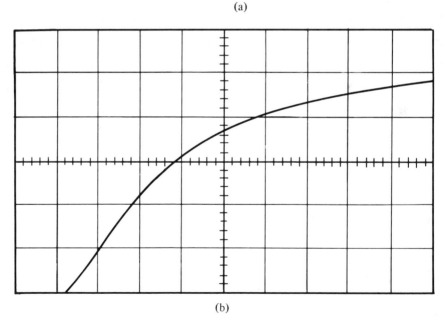

(b)

Fig. 6-22 Rise time measurement of video amplifier response: (a) definition of rise time, (b) expansion of leading edge for accurate measurement.

normal amplitude and is undistorted, the trouble will be found in the preceding IF or RF sections. The normal ampli-tude for the detector output waveform will be specified in the receiver service data; from 1 to 3 V peak to peak is typical. Serious distortion of the waveform can also be noted in this test. For example, the top or bottom of the waveform might be clipped off, or there might be obvious interference in the signal. IF amplifier faults are generally responsible for a distorted detector output waveform.

In case the detector output waveform is weak or absent, the picture detector may be at fault. The most common defect is an open- or short-circuited semiconductor diode. A quick check can be made by applying a demodulator probe at the output of the IF section and observing the demodulated IF waveform (if any) on the scope screen. If normal signal output is present from the IF section, there is a defective component in the picture detector section. To check the semiconductor diode, one lead should be disconnected, and the front-to-back resistance ratio of the diode measured with an ohmmeter. A good diode has a low-forward resistance (often less than 100 Ω), and a very high-back resistance (often more than 0.5 MΩ). When replacing a semiconductor diode, it is

essential to observe correct polarity. Otherwise, a negative picture will be displayed, with accompanying sync and AGC trouble symptoms. Figure 6-23 shows the configuration for a typical demodulator probe, used with a service-type oscilloscope. Note that a demodulator probe distorts the composite video signal; however, it is a useful indicator for presence or absence of IF signal.

In the event that a normal composite video signal is observed at the output of the picture detector, the trouble will often be found in the video-amplifier section. However, it is possible that a weak picture or no-picture symptom can be caused by a defective picture tube. Therefore, it is good

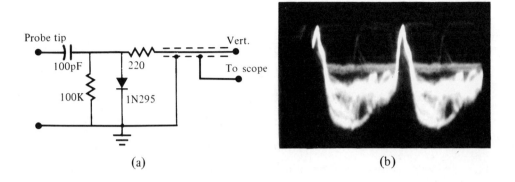

Fig. 6-23 Demodulator probe for oscilloscope: (a) typical
configuration, (b) oscilloscope display.

practice to observe the output waveform from the video amplifier with an oscilloscope. A low-capacitance probe is
generally used with the scope in this test, to avoid the
possibility of circuit loading and disturbance. Figure 6-24

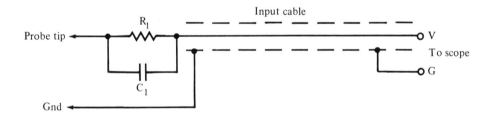

Fig. 6-24 Basic low-capacitance probe configuration.
shows the configuration for a typical low-capacitance probe.
This type of probe exploits a trade-off between signal amplitude and input impedance. Most probes provide a signal
attenuation of 10 to 1, and an impedance increase of 10 times.
Thus, R_1 has a resistance equal to 9 times the scope input
resistance, and C_1 has a capacitance equal to $\frac{1}{9}$ of C.

When normal video-signal amplitude is observed at the
output of the video amplifier, the picture tube is at fault

and requires replacement.   Note that the   normal signal
amplitude is   specified in the   receiver service   data; a
value of 50 V peak to peak is typical.   If the video-signal
amplitude is seriously subnormal, or seriously distorted at
the output of the video amplifier, the trouble will be found
in the video-amplifier section.   Preliminary localization can
be accomplished by signal-tracing with a scope and low-
capacitance probe.   Thus, the fault might be localized to
the driver stage, or to the output stage.   To close in on the
defective component, dc voltage measurements are made and
compared with the values specified in the receiver service
data.   Logical reasoning concerning a group of incorrect
voltage values will lead the technician to a leaky capacitor,
a defective transistor, open peaking coil, or an off-value
resistor.

Questions

Short Answer

1.   What is the function of the video amplifier?
2.   Why is the amplitude of the sound signal restricted to
     about 10% of the composite video level?
3.   What is the function of the video detector?
4.   What is the function of the sync separator?
5.   What is the typical range of the frequency response of
     a video amplifier?
6.   What is the purpose of the contrast control?
7.   What is the purpose of the photo resistor LDR_1 in
     Fig. 6-5?
8.   What is the purpose of blanking pulses?

9. Why are blanking pulses required?

10. What is the function of the picture detector?

11. What is the relationship between the dc voltage level of the output of the picture detector and the brightness of the scene?

12. Why do most television manufacturers use ac-coupled video amplifiers?

13. What is the source of the blanking waveforms?

14. What is the purpose of transformer T_2 in the schematic diagram in Fig. 6-10?

15. What is the purpose of diode CR2 in the circuit shown in Fig. 6-10?

16. What is the purpose of the spark gap device in the circuit shown in Fig. 6-10?

17. What is the purpose of the diode shown in the circuit in Fig. 6-11?

18. What is the bandwidth of a video amplifier in which the rise time of a square wave response is 80 nsec?

True-False

1. Two functions of the video amplifier are to amplify the picture signal and to amplify the sound signal.

2. A video-amplifier section usually consists of only one stage.

3. The output of the video amplifier is about 10 V peak to peak.

4. The sound level must be kept to a low level in the video-frequency channels.

5. The 4.5-MHz sound signal is formed by heterodyning of the picture-IF carrier with the sound-IF signal in the video-detector stage.

6. The first video amplifier often provides no voltage gain, although it provides power gain.

7. The dB gain of a typical video-frequency channel is around 60 dB.

8. The bandwidth of the video section of a typical television receiver is about 6 MHz.

9. One purpose of an emitter follower amplifier is to match a high impedance to a low impedance.

10. Peaking coils are used in the video section to extend the low-frequency response.

11. A photoresistor changes in value as the light on the resistor changes.

12. Blanking pulses are not required during the retrace time.

13. The picture detector is basically a rectifier.

14. A capacitor blocks dc voltages.

15. The purpose of the blanking pulses is to reduce the brightness level on the CRT during a night scene.

16. Misadjustment of the 4.5-MHz sound trap will cause loss of sound in a television receiver.

17. Transistor Q1 in the schematic diagram in Fig. 6-10 is connected as an emitter follower.

18. Transistor Q1, in Fig. 6-10, operates as an emitter follower in respect to the sound takeoff branch and as a common emitter with respect to the keyed AGC takeoff branch.

19. Blanking pulses are not used in the circuit shown in Fig. 6-10 because dc coupling is employed.

20. Unless blanking was employed in the dc-connected circuit shown in Fig. 6-10, retrace lines would be visible as the picture tube aged.

21. The problem with IC circuits being used in video amplifiers is that they have a very low high-frequency response.

22. The chief advantage of an IC driver is its simplicity from the standpoint of production.
23. The diode shown in Fig. 6-10 is used as an AGC rectifier.
24. One disadvantage of the IC amplifier shown in Fig. 6-14 is its low gain.

Multiple Choice

1. The circuit that is used to step up the amplitude of the composite video signal from the picture amplifier to a level for operation of the picture tube is the:
   (a) picture detector.
   (b) video amplifier.
   (c) picture amplifier.
   (d) tuned amplifier.
2. The output of the video amplifier is about:
   (a) 1.5 V.
   (b) 15 V.
   (c) 50 V.
   (d) 150 V.
3. The amplitude of the sound signal is approximately _____ of the composite video signal.
   (a) 1%
   (b) 10%
   (c) 50%
   (d) 90%
4. The 4.5-MHz sound-IF carrier with the sound signal is developed in the:
   (a) transmitter.
   (b) RF amplifier.
   (c) RF detector.
   (d) video detector.

5. Typically, a video frequency provides a gain of approxi-
    mately:

    (a) 2.8 dB.   (c) 28 dB.

    (b) 15 dB.   (d) 150 dB.

6. A typical television receiver has a video section with
    a bandwidth of about:

    (a) 2.2 MHz.   (c) 6.2 MHz.

    (b) 3.5 MHz.   (d) 8.1 MHz.

7. A picture detector is basically a/an:

    (a) rectifier.   (c) oscillator.

    (b) amplifier.   (d) CRT.

8. In reference to the schematic diagram in Fig. 6-10,
    misadjustment of T_2 will cause:

    (a) sound gain in the picture image.

    (b) retrace lines in the picture.

    (c) blanking of the picture.

    (d) blooming of the picture.

9. The purpose of a transistor amplifier being connected
    as an emitter follower is primarily for:

    (a) voltage gain.   (c) power gain.

    (b) frequency response.   (d) impedance matching.

10. Capacitors C_{10} and C_{11} in Fig. 6-10 are used:

    (a) as dc filters for the emitter voltage.

    (b) as high-frequency compensating capacitors.

    (c) as low-frequency compensating capacitors.

    (d) as a voltage divider for the video-output signal.

11. The purpose of the spark gap protection in transistor
    Q2 is to:

    (a) protect the operator.

    (b) protect the picture tube.

    (c) protect the high-voltage circuit.

    (d) protect transistor Q2.

12. The maximum practical bandwidth of a video amplifier is obtained by:

(a)   use of series peaking coils.

(b)   parallel peaking coils.

(c)   purely resistive loads.

(d)   a combination of series and parallel peaking coils.

13. The purpose of connecting transistors in a differential amplifier configuration is:

(a)   for maximum signal gain.

(b)   for temperature stability.

(c)   for impedance matching.

(d)   for a better signal-to-noise ratio.

14. Malfunction of either of the transistors in the IC package shown in Fig. 6-13 would be corrected by:

(a)   replacing the entire package.

(b)   replacing the faulty transistor.

(c)   replacing all transistors.

(d)   sending the set to the factory.

15. Transient response of a video amplifier is usually checked with a/an:

(a)   sine wave generator.

(b)   spectrum analyzer.

(c)   oscilloscope.

(d)   square wave generator and an oscilloscope.

16. The rise time of a pulse or square wave is measured as the time between:

(a)   0% and 90%.

(b)   10% and 90%.

(c)   50% and 50%.

(d)   90% and 100%.

Chapter **7**

AUTOMATIC GAIN
CONTROL

7.1 Principles of AGC Action

Although the picture tube requires a certain video-
signal amplitude for normal operation, the antenna input
signal generally varies over a wide range from one channel
to another.   Thus, the antenna might supply 5 μV of signal
on one channel, and 300,000 μV of signal on another channel.
A television receiver should display each of these signals
with approximately equal contrast on the picture tube screen;
automatic control of the output signal level is essential.
Therefore, an AGC section is required.

Good picture and sound reproduction necessitate that
the video detector operate at about 2 or 3 V peak to peak.
The detector diode is a nonlinear device; if the diode is

operated at a low level, the gray range of the picture becomes distorted, and sync buzz is introduced into the intercarrier sound signal. When a detector diode is operated on the highly curved portion of its characteristic (Fig. 7-1), the highlights of the image become compressed.

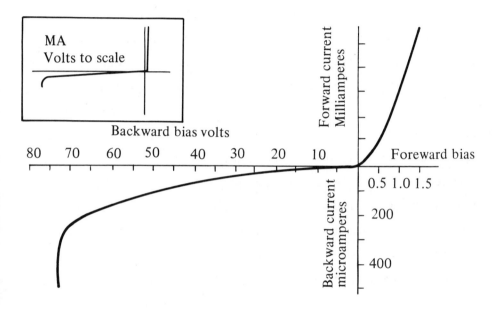

Fig. 7-1 E-I characteristics of a germanium diode.

As explained in greater detail subsequently, highlight compression in the video detector also causes the intercarrier sound signal to become amplitude modulated by the vertical sync pulse.

Because the video detector needs to be operated at a comparatively fixed level, AGC is employed only in the RF and IF sections. The last IF stage operates at constant gain and is not included in the AGC system. The reason is that the last IF stage must process a high-level IF signal. The last IF stage necessarily operates with a large signal swing; because AGC reduces the dynamic range of a stage, the last IF stage is the least desirable point to apply AGC. If AGC were applied in the last IF stage, objectionable picture and sound distortion would occur due to driving the stage into excessively nonlinear regions of its characteristic.

AGC voltage is applied to the RF tuner and to all but the last IF stage. However, delayed AGC is generally employed in the RF tuner. That is, the RF tuner operates at maximum gain until the incoming signal strength is sufficient so that AGC action has reduced the IF gain appreciably. Then, AGC voltage is applied to the RF amplifier, and the gain of the RF stage decreases as the applied signal level increases. The advantage of delayed AGC is an improvement in receiver sensitivity at weak signal levels. The signal-to-noise ratio is poor in weak signal reception, and the noise voltages would otherwise prevent operation at maximum gain, unless delayed AGC were used. This is an important factor in weak signal reception, because the incoming signal needs to be processed at maximum available gain.

7.2 Types of AGC Systems

Two fundamental types of AGC action are used to vary the beta (gain) of RF and IF transistor stages. Reverse AGC operation consists in reducing the forward bias on a transistor, so that collector current cutoff is approached. Forward AGC operation consists of increasing the forward bias on a transistor, with simultaneous reduction in collector voltage and shift of operation into the collector saturation region. Forward AGC requires substantial series resistance in the collector circuit. Consequently, as the collector current is increased, more of the collector supply voltage appears as an IR voltage drop across this series resistance. In turn, the collector voltage approaches zero at high values of forward bias. The beta value of a transistor decreases when either the collector current or the collector voltage is greatly reduced. Mesa transistors provide more gradual control with reverse AGC, whereas MADT's provide more gradual control with forward AGC.

Subclassifications of AGC arrangements include delayed AGC, unkeyed AGC, keyed AGC, and amplified AGC. These subclasses can be divided further into IF or video-takeoff points, combined video and AGC or separate video and AGC detectors, combined IF and AGC or separate IF and AGC amplifiers, and various other design methods. Figure 7-2 shows

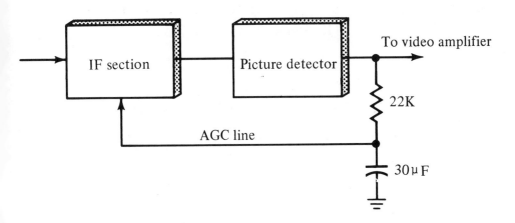

Fig. 7-2 Plan of a simple AGC arrangement.

the plan of a simple AGC arrangement. The composite video signal from the picture detector branches into a low-pass filter comprising a 22-kΩ resistor and a 30-μF capacitor. The voltage on the AGC line is the dc component of the composite video signal. All of the ac components in the signal are removed by the low-pass filter. If the amplitude of the picture detector output increases, the AGC voltage will increase also. The AGC voltage can be used to control the gain of the IF amplifier and thereby maintain the output from the picture detector at a comparatively constant strength.

As shown in Fig. 7-3, the gain of a conventional IF

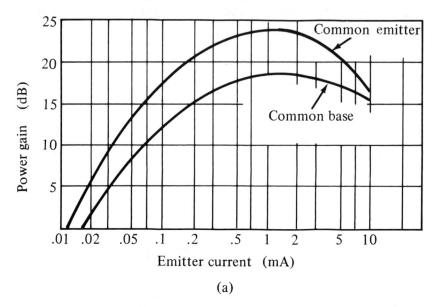

(a)

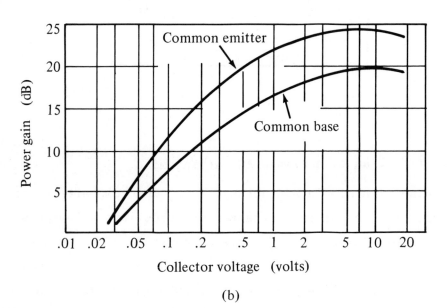

(b)

Fig. 7-3 Examples of AGC action for a typical transistor:
(a) reverse AGC in CE and CB configurations, (b) forward
AGC in CE and CB configurations.

transistor can be varied over a range of approximately 20 dB either by control of emitter current (reverse AGC), or by control of collector voltage (forward AGC). The basis of reverse AGC action is seen in Fig. 7-4; the collector current

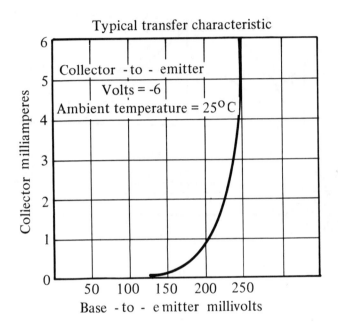

Fig. 7-4 Transfer characteristics for a typical transistor. (Courtesy, Radio Corporation of America)

increases slowly as the base emitter voltage is increased from 100 to 200 mV. The collector current increases rapidly as the base emitter voltage is increased from 200 to 250 mV. Thus, if the operating point of the transistor were placed at 100-mV base emitter bias by the AGC line, an applied signal would produce practically no collector output signal. However, if the operating point of the transistor were placed at 225-mV base emitter bias by the AGC line, an applied signal would produce quite a substantial collector output signal. With an operating point of 250 mV, a very large collector-output signal would be produced.

Figure 7-5 shows a family of collector characteristics for

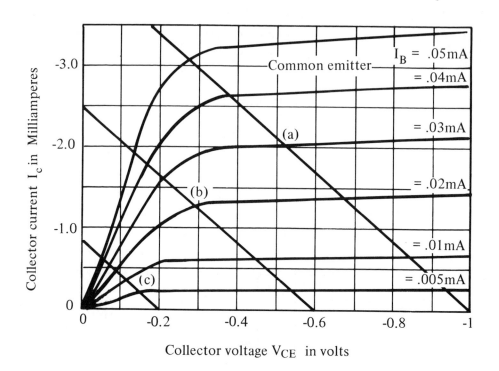

Fig. 7-5 Basis of forward AGC action.

the region of collector potential below 1 V. A 240-Ω load line
(a) is drawn from V_{ce} = 1; the 240-Ω load line (b) is drawn
from V_{ce} = 0.6; and the 240-Ω load line (c) is drawn from
V_{ce} = 0.2. An I_b swing from 0.02 to 0.03 mA produces different
I_c swings on the three load lines. Thus, there is a swing of
0.6 mA on (a), 0.3 mA on (b), and 0.1 mA on (c). As the collector voltage is reduced to small values, the gain of the
transistor also decreases.

As depicted in Fig. 7-6, the AGC system controls the
gain of both the RF section and the IF section.   In most
receivers, delayed AGC is employed.   This term denotes the
fact that the RF section operates at maximum gain on weak
signals, and that gain reduction is applied to the IF section

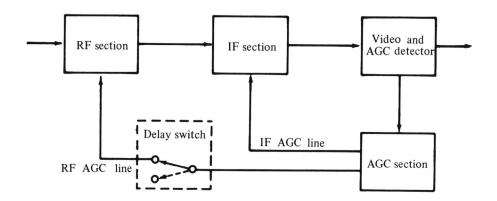

Fig. 7-6 The AGC system controls the gain of both the RF and the IF sections.

first.   On stronger signals, the gain of the RF section is reduced somewhat, while the gain of the IF section continues to be reduced.   This arrangement prevents noise voltages from impairing the gain of the receiver when tuned to weak signals.   Delayed AGC is obtained by means of switch action in the RF AGC line.   This is an electronic switch, such as a reverse-biased diode.   The diode represents an open cir- cuit until the AGC voltage increases past a certain value; thereupon, the diode becomes forward biased and represents a closed circuit.

Deluxe receivers employ keyed AGC.   A common form of keyed AGC system is depicted in Fig. 7-7.   This arrangement does not exploit the dc component of the composite video signal.   Instead, the AGC voltage is obtained by sampling the tips of the horizontal sync pulses.   The output from a dc-coupled video amplifier is fed into a sampler device, which is also gated on and off by pulses from the horizontal deflection system.   Thus, the output from the sampler device consists of pulses with a 15,750-Hz repetition rate.   These are dc pulses with an amplitude corresponding to the ampli-

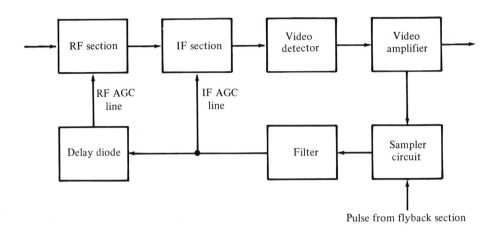

Fig. 7-7 Plan of a keyed AGC system.

tude of the horizontal sync pulses in the composite video
signal.   An RC filter smooths the pulse train into nearly
pure dc, which is utilized as AGC voltage. The chief advantage of keyed AGC is the fact that 60-Hz vertical sync
pulses are not utilized.   In turn, the filter can have a
much shorter time constant, and the AGC system becomes more
quickly responsive to changing signal levels.   For example,
airplane flutter in the signal is much less annoying to the
viewer when keyed AGC is utilized.

    Amplified AGC, as depicted in Fig. 7-8, can be used

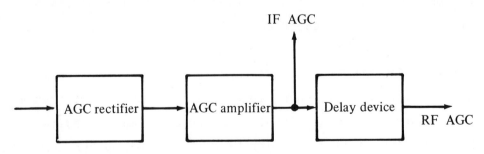

Fig. 7-8 Plan of an amplified AGC system.

with any type of AGC source.   Most receivers have at least one stage of AGC amplification. This is a dc amplifier that steps up the level of the control voltage from the source. The advantage of amplified AGC is greater uniformity of receiver response when going from very weak to very strong signals. No AGC system can keep the picture contrast at exactly the same level when the RF tuner is switched from a weak channel to a strong channel. However, the control action provided by an AGC system becomes more efficient if AGC amplification is used. The AGC control function approaches the ideal to the extent that greater amplification is provided for the AGC voltage.

7.3 AGC Circuitry

Economy-type receivers often utilize the same semiconductor diode for the video detector and AGC detector. This configuration is shown in Fig. 7-9. The 22-kΩ resistor

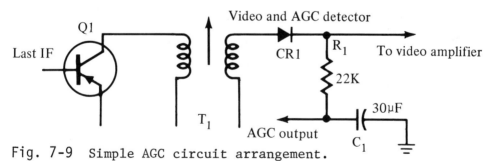

Fig. 7-9 Simple AGC circuit arrangement.

and 30-µF capacitor operate as an RC filter to develop the dc component of the composite video signal. Note that the time constant of this arrangement is 0.66 sec. Because the period of the vertical sync pulse is 0.016 sec, approximately, the AGC output is practically pure dc. The polarity of the AGC voltage is positive in this example. This configuration is termed a simple AGC system, because it utilizes a minimum number of components. For the same reason, its control efficiency is less than for more elaborate configurations.

Improved control action could be obtained using a separate AGC detector diode with a takeoff point from a dc-coupled video amplifier. Although this variation is theoretically attractive, it is not used extensively, due to difficulties from residual drift encountered in dc video amplifiers.

Separate AGC detectors are often utilized in simple AGC systems as shown in Fig. 7-10.   The arrangement in (a)

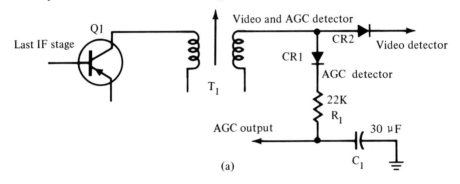

(a)

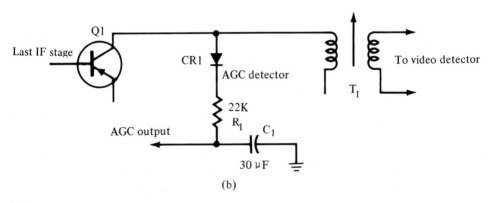

(b)

Fig. 7-10 Simple AGC circuits using a separate AGC detector: (a) takeoff from secondary of last IF transformer, (b) takeoff from primary of last IF transformer.

employs AGC takeoff from the secondary of the last IF transformer. It has a minor advantage in that the AGC detector diode isolates the AGC system from the video-amplifier channel so that the AGC voltage cannot back up from the RC

filter into the video-detector diode. A variation of the
foregoing arrangement is seen in (b). In this configuration
the AGC takeoff point is located on the primary side of the
last IF transformer. Its performance characteristics are
practically the same as in (a). Note in passing that circuit
equivalents which are based on personal preferences of design
engineers, or to avoid patent infringements, are often
encountered.

Two general types of AGC amplifiers are utilized in
the more elaborate AGC systems. Figure 7-11 shows a widely

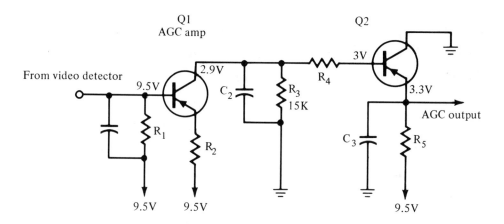

Fig. 7-11 An AGC amplifier configuration.

used configuration for an AGC amplifier section. This type
of amplifier processes the AGC control voltage only. Q1 and
Q2 are dc coupled to each other and to the video-detector
source voltage. A video detector has a comparatively high
impedance (1500 Ω) with respect to an AGC line (typically
300 Ω). Therefore, the AGC line is usually driven by an
emitter follower (Q2 in this example). An approximate impedance match is thereby obtained, which optimizes the efficiency
of the amplifier. Because Q2 does not provide as much power

gain as desired in the system, Q1 is also employed to drive Q2. This AGC amplifier stage operates in the common emitter mode and provides considerably increased dynamic range.

Three AGC filter sections are provided in the configuration of Fig. 7-11. C_1 serves the same function as the 30-μF capacitor C_1 in Fig. 7-9. Additional filtering is provided by C_2 and C_3 in Fig. 7-11. A 220-Ω resistor R_2 is connected in series with the emitter branch of Q1. This resistor develops emitter degeneration (current feedback) which provides bias stability for this stage. A similar function is served by R_5 in the emitter follower stage. C_3 bypasses R_5 for ac only, and R_5 develops emitter current feedback. Although the AGC voltage range varies considerably according to design, a variation of 1 V from weak signal to strong signal reception is typical.

Now consider the keyed AGC configuration shown in Fig. 7-12. Note that Q1 processes the IF signal; however, it is not a conventional IF amplifier stage. A keying pulse from the horizontal flyback section is applied to Q1 via pulse-gate diode CR1. The function of CR1 is to insure that a negative dc pulse is applied to the transistor. This is

the supply voltage for Q1, and the -0.95 V at its collector represents the average value of this pulse-gate voltage. Because Q1 is pulsed, the ac voltage applied to T_1 consists of a train of pulsed bursts, as depicted in Fig. 7-13. The ac component has a frequency of approximately 42 MHz, which is rectified by diode CR1. Thus, a negative dc voltage appears at the output of the RC filter $C_8 R_7 C_7$ (Fig. 7-12). This AGC voltage is applied to the base of Q2. An emitter follower configuration is utilized to provide a low-output impedance to the AGC line.

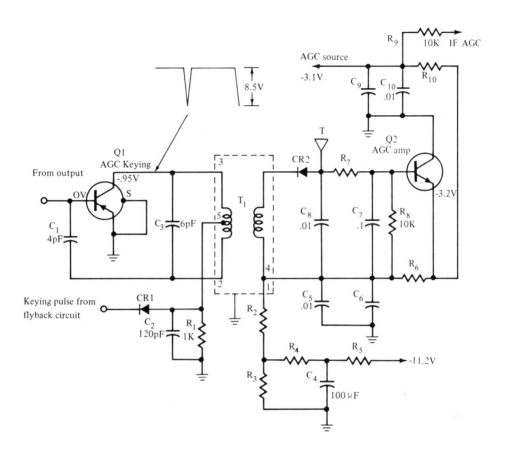

Fig. 7-12 A keyed AGC section.

Transistor Q1 in Fig. 7-12 operates as a common emitter amplifier, in addition to serving as a switching device. In operation, the collector voltage of Q1 remains practically unchanged from weak signal to strong signal conditions. This constant collector potential results from the fact that the 8.5-V gating pulse drives the transistor into saturation, regardless of the base signal amplitude. However, due to the base emitter characteristic, the amplified IF signal applied to T_1 varies in amplitude according to the amplitude of the IF signal applied to the base of Q1. Note that the emitter voltage of Q2 has a range of about 1 V;

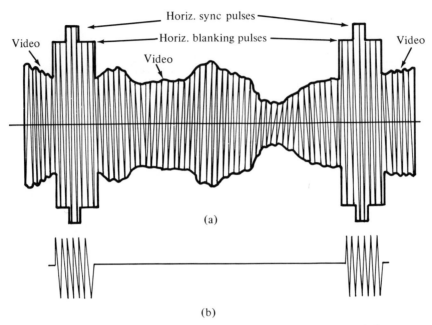

(a)

(b)

Fig. 7-13 Sampling process of keyed AGC stage: (a) IF
signal input to keyed transistor, (b) sampled horizontal
sync-pulse output.

that is, during weak signal reception the emitter voltage is
about -3.2 V, but during strong signal reception the voltage
changes to approximately -2.2 V.

   Now observe the configuration shown in Fig. 7-14. This
arrangement employs the IF transistors as AGC amplifiers,
in addition to their conventional function as IF signal amplifiers. AGC voltage is directly applied to the first stage.
The control voltage is dc coupled through the IF amplifier
circuitry and is applied to the second and third IF stages
also. The first and second stages operate as current amplifiers with respect to the applied AGC current. Forward AGC
is employed in the first and second IF stages, whereas reverse
AGC is utilized in the third stage. Thereby, bandwidth variation is practically eliminated over a wide range of signal
levels. The disadvantages of forward AGC are largely cancelled

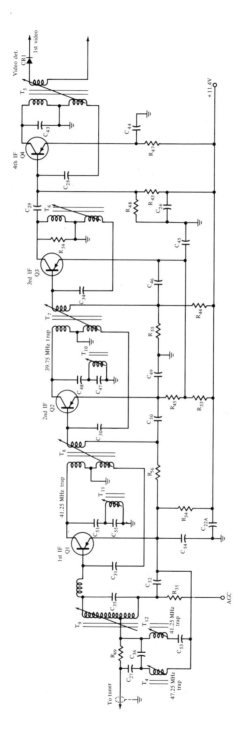

Fig. 7-14 A configuration in which IF transistors double as AGC amplifiers.

out by reverse AGC.

When there is no incoming IF signal in Fig. 7-14, a
positive reference voltage of approximately 2.1 V appears at
the AGC terminal. The emitter is returned through R$_{34}$ to a
+12-V supply. Therefore, the base is negative with respect to
the emitter, and the transistor is forward biased. This circuit is shown in equivalent form in Fig. 7-15. Transistor

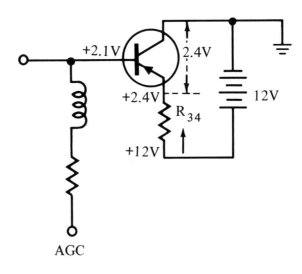

AGC

Fig. 7-15 Equivalent circuit for the first IF stage.

conduction causes the emitter voltage to level off at about
2.4 V, with the result that a forward bias of about 0.3 V
occurs between base and emitter. Under this condition, the
total drop across the emitter resistor is 9.6 V, and the collector-to-emitter voltage is 2.4 V.

As the IF signal strength increases from zero, the
voltage at the AGC terminal becomes less positive. The forward bias increases at the emitter junction, and I$_E$ rises
along with an increase in voltage drop across the emitter
resistor. The resulting decrease in collector-to-emitter

voltage provides forward AGC action. When the collector-to-emitter voltage decreases below 1 V, the gain diminishes rapidly. A variation of collector voltage between 1 and 2 V causes little change in gain, so that the arrangement has an inherent delay action.

Observe in Fig. 7-14 that the first-stage emitter voltage with respect to ground will drop from a high value of +2.4 V and decrease toward zero as the AGC voltage is increased. This emitter voltage provides AGC bias for the next stage. Coupling is provided through the isolating resistor R_{56}. The second stage is AGC controlled in the same manner as the first stage. That is, an increase in IF signal strength causes the base voltage to decrease from 2.4 V toward zero. The emitter voltage of the second stage is applied as AGC bias to the third stage. However, the second stage operates to control the emitter voltage, and not the base voltage. The base voltage is held constant by the voltage divider R_{44} and R_{45}. Note that the emitter voltage is tapped from the divider $R_{33}R_{45}$ in the emitter branch of the second stage. The sequence of operation at the third stage is as follows.

When there is no IF signal present in Fig. 7-14, the voltage tapped off at the junction of R_{33} and R_{45} makes the emitter slightly positive with respect to the fixed base voltage on the transistor. In turn, the third stage operates at maximum gain. Next, as the IF signal level increases from zero, the emitter voltage on the second stage becomes less positive; similarly, the emitter voltage on the third stage becomes less positive. The emitter of the third stage then becomes less positive with respect to its base, and its forward bias decreases. Therefore, reverse AGC action takes place.

7.4 Troubleshooting the AGC Section

Defects that seem to be in the AGC section at the
outset may actually be located in other receiver sections,
such as the IF or video amplifier.   For example, if there
is no sound and no picture with a normal raster, the trouble
could be in the AGC section, but it could also be located
in the RF tuner, IF amplifier, picture detector, or driver
stage of the video amplifier.   A muddy and filled-up
(overloaded) picture, which may be accompanied by intercarrier sound buzz, could be caused by AGC trouble, but might
also result from a leaky capacitor in the IF or video-
amplifier section.   When sync action is poor, the trouble
could be in the AGC section, but it might result instead from
a fault in the sync section, or from a defect in the picture
signal channel. Therefore, preliminary troubleshooting is
concerned with sectionalization of the trouble area.

The first   step in analyzing   apparent AGC trouble
is to clamp the AGC line(s) with a dc source such as bat-
teries.   The clamping voltage should be equal to the normal
AGC voltage(s) specified in the receiver service data.
Then, observe receiver operation on a fairly strong television
station signal.   If reception is normal, the trouble will be
found in the AGC section. On the other hand, if the trouble
symptom persists, it is logical to conclude that the defect
is not in the AGC section. When it appears that there is a
component defect in the AGC section, dc voltage measurements
are basic. Measured values are compared with specified values
in the receiver service data, and the technician is lead to a
defective component in most cases by a group of incorrect
voltage values.

In some cases, receiver service data will specify dc

voltage values under no-signal and strong signal conditions. The shift in voltage values which occurs can often be very helpful in analysis of abnormal circuit operation. A defect that causes little or no dc voltage change under no-signal conditions may show up prominently under strong signal conditions. In keyed AGC systems, it is essential to check the amplitude of the keying pulse from the horizontal sweep section. If the keying pulse is weak or absent, a keyed AGC system becomes inoperative. A weak keying pulse can result from a capacitor defect and can also be due to leakage to core or shorted turns in keyer winding on the flyback transformer.

Questions

Short Answer

1. If the signal from the antenna is 10 ΩV and the output from the video detector is 1 V, what is the gain to that point?
2. What is the reason for AGC in a television receiver?
3. Why is it necessary to have a 2- to 3-V output from the video detector?
4. Why is AGC not applied to the last IF amplifier?
5. Explain the two types of AGC action, forward and reverse.
6. What is the advantage of each of the AGC methods in Question 5?
7. Explain the term "keyed AGC."
8. What component of the television signal does keyed AGC use?
9. What causes airplane flutter?

10. What is the primary advantage of keyed AGC?

11. What is the advantage of amplified AGC?

12. Explain the generation of the AGC circuit shown in
    Fig. 7-11.

13. What is the purpose of diode CR3 in Fig. 7-11?

14. Explain the operation of the AGC circuit in Fig. 7-14.

15. Why does the AGC arrangement in Fig. 7-15 have a delayed
    action?

16. Why is it difficult to locate trouble in the AGC section?

17. Explain how you would check the AGC section of a tele-
    vision receiver.

18. How would you locate a resistor in an AGC circuit that
    had a low value of resistance?

19. How would you locate a leaky capacitor in a faulty AGC
    circuit?

True-False

1. AGC in a television receiver compensates for differences
   in amplitude of the received signal.

2. If the diode detector is operated at a low level, the
   gray range of the picture becomes distorted; however the
   sound signal improves.

3. High light depression in the video detector causes the
   intercarrier sound signal to become amplitude modulated.

4. The advantage of delayed AGC is a reduction of snow in
   the picture at weak signal levels.

5. Delayed AGC increases the noise introduced by the
   receiver signal channel.

6. The gain of a conventional IF transistor can be varied
   over a range of only 5 dB by control of emitter current.

7. Delayed AGC is obtained by means of operation of an electronic switch in the RF AGC line.

8. Keyed AGC uses the dc component of the composite video signal.

9. Airplane flutter is reduced by keyed AGC.

10. The AGC signal must not be amplified in a receiver, because of the phase shift of the amplifier.

11. The control action provided by an AGC system is more efficient if AGC amplification is used.

12. Some receivers use the same diode as both the video detector and the AGC detector.

13. A short in diode CR3 (Fig. 7-11) would result in no AGC action.

14. One advantage of the AGC circuit shown in Fig. 7-15 is that there is no delayed action.

15. The AGC section is possibly the simplest circuit to troubleshoot in the television receiver.

16. Noting that clamping of the AGC lines to approximately 4 V with a battery returns receiver operation to normal, we would conclude that the problem was not in the AGC section.

Multiple Choice

1. Good picture and sound reproduction require that the video detector operate at about _____ V peak to peak.
   (a) 2 or 3
   (b) 5 or 6
   (c) 6 or 7
   (d) 7 or 8

2. High light compression in the video detector causes:

    (a) the picture to be amplitude modulated.

    (b) the sound to be amplitude modulated.

    (c) the picture to be frequency modulated.

    (d) the sound to be frequency modulated.

3. The most important advantage of delayed AGC at weak signal levels is:

    (a) better sound signal.

    (b) improved signal-to-noise ratio.

    (c) elimination of retrace lines.

    (d) greater tube brightness.

4. Reverse AGC causes a variation in the _____ of a transistor.

    (a) collector voltage

    (b) base current

    (c) emitter voltage

    (d) emitter current

5. Keyed AGC is controlled by:

    (a) tips of the horizontal sync pulse.

    (b) the dc component of the video signal.

    (c) the dc component of the RF signal.

    (d) tips of the vertical sync pulse.

6. The greatest advantage of amplified AGC over other types is:

    (a) greater uniformity of receiver response.

    (b) better signal-to-noise ratio.

    (c) quicker response.

    (d) less snow in the picture.

7. In reference to Fig. 7-11, the AGC amplifier operates in the _____ mode.

    (a) common base   (c) common emitter

    (b) common collector   (d) cutoff

8. In Fig. 7-11, diode CR3 is used as a:

(a) detector.

(b) rectifier.

(c) limiter.

(d) clamper.

9. In Fig. 7-14, no IF signal will result in the:

(a) maximum gain in the third stage.

(b) cutoff of the third stage.

(c) maximum gain of the first stage.

(d) development of a forward AGC action.

10. To analyze an apparent AGC trouble, the first step is to:

(a) clamp the AGC lines with a dc source.

(b) disconnect the antenna.

(c) clamp the AGC lines to ground.

(d) remove one of the IF stages.

11. A weak keying pulse in a keyed AGC circuit can result from:

(a) shorted turns in the flyback.

(b) leakage to the core of the flyback transformer.

(c) leaky capacitor.

(d) all of the above.

Chapter 8

HORIZONTAL AND VERTICAL SYNC SECTIONS

8.1 Functions of the Sync Sections

The synchronizing section has the function of timing the operation of the horizontal and vertical sweep sections, as depicted in Fig. 8-1. The sync section is composed of several subsections, as shown in Fig. 8-2. The clipper or stripper circuit is driven by the composite video signal; it rejects the camera signal and blanking pedestals, and passes the sync tips to the sync amplifier. In turn, the sync amplifier steps up the amplitude of the sync pulses and feeds them to integrator and differentiator circuits. Because the horizontal sync pulses are much narrower than the vertical sync pulses and have a much faster repetition rate, simple RC filters can be used to separate the hori-

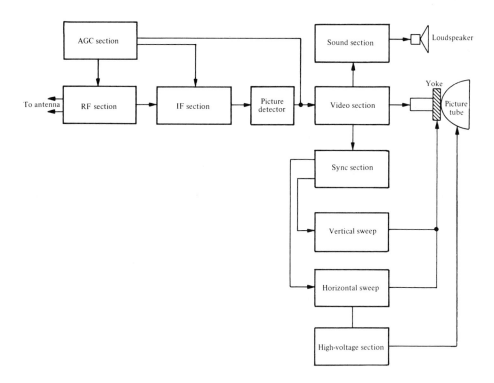

Fig. 8-1 The sync section times the operation of the vertical and horizontal sweep sections.

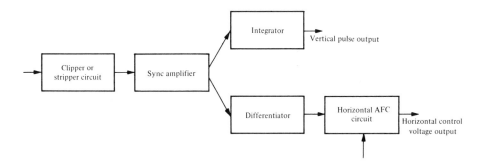

Fig. 8-2 Subsections of a synchronizing system.

zontal pulses from the vertical pulses. The vertical pulse
output is generally applied directly to the input of the

vertical sweep oscillator.   However, nearly   all receivers
employ a horizontal   automatic frequency   control (AFC) circuit between the differentiator output and the horizontal
sweep oscillator input.   Consider the processing circuitry
that is utilized in the synchronizing system.

8.2 Clipper Circuitry

The sync clipper   (also called the   sync separator)
effectively   slices the sync tips from the   composite video
signal as depicted   in Fig. 8-3.   In (a), a diode clipper

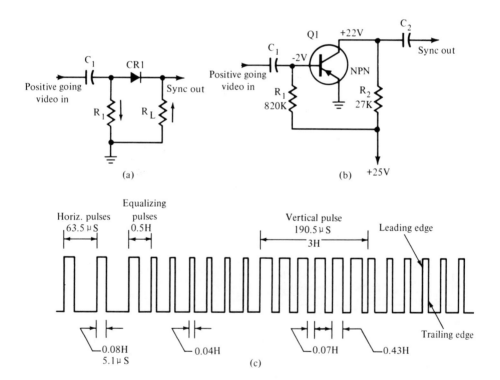

Fig. 8-3 Sync tips are stripped from the composite video
signals: (a) diode clipper circuit, (b) bipolar transistor
clipper circuit, (c) ideal stripped-sync output waveform.

circuit resembles a detector circuit in its general appearance. However, there is an essential difference in that the

RC time constant is sufficiently great that a substantial
negative charge builds up on the right-hand plate of C. The
sequence of clipping action is as follows:

1. Positive-going composite video signal is applied
   at the input of the clipper circuit.

2. Semiconductor diode CR is polarized so that conduction occurs.

3. Electrons flow up through R_L and CR and charge C
   to the positive peak voltage of the applied video
   signal.

4. Between successive sync pulses, some of the charge
   on C leaks off to ground through R.

5. Because diode CR is reverse biased, conduction can
   occur only on the peaks of the composite video
   signal, as depicted in Fig. 8-4.

The RC time constant employed in the diode clipper circuit provides a decay rate such that the difference between
E and E_2 in Fig. 8-4 is equal to the amplitude of the sync
tip. The time constant is typically 0.01 sec. The clipper
diode is reverse biased sufficiently so that the camera signal
and blanking pedestals are rejected. The configuration in
Fig. 8-3(a) is a self-biased clipper; diode CR operates with
signal-developed bias. This is an essential feature of the
circuit action, because clipping action must occur on weak
signals as well as strong signals. Because the value of
reverse bias voltage on diode CR must "follow" the prevailing
video-signal amplitude, the sync tips are sliced from a weak
signal in the same manner as from a strong signal.

Next, consider the configuration shown in Fig. 8-3(b).
This is a clipper amplifier arrangement. The base emitter

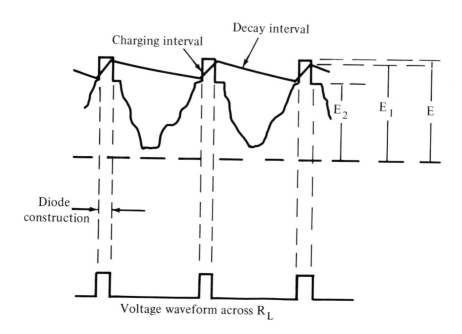

Fig. 8-4 Sequence of circuit action in a diode clipper
configuration.

circuit operates in the   same manner as the   diode clipper
described above.   In typical operation,   the base emitter
junction is reverse biased approximately 2 V.   Thus, emitter
current flows only during the sync tips, as shown in Fig. 8-5.
In turn, the pulses of emitter current flow into the collector
circuit (Fig. 8-3b) where they appear in amplified form across
the load resistor R_2. Because a CE configuration is employed
in this example, positive-going pulses appear as negative-
going pulses across the collector load resistor.

    The composite video signal applied to the sync clipper
may be obtained from the video-detector output circuit or
from a video-amplifier stage. Because the input impedance
of the clipper jumps to a low value (several hundred Ω)
during conduction intervals, and because a transistor clipper
arrangement has a rather high-input capacitance, loading of

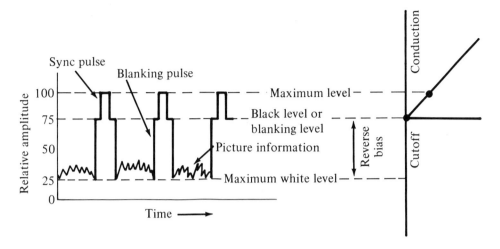

Fig. 8-5 Operation of reverse-biased base emitter junction.

the source is a basic consideration. Most receivers employ sync takeoff in the collector branch of a video-amplifier stage, as shown in Fig. 8-6. In case direct coupling is

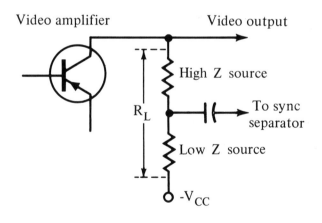

Fig. 8-6 The sync takeoff point is often tapped from the collector load in a video amplifier stage.

used to the input of the clipper stage, signal-developed bias is produced by an RC circuit in the emitter branch, as shown in Fig. 8-7. The output pulse amplitude will be greater, in any case, when the applied composite video signal has a greater amplitude. Therefore, the sync clipper is followed by a limiter stage that provides a constant output amplitude.

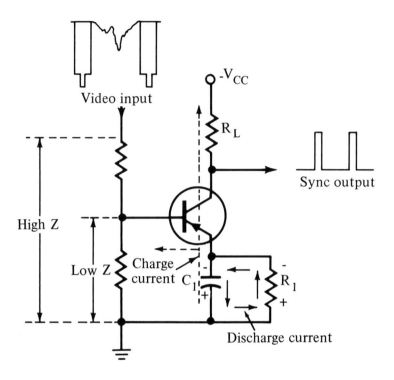

Fig. 8-7 A clipper circuit with self-bias voltage developed in the emitter branch.

8.3 Limiter Circuitry

Sync pulses are used to control the repetition rate of the sweep system, as in Fig. 8-1. Noise pulses may simulate sync pulses under some conditions of reception and produce false triggering of the sweep oscillators.   Therefore, it is desirable to employ sync systems that minimize the disturbing effects of noise pulses insofar as practical considerations permit.   Several approaches are utilized; in many systems, strong noise pulses are clipped in the video amplifier, as depicted in Fig. 8-8.   That is, the video-driver stage has a configuration such that strong noise pulses drive the transistor into cutoff.   Thus, the composite video signal applied

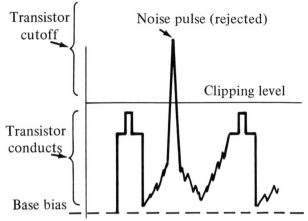

Transistor cutoff

Noise pulse (rejected)

Clipping level

Transistor conducts

Base bias

Fig. 8-8 Noise-pulse clipping improves the signal-to-noise ratio in an amplifier stage.

to the input of the sync system has been "cleaned up" to some extent, in that any noise pulses cannot greatly exceed the amplitude of the sync pulses.

Additional clipping is generally utilized in the sync section, not only to supplement video-amplifier clipping, but also to square off the separated sync pulses and to ensure that their amplitude remains constant regardless of fluctuations in signal strength. In an economy-type receiver, the clipper circuit may do double duty as a sync limiter. For example, with reference to Fig. 8-7, the value of R_L and $-V_{cc}$ may be chosen such that the sync tips drive the transistor into collector saturation. Residual strong noise pulses are clipped to the same height as the output sync pulses, and the output pulses have a constant amplitude regardless of reasonable variations in driving signal amplitude. This method reduces the gain that can be realized in the stage; another disadvantage is that the amplitude of the driving signal becomes marginal in weak signal reception, with the result that limiting action is impaired. Consequently, synchronizing action becomes uncertain, and the picture tends to "tear" and "roll."

A secondary disadvantage of a clipper limiter stage
becomes apparent when the incoming signal is quite strong.
In such a case, the strong signal drives the transistor
further into saturation than does a medium strength signal.
Transistors have certain storage delay and turn-off times.
These periods are a function of drive signal amplitude.
Therefore, high-level drive causes the output sync pulses
to be "stretched" or abnormally increased in pulse width.
Engineers call this distortion the "back porch" effect.
Because variation in sync pulse width tends to disturb the
control action of a sync system, the more elaborate designs
employ a limiter stage which is arranged to prevent objectionable minority carrier storage in the base region of the
transistor.

With reference to Fig. 8-9, Q1 operates as an ampli-

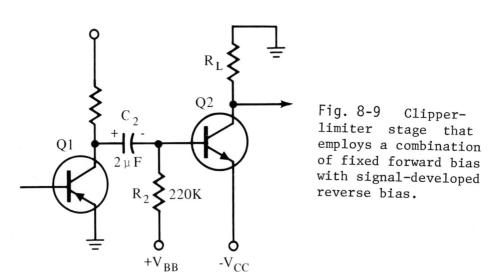

Fig. 8-9 Clipper-
limiter stage that
employs a combination
of fixed forward bias
with signal-developed
reverse bias.

fier, and Q2 operates as a forward-biased clipper limiter.
The output from Q1 is a positive-going signal, and the sync
tips drive Q2 into saturation. Forward bias is provided by

+V$_{BB}$, so that Q2 is driven into saturation by weak signals, and noise pulses are clipped to the sync tip level. R$_2$ has a comparatively high value, and Q2 operates with considerable signal-developed reverse bias when driven by strong signals. In turn, minority carrier storage in the base region is minimized, and the output pulses have a practically constant width regardless of the amplitude of the driving signal. To summarize, the foregoing combination of forward and reverse bias provides an operating characteristic such that weak, medium, and strong signals drive Q2 into approximately the same depth of saturation.

8.4 Separation of Horizontal and Vertical Sync Pulses

Practically all present-day receivers employ RC filters to separate horizontal and vertical sync pulses from the stripped sync waveform. As depicted in Fig. 8-10, horizontal sync pulses are passed by a differentiating circuit (high-pass RC filter). Incoming pulses have a width of approximately 5 μsec, and the differentiating circuit has an RC product (time constant) of about 1.5 μsec. The output pulse waveform is distorted as shown; however, the peak voltage of the output pulse is substantial, so that it can be utilized by subsequent circuits. Vertical sync pulses are effectively rejected by the differentiating circuit. Consider this circuit action.

With reference to Fig. 8-11, the incoming vertical sync pulse has the waveform shown in (a). This is a very wide pulse, compared with a horizontal sync pulse. It is serrated at half-line intervals, so that complete rejection does not take place in the differentiating circuit. Although the wide portions of the pulse are rejected, each serration produces a differentiated output, as shown in Fig. 8-12(b). The reason

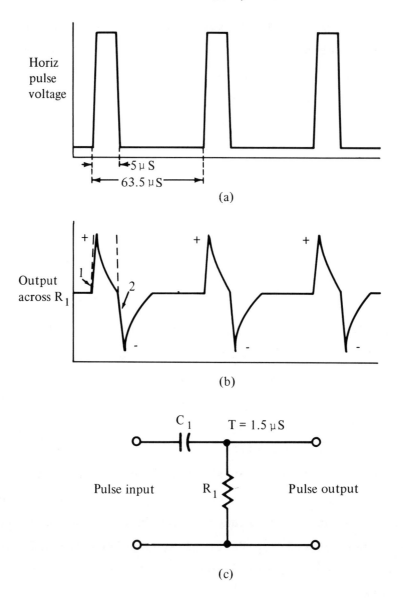

Fig. 8-10 Processing of horizontal sync pulses by a differentiating circuit: (a) incoming sync pulses, (b) differentiated pulses, (c) RC differentiating circuit.

that serrations are employed is to provide a means of main-taining sync lock in the horizontal deflection system during passage of the vertical sync pulse. In other words, if serra-tions were not provided, the horizontal oscillator would

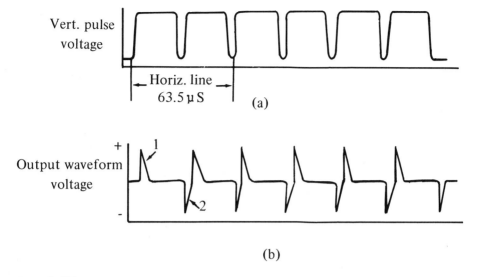

Fig. 8-11 Processing the vertical sync pulse by a differentiating circuit: (a) incoming sync pulses, (b) only differentiated serrations appear in the output waveform.

"wander" during the time that the vertical sync pulse occurs. Consequently, the top of the picture would appear bent or pulled. On the other hand, the serrations in the vertical sync pulse keep the horizontal oscillator correctly timed so that it does not drift off frequency during the vertical flyback interval.

The vertical sync pulses are separated from the horizontal sync pulses. This is accomplished by means of an integrating circuit (low-pass RC filter), as shown in Fig. 8-12(a) and (b). The width of the vertical sync pulse is approximately 190 μsec, and it is divided by the serrations into six sections, each of which has a width of about 28 usec. Because the integrating circuit has an RC product (time constant) of about 100 μsec, an applied vertical sync pulse builds up a charge on the capacitor, thereby producing an output pulse waveform. Because horizontal sync pulses have a

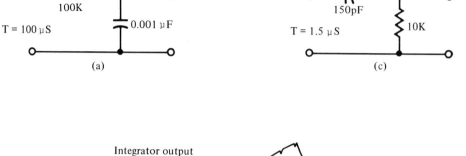

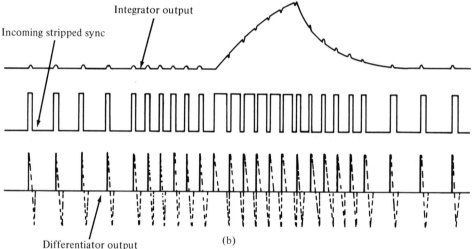

Fig. 8-12 Separation of vertical and horizontal sync
pulses: (a) simple integrating circuit, (b) integrated
and differentiated stripped-sync waveforms, (c) differentiated circuit.

width of only 5 μsec, they produce very little charge build-up
on the integrating capacitor.

     Observe in Fig. 8-12 that equalizing pulses produce a
slight response from the integrating circuit.   Equalizing
pulses are necessary because interlaced scanning is employed.
That is, the start of the vertical sync pulse is shifted by

half a line from the last horizontal sync pulse from odd to
even fields.   Therefore, the narrow equalizing pulses serve
to minimize the effect of horizontal pulses on the charge
of the integrating capacitor at the start of the vertical
sync pulse.   The start of the vertical sync pulse is always
half a line from the last equalizing pulse on successive
fields.   It is instructive to note that in case horizontal
pulses should affect integrator action, interlacing action
is disturbed.   This is called "line pairing" and is explained
in greater detail subsequently.

Because the serrations in the vertical sync pulse tend
to produce irregularities in the output waveform from a simple
integrator (Fig. 8-12), two-section integrators are generally
utilized, as depicted in Fig. 8-13.   Some receivers use a
three-section integrator.   Still others employ a packaged-
circuit (PC) integrator.   Any of these designs produces a
smooth output waveform, compared with a simple integrator
(see Fig. 8-14). Greater output amplitude is also provided.
The effective time constant of a multiple-section integrator
is made approximately the same as that of a single-section
integrator.   Note that a PC integrator contains resistance
with distributed capacitance.   In other words, a PC integrator
is the equivalent of a multiple-section arrangement with an
extremely large number of sections.

8.5 Noise-Immunity Techniques

Improvement of the sync signal-to-noise ratio by clipping
of high-amplitude noise pulses was noted previously.   Integration of the sync signal also assists in minimizing the disturbing effect of noise pulses. For example, if a noise pulse
is included in the integrator waveform (Fig. 8-14), its effect
is largely masked by the magnitude of the total charge build-up

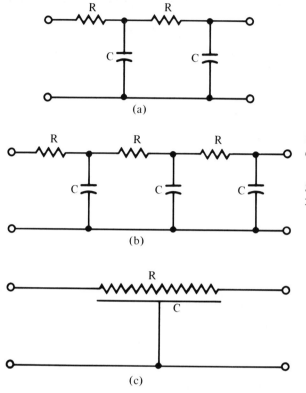

Fig. 8-13 Integrator
circuit arrangements:
(a) two-section inte-
grator, (b) packaged
integrator circuit.

Fig. 8-14 Output
waveforms from typi-
cal integrators:
(a) single RC sec-
tion, (b) two RC
sections.

on the integrating capacitor. Noise pulses are generally

narrower than a horizontal sync pulse. That is, the shape and

amplitude of the integrator output waveform are not substan-

tially changed by a noise pulse that occurs with the vertical

sync pulse. Unless a large number of noise pulses occurs

during the vertical sync pulse interval, the integrator output waveform is not seriously disturbed.

On the other hand, differentiation of the sync signal does not improve the sync signal-to-noise ratio. It is evident from the differentiator action depicted in Fig. 8-12 that noise pulses necessarily appear in the output waveform in the same general manner as horizontal sync pulses. Therefore, additional signal processing is required to minimize the disturbing effect of noise pulses in the differentiator output waveform. The differentiator is followed by horizontal AFC section. An AFC circuit can be compared with an integrator, in that it has a masking action with respect to noise pulses. Details are explained subsequently.

Noise-immunity techniques are also employed in the sync separator section of the more elaborate receiver designs. With reference to Fig. 8-9, it is evident that a strong noise pulse, or a series of weaker noise pulses, can disturb the clipping level substantially. If a high-amplitude noise pulse is applied to the base of Q2, the bias on C_2 jumps up suddenly. In turn, the output waveform amplitude is reduced until the excessive charge leaks off through R_2. A series of strong noise pulses can cause temporary cutoff of Q2 with respect to the incoming sync pulses, so that there is a gap in the output waveform. Disturbances of this kind can be minimized by supplementing a clipper limiter stage with a noise-absorbing circuit, or equivalent configuration.

Figure 8-15 shows a typical sync clipper with a noise-absorption network. This network comprises R_1C_1 and the noise-switch diode CR1. Clipping action results from signal-developed bias on transistor Q1. Although the signal-developed bias is determined primarily by the charge on C_2,

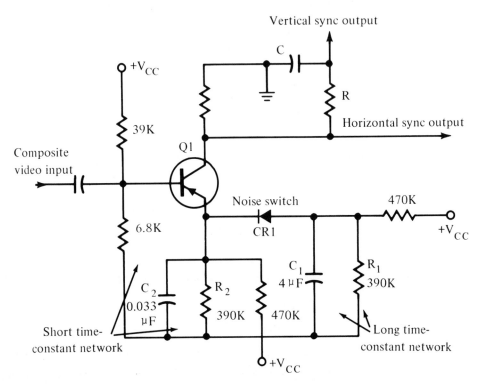

Fig. 8-15 A noise absorber arrangement for a sync clipper.

it is also determined to some extent by the charge on C_1.
When a strong noise pulse is applied to Q1, the signal-
developed bias is completely dominated by the charge on C_1.
Note that R_2C_2 has a short time constant, whereas R_1C_1 has
a long time constant. Because C_1 has a large capacitance
value, it effectively absorbs a strong noise pulse without
substantial change in its terminal voltage.

The signal-developed bias provided by R_2C_2 in Fig. 8-15
is adequate to provide normal clipping action, as depicted in
Fig. 8-7. However, the "shock-absorber" action of R_1C_1 is
also available via CR1 to prevent overcharge of C_2 when a
strong noise pulse is applied to Q1. When a sync tip is
applied to the base of Q1, the transistor conducts and its
emitter voltage falls to a less positive value. Depending on

the prevailing signal amplitude, this voltage decrease forward biases CR1 more or less for the duration of the sync tip, and the voltage across C_1 tends to "follow" the voltage across C_2. During the quiescent time between successive sync tips, C_2 discharges through R_2, and C_1 discharges at a slower rate through R_1.

Consider the circuit action in Fig. 8-15 when a strong noise pulse is applied to the base of Q1. The high-amplitude pulse drives Q1 into maximum conduction, and the noise-switch diode CR1 is simultaneously driven into maximum conduction. In effect, R_1C_1 is directly connected to R_2C_2 for the duration of the strong noise pulse. Because C_1 has a high value of capacitance, the noise pulse cannot change its terminal voltage greatly. Moreover, as C_1 is effectively connected parallel to C_2, the noise pulse cannot change the terminal voltage of C_2 greatly. Therefore, Q1 is not blocked following passage of the noise pulse, and there is no gap in the output waveform.

8.6 Sync Channel Bandwidth

Noise pulses are generally quite narrow. Accordingly, a noise pulse has a broad frequency spectrum from very low frequencies to very high frequencies. In turn, the amplitude of noise voltages can be attenuated by reducing the bandwidth of a sync channel. However, there is a practical limit to bandwidth reduction, because a sync pulse will also be attenuated by passage through an excessively narrow channel. For example, unless the sync channel passes about 10 harmonics of the horizontal sync pulse, the output waveform will be objectionably attenuated. In other words, a horizontal sync channel requires a passband from approximately 15 kHz to 150 kHz. Greater bandwidth results chiefly in an output with a poorer signal-to-noise ratio.

Figure 8-16   exemplifies sync channel   circuitry with

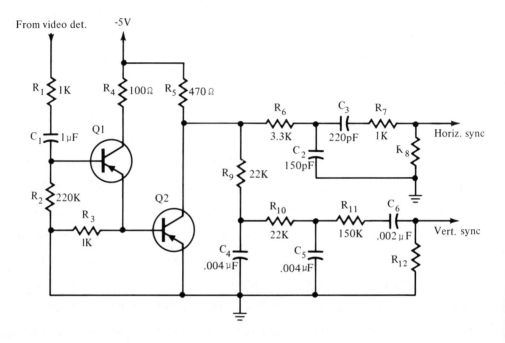

Fig. 8-16 Sync channels with limited bandwidth.

limited bandwidth.   Transistor Q1 operates as a sync clipper
in the CC configuration with   signal-developed bias from C_1
and R_2.   Resistor R_1 serves to reduce   the loading imposed
on the video detector.   Stripped sync output from   Q1 is fed
to the base of Q_2, which operates in a   CE configuration,
with R_3 as the   emitter load resistor; R_3 also   serves as a
bias resistor with R_4.   Because Q2 is dc coupled to Q1, its
base resistance also operates in the bias network for the
emitter of Q1.   As Q2 has a   low-collector voltage and a
high-load resistance (R_5), it saturates easily.   Thereby, sync
limiting is provided in addition to sync clipping.

Stripped sync pulses from Q2 (Fig. 8-16) are fed to a
horizontal sync channel and to a vertical sync channel.   This
horizontal channel consists basically of a differentiating

network composed of $C_3R_7R_8$. However, the differentiating network is preceded by an integrating circuit R_6C_2. This integrating circuit has a time constant of approximately 0.5 μsec and reduces the high-frequency response of the channel to about 150 kHz. The amplitude of the horizontal sync pulses is practically unaffected, whereas most noise pulses are considerably attenuated.

Comparable circuit design is employed in the vertical sync channel of Fig. 8-16 to provide limited bandwidth. A two-section integrator is utilized, composed of R_9C_4 and $R_{10}C_5$. The integrator time constant is a compromise between minimum vertical sync attenuation and maximum noise-pulse attenuation. R_{11} serves as an isolating resistor between the integrator and its utilization or load circuit. Note that the load circuit starts with a differentiating circuit composed of C_6 and R_{12}. This differentiating circuit has a time constant of approximately 300 μsec and limits the low-frequency response of the channel to approximately 50 Hz. Thereby, any low-frequency transients that may enter the channel are attenuated or suppressed in the output circuit.

8.7 Interlaced Scanning and Information Transfer

Interlaced scanning is used in the NTSC system to minimize flicker, particularly on high brightness images. To avoid picture element displacement both horizontally and vertically, the odd field lines must fall precisely halfway between the even field lines. This places stringent demands on the sync system; output pulses from the sync channels should not only be as free from noise as possible, but the pulses should have reasonably constant amplitude under conditions of signal strength fluctuation, or when going from strong signal reception to weak signal reception. It is essential to minimize crosstalk between the horizontal and vertical sync channels.

Note that flicker could also be minimized by means of a sync system controlling successive fields containing 525 lines each, at a rate of 60 fields/sec. In such a case, the demands on the sync system would be relaxed and there would be no interlacing problems to contend with. However, the NTSC stipulates that successive fields shall contain $262\frac{1}{2}$ lines each, in even line and odd line order, at the rate of 60 fields/sec. This two-field-per-frame scanning arrangement with interlaced even and odd lines is employed because it doubles the picture information transfer within the 4-MHz video band. This fact is not obvious until the factors that are involved are analyzed. Information transfer is doubled by employment of interlaced scanning as follows.

In any scanning arrangement, 60 fields/sec are required to obtain a satisfactorily low-flicker level. For example, 30 fields/sec produce objectionable flicker in high brightness scenes. In the transmission of 60 fields/sec, the required bandwidth depends on the number of lines in each field. Therefore, if $262\frac{1}{2}$ lines are contained in each field, the required video bandwidth is only half as great as would be the case if 525 lines were contained in each field. Therefore, the NTSC system has standardized $262\frac{1}{2}$ lines per field, plus a scanning pattern in which odd lines are interlaced with even lines. Because of persistence of vision, the viewer in effect observes a 525-line image, in spite of the fact that only $262\frac{1}{2}$ lines are displayed per vertical scanning interval. Effectively, interlaced scanning provides double the amount of picture detail in the overall result.

However, it is interesting and instructive to note that

there is a trade-off involved in the interlaced scanning process. In other words, the foregoing analysis implies a still picture, in which there is no movement. As long as no moving objects are being televised, double information transfer in the 4-MHz passband is realized. When a moving object is being televised, it is obvious that picture elements in the second field will be more or less displaced horizontally with respect to the same picture elements in the first field. This is just another way of saying that there is a time delay involved between "writing" the second field in between the lines of the first field. This picture degradation is not noticeable when televised objects move at moderate speeds. However, if a high-speed object is being televised, the odd and even line elements are considerably displaced, with the result that the moving object is displayed with ragged edges. This disadvantage is greatly outweighed by the doubling of information transfer on ordinary images, and this is the reason that interlaced scanning is specified in the NTSC standards.

Note in passing that three fields per frame, or four fields per frame, could be transmitted at a 60-Hz repetition rate, if desired. However, there are serious disadvantages involved in multiple-field operation, which preclude its adoption. First, it is prohibitively difficult to design a sync system that operates with adequate precision to control a three-field or four-field display satisfactorily. Second, the trade-off between increased information transfer and element displacement in moving objects becomes marginal, and the benefit for the viewer is questionable. Therefore, practical television systems are restricted to transmission of two fields per frame.

8.8 Vertical Interval Test Signals

In the past, test patterns such as illustrated in Fig. 8-17 were televised in the morning and late at night to serve

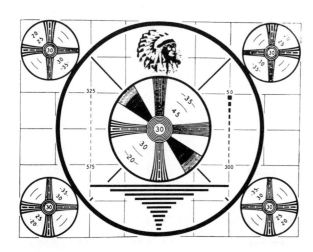

Fig. 8-17 A stand-ard test pattern. (Courtesy, RCA Elec-tronic Components Division)

as a handy means of evaluating receiver adjustment and opera-tion.   At the present time, however, television stations seldom transmit test patterns, and technicians who wish to make use of such patterns employ specialized generators called flying-spot scanners (Fig. 8-18).   The present-day trend of televising test signals includes vertical interval test sig-nals (VIT's) with the train of sync pulses. They are trans-mitted in nearly all network color programs and appear to the casual viewer as bright lines in the vertical blanking inter-val when the picture is rolled on the screen.

Figure 8-19 shows how VIT's appear on a scope screen during two consecutive fields.   The multiburst consists of a white flag followed by six groups of video frequencies; the flag identifies the start of the frequency sequences.   These are groups of sine waves with frequencies of 0.5, 1.5, 2.0, 3.0, 3.6, and 4.2 MHz.   Each group or burst is transmitted at the same amplitude.   Therefore, by observing the repro-

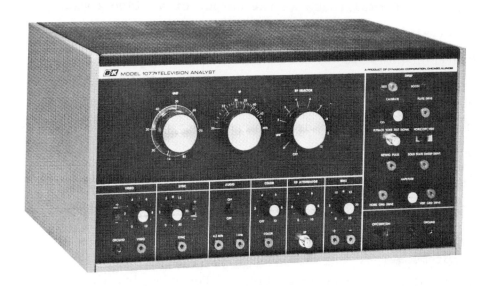

Fig. 8-18 A flying-spot scanner that provides a test pattern signal. (Courtesy, B & K Manufacturing Co.)

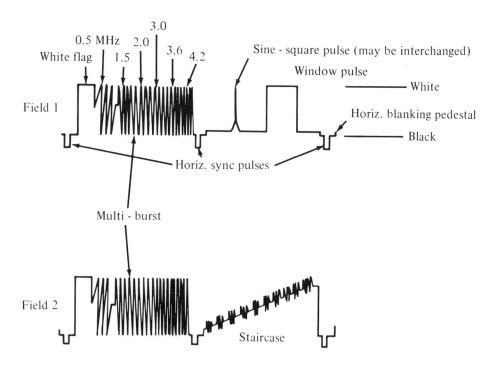

Fig. 8-19 A standard VIT signal waveform.

duced burst amplitudes at the output of a video amplifier in
a television receiver, the frequency response of the receiver
system can be easily evaluated. Other portions of the VIT
signal such as the sine-squared pulse, window, and staircase
components are of less interest to the service technician.
Engineering students are referred to technical handbooks for
additional information.

8.9 Troubleshooting the Sync Sections

When vertical or horizontal synchronization trouble
symptoms arise, the first consideration of the technician is
to localize the faulty section.   For example, the defective
component might be in a sweep oscillator section, instead of
the sync section.   This preliminary localization is accomplished to best advantage by signal tracing with an oscilloscope from the sync takeoff point through the sync section
to the vertical and horizontal sweep oscillators. Waveforms
within the sync section are compared in shape and amplitude
with those specified in the receiver service data. If distortion and/or attenuation or blocking of the sync signals
is found at some point in the sync section, attention is then
turned to the circuitry in this vicinity.

Pinpointing of a defective component in a network or
branch circuit is generally accomplished to best advantage
with a dc voltmeter. Measured values are compared with those
specified in the receiver service data.   Due allowance is
necessarily made for normal component tolerances. Thus, a
dc voltage value is generally acceptable if it is within
$\pm 20\%$ of the specified value (unless noted for closer tolerance in the service data). It is highly advisable to check
the line supply voltage when making dc voltage measurements;

the standard value is usually 117 V. If the line voltage is high or low, it will shift the measured values of dc voltages accordingly. Service data sometimes provide dc voltage values both in the presence and in the absence of incoming signal.

Most trouble symptoms in the sync section are caused by leaky or open fixed capacitors. Accordingly, capacitors fall under suspicion from the outset simply on a statistical basis. However, other component failures, such as off-value resistors, defective transistors, cold-soldered connections, broken printed circuit conductors, or leakage paths between PC conductors, will be encounted. For example, a small solder splash can cause a short circuit in a PC board. Resistance measurements are generally less useful than dc voltage measurements to pinpoint a trouble condition. However, an ohmmeter is useful as a continuity tester. It is also useful to check the value of a resistor after it has been disconnected from branch circuits.

Questions

Short Answer

1. What is the function of the clipper, or stripper, circuit?
2. What is the function of the sync amplifier?
3. How are the vertical and horizontal sync pulses treated differently after they leave the sync separator?
4. What is the sequence of clipping action in the circuit in Fig. 8-3?
5. How do the clipper circuits in Fig. 8-3(a) and (b) differ in their operation?

6. What is the purpose of the limiter stage that follows the sync clipper?

7. Why is it necessary to use sync systems that minimize the effects of noise pulses?

8. How are noise pulses clipped in the circuit in Fig. 8-7?

9. What are the disadvantages of the circuit in Fig. 8-7?

10. What causes the back porch effect in a clipper limiter?

11. With reference to Fig. 8-11, why are serrations employed?

12. Why are equalizing pulses employed in the circuit in Fig. 8-12?

13. What is "line pairing"?

14. How does integration of the sync signal assist in minimizing the disturbing effect of noise pulses?

15. Explain the operation of the noise-absorption network in the circuit in Fig. 8-15.

16. How is sync clipping accomplished in the circuit in Fig. 8-16?

17. How are the low-frequency transients attenuated or suppressed in the output circuit in Fig. 8-16?

18. What is the advantage of two-field-per-frame scanning?

19. Why is it not expedient to use a three-field or four-field-per-frame scanning at a 60-Hz repetition rate?

20. Explain the purpose of a VIT test signal.

21. What is the first consideration of the technician in repairing vertical and horizontal synchronization problems?

22. What are several of the possible causes of trouble in the sync section of a receiver?

True-False

1. The synchronizing section of a television receiver has

the function of timing the horizontal and vertical sweep sections.

2. Most receivers employ an AFC circuit in the vertical amplifier.

3. The sync separator slices the tips from the composite video signal.

4. The base emitter junction of the transistor shown in Fig. 8-36 acts as a diode.

5. Because of its self-biasing action, there is no need for the sync clipper to be followed by a limiter stage.

6. Noise pulses may simulate sync pulses under some conditions.

7. Clipping is never used in both the video amplifier and the sync separator.

8. In economy-type receivers, the clipper circuit may do double duty as a sync limiter.

9. In Fig. 8-9, weak, medium, and strong signals drive Q2 into saturation.

10. Practically no present-day receivers employ RC filters to separate horizontal and vertical sync pulses from the stripped sync waveform.

11. In Fig. 8-11, serrations are used to keep the vertical sync pulse locked in during retrace time.

12. In Fig. 8-11, the vertical sync pulses are separated from the horizontal sync pulses by a low-pass RC filter.

13. Two- and three-section integrated circuits are often employed in a sync separator.

14. Differentiation of the sync signal improves the sync signal-to-noise ratio.

15. Noise pulses are generally quite narrow.

16. It is essential to minimize crosstalk between the horizontal and vertical sync channels.

17. Sixty fields/sec are required to obtain a satisfactorily low-flicker level.

18. If a high-speed object is being televised, the result is that the moving object is displayed with ragged edges.

19. Fixed capacitors are very seldom at fault when trouble occurs in the sync section of a receiver.

20. The dc voltage values in a television receiver should be tested with the same general type of voltmeter as used for the measurements on the service data sheets.

Multiple Choice

1. The vertical and horizontal sync pulses are separated by a/an:
    (a) tuned transformer.
    (b) resonant LC circuit.
    (c) RC filter.
    (d) diode detector.

2. The vertical sync pulses are fed from the sync separator to the:
    (a) vertical sweep oscillator.
    (b) vertical deflection coils.
    (c) pulse-shaper circuit.
    (d) AFC circuit.

3. The horizontal sync pulses are fed from the sync separator to the:
    (a) horizontal sweep oscillator.
    (b) horizontal deflection coils.
    (c) pulse-shaper circuit.
    (d) horizontal AFC circuit.

4. The camera signal and blanking pedestals are rejected by diode CR in Fig. 8-3(a) because of the:

   (a) fixed bias in the diode.

   (b) self-bias developed on the diode.

   (c) RC time constant of the diode circuit.

   (d) tuned circuit in the cathode circuit of the diode.

5. The effect of noise pulses in the sync system is reduced by clipping in the:

   (a) IF amplifier.

   (b) RF section.

   (c) video amplifier.

   (d) sync separator.

6. The storage delay and turn-off time delay of a transistor in a clipper limiter stage cause a distortion called the _____ effect.

   (a) back porch

   (b) fall time

   (c) expansion time

   (d) storage time

7. In Fig. 8-9, Q1 operates as _____, and Q2 operates as _____.

   (a) a clipper, a limiter

   (b) an amplifier, an amplifier

   (c) a limiter, an amplifier

   (d) an amplifier, a forward-biased clipper limiter

8. Serrations of the vertical sync pulse are necessary to keep the _____ oscillator timed during _____ flyback time.

   (a) horizontal, vertical

   (b) vertical, vertical

   (c) horizontal, horizontal

   (d) vertical, horizontal

9. Equalizing pulses are necessary because:

    (a) of the temperature drift of a transistor.

    (b) of the neutralization in the video amplifier.

    (c) interlaced scanning is employed.

    (d) clipping has been employed.

10. Differentiation of the sync signal:

    (a) improves the sync signal-to-noise ratio.

    (b) separates the horizontal sync pulses.

    (c) separates the vertical sync pulses.

    (d) clips the sync pulses.

11. One factor that is common to most noise pulses is that they are generally:

    (a) quite narrow.   (c) small in amplitude.

    (b) quite wide.   (d) large in amplitude.

12. The horizontal sync channel requires a passband of:

    (a) 50 Hz to 150 Hz.   (c) 1500 Hz to 15 kHz.

    (b) 150 Hz to 11,500 Hz.   (d) 15 kHz to 150 kHz.

13. Interlaced scanning is used in the NTSC system to prevent:

    (a) snow.

    (b) flicker.

    (c) noise in the sound section.

    (d) loss of vertical sync.

14. The two-field-per-frame scanning arrangement with interlaced even and odd lines is employed because:

    (a) it prevents shutter.

    (b) it doubles the picture information transfer, within the 4-MHz video band.

    (c) it decreases snow.

    (d) it decreases flutter.

15. Most troubles in the sync section are caused by:

    (a) leaky or open capacitors.

    (b) shorted resistors.

    (c) open resistors.

    (d) shorted capacitors.

16. An ohmmeter is useful to:

    (a) measure the value of a capacitor.

    (b) check continuity.

    (c) measure the value of an inductor.

    (d) measure circuit current.

Chapter **9**

VERTICAL SWEEP SECTION

9.1 Function of the Vertical Sweep Section

Vertical motion of the scanning beam in a picture tube is determined by the vertical sweep section.   As noted previously, electromagnetic deflection is almost always utilized. Figure 9-1 shows a block diagram for a typical vertical sweep

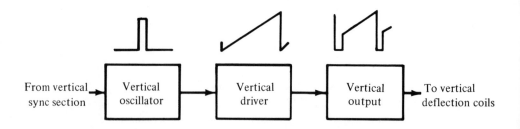

Fig. 9-1 Block diagram of a typical vertical sweep system.

system. It consists of a vertical oscillator section synchro-
nized by the vertical sync section. A 60-Hz pulse output
from the vertical oscillator energizes the vertical driver
section. In turn, the vertical driver produces a sawtooth
waveform which energizes the vertical output section. This
output section develops increased waveform voltage and power,
and also shapes the sawtooth wave into a peaked sawtooth wave.
This voltage waveform is required to produce a sawtooth current
flow through the vertical deflection coils, subsequently
explained in greater detail.

9.2 Vertical Oscillator Circuitry and Operation

Blocking oscillators are generally utilized in vertical
sweep systems. A common configuration is shown in Fig. 9-2.

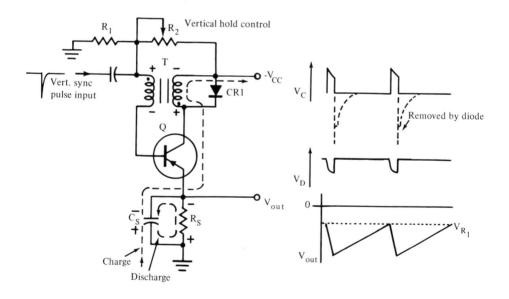

Fig. 9-2 A vertical blocking oscillator configuration that
generates a positive-going sawtooth.

This arrangement generates a 60-Hz sawtooth output waveform.
The circuit action takes place as follows: When the oscil-

lator is switched on, a negative bias voltage is applied to the base of transistor Q. In turn, the transistor conducts, and capacitor C_S charges toward the bias value. Simultaneously, collector current flows, and a transient voltage is induced into the base circuit by transformer T. This induced voltage is polarized to drive the base more negative, and Q is rapidly driven into saturation. At this instant, C_S has been charged almost to the collector supply voltage value.

When transistor Q in Fig. 9-2 is driven into saturation, collector current flow stops, and no more voltage is induced into the base circuit. This leaves the emitter more negative than the base, due to the charge on C_S, and the transistor cuts off. Observe that transistor cutoff continues while C_S discharges through R_S and produces the rising slope interval of a sawtooth wave. Finally, C_S discharges sufficiently so that Q comes out of cutoff, and the positive feedback action through transformer T takes place once more, thereby forming the flyback portion of the sawtooth wave. Note that the vertical sync pulse is coupled into the base circuit of Q. R_2 is adjusted so that the blocking oscillator has a free-running frequency slightly slower than 60 Hz. In turn, the sync pulse brings Q out of cutoff sooner than in the free-running mode. Accordingly, the repetition rate of the sawtooth output is locked to the sync pulse repetition rate.

Note that adjustment of R_2 in Fig. 9-2 established the free-running frequency of the blocking oscillator, because the base bias value determines the level, and therefore the time, at which Q will come out of cutoff. Potentiometer R_2 is called the vertical hold control. When set within its normal operating range, the image on the picture tube screen is locked in sync. However, if R_2 is set out of this range, the image will "roll" up or down on the screen. Protective diode X is shunted across the primary of T to eliminate the "kickback" transient voltage which would otherwise cause transistor breakdown. This diode goes into conduction when Q cuts off suddenly, thus dissipating the stored magnetic energy in T. The V_C waveform in Fig. 9-2 shows this diode action.

Waveform V_{R_1} in Fig. 9-2 is called a positive-going sawtooth. In other words, the waveform rises from a more negative value to a less negative value. When a vertical sweep system requires a negative-going sawtooth source, the configuration depicted in Fig. 9-3 may be used. The circuit action is as

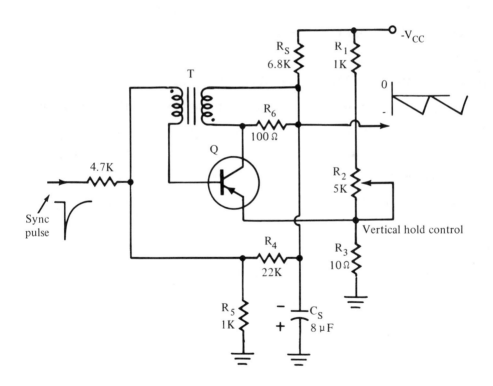

Fig. 9-3 A vertical blocking oscillator configuration that generates a negative-going sawtooth.

follows: When the transistor is switched on, capacitor C_S is uncharged, and the base voltage on transistor Q is zero. The transistor is cut off at this time, due to the negative emitter

bias from R_3.   Capacitor C_S charges   through R_S and produces
the falling slope   interval of a negative-going   sawtooth wave.
At the same time, the base voltage of Q is becoming more negative from R_5.   Suddenly the transistor   goes into conduction,
and feedback action   via T drives the   base highly negative.
In turn, the transistor is driven into saturation, and C_S
quickly discharges through T and R_3 to ground.   Thereby, the
flyback portion of the sawtooth wave is formed, and the cycle
of operation repeats.

Observe in Fig. 9-3 that a 60-Hz sync pulse is fed into
the base circuit of Q to lock the operation of the blocking
oscillator, as described previously.   That is, R_2 is the vertical hold control; it is adjusted so that the free-running frequency of the oscillator is slightly slower than 60 Hz.   In
turn, the arrival of the negative-going sync pulse triggers Q
out of cutoff sooner than would occur in the free-running mode.
In this example, a protective diode is not used.   Instead, a
100-Ω resistor R_6 is connected across the primary of transformer T.   This resistor has a sufficiently low value that it
dissipates the stored magnetic energy in T rapidly when Q cuts
off.   Thereby, the "kickback" transient is reduced to a low
value, and transistor breakdown is avoided.

9.3 Buffer or Driver Section Circuitry

Because the   vertical deflection   coils in   the yoke
require substantial current, they cannot be driven directly
from the   sawtooth-forming   capacitor in   the vertical oscillator section.   A low-impedance vertical output section is
accordingly required to provide substantial sawtooth driving
current.   Inasmuch as the vertical oscillator section has a
comparatively high-output impedance, a buffer or driver section
is desirable to match circuit impedances and obtain maximum

power transfer, with resulting high operating efficiency. A
buffer section also serves to isolate the oscillator from the
output section, thereby improving stability. It also minimizes
interaction between the height and linearity controls with the
hold control.

A vertical buffer stage generally employs a common
collector configuration, as shown in Fig. 9-4. This arrange-

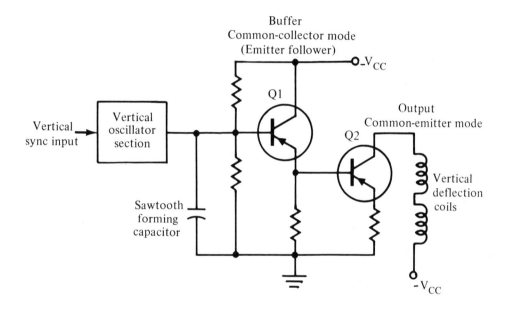

Fig. 9-4 The buffer stage drives the output stage at high
efficency.

ment is also called an emitter follower. It provides a high-
input impedance, with a low-output impedance. A power gain is
developed, so that the output stage can be driven without
placing appreciable load on the oscillator stage. In this
example, direct coupling is employed between the buffer transistor Q1 and the output transistor Q2. Note that Q2 operates
in the common emitter mode. A power transistor is used in the
output section.

Buffer stages that operate in the common emitter mode

are also found. An example is seen in Fig. 9-5. When the CE
mode is used, some circuit means is included to increase the
effective input impedance of the buffer stage. With reference
to Fig. 9-5, series resistor R_S servies this purpose.   The

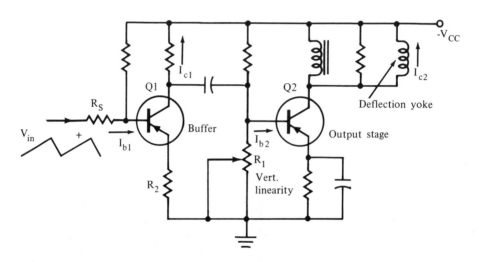

Fig. 9-5 Example of a CE buffer configuration.

input impedance is also increased by the unbypassed emitter
resistor R_2.   Both of these resistors reduce the gain of the
buffer stage. However, because the CE mode provides inherently
high gain, the foregoing losses are tolerable.

Unless a comparatively linear sawtooth is generated by
the vertical deflection system, scanning distortion will
result.   That is, the image will be compressed at the top
and expanded at the bottom, or vice versa.   A basic method
for optimizing linearity and also increasing operating stability
is to use negative feedback, as depicted in Fig. 9-6.   In this
example, the current through the vertical deflection coils is
sampled and is fed back in opposing phase to the emitter of the
buffer transistor. Note that the yoke return circuit is made
through emitter resistor R_E.   The resulting negative feedback

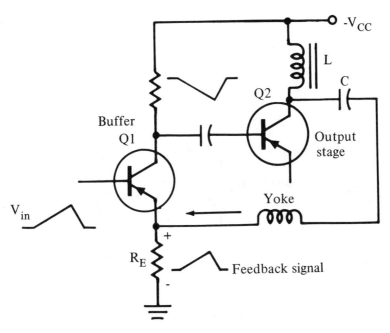

Fig. 9-6 Negative feedback to the buffer section improves system linearity.

linearizes operation of both Q1 and Q2. Coupling capacitor C is utilized to avoid disturbance of the emitter bias on Q1. Choke inductor L provides shunt feed of dc collector voltage to Q2.

9.4 Vertical Output Section Circuitry

To obtain linear vertical deflection, the current flow through the vertical deflection coils must have a good saw-tooth waveform. The corresponding voltage waveform across the coils does not have the same shape. Appreciable current is required, and the vertical output stage accordingly employs a power-type transistor. For example, a current waveform with an amplitude of approximately 400 mA peak to peak is utilized with 48-mH vertical deflection coils in a typical receiver.

A basic vertical output configuration is shown in Fig. 9-7. Drive demand is minimized by operation in the CE mode. Observe that sawtooth current flow through the vertical

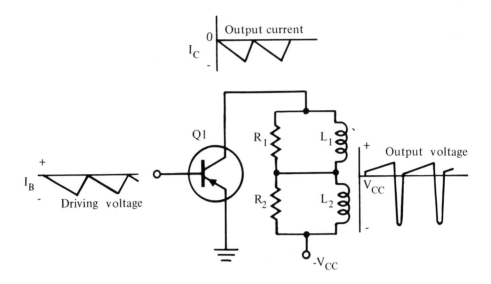

Fig. 9-7   A basic vertical output configuration.

deflection coils is produced by a peaked sawtooth voltage waveform. The reason for this relation is seen in Fig. 9-8. That is, a voltage sawtooth produces a current sawtooth in a resistive load. On the other hand, a pulse voltage produces a sawtooth current in a pure inductive load. Therefore, it is logical to conclude that a combination of these two voltage waveforms, or a peaked sawtooth comprising a sawtooth and a pulse, will produce a sawtooth current in an inductive imped- ance load.

With reference to Fig. 9-7, the sawtooth component of the output voltage can be regarded as deriving from the driving sawtooth. During the brief flyback or retrace inter- val, the magnetic field in the vertical deflection coils collapses rapidly. This collapse generates a counter emf (kickback) pulse across the coils. It appears in the output voltage waveform as a negative peaking pulse. A peaked saw- tooth waveform is also called a trapezoidal waveform. Note

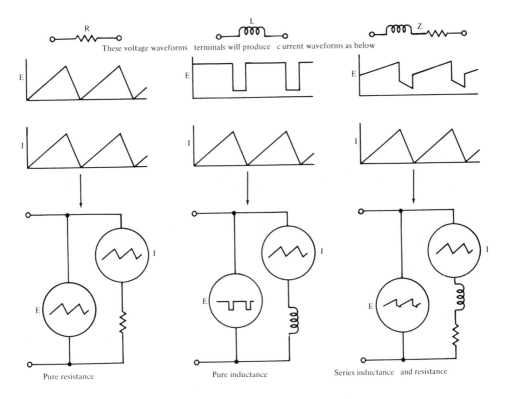

Fig. 9-8 Voltage-current relations for resistance, inductance, and impedance.

that negative-going sawtooth drive is employed in this configuration; a negative-going drive waveform prevents the kickback pulse from making the collector forward biased. This would distort the output waveform. Of course, the transistor that is used must be rated to withstand the peak-to-peak voltage of the output waveform.

Because abrupt voltage changes are applied across L_1 and L_2 in Fig. 9-7, the Q value of the vertical deflection coils must be established below the critical value.   Otherwise, the output circuit will "ring," or be shock-excited into transient oscillation as depicted in Fig. 9-9.   In turn, the output waveform would be distorted.   To reduce the Q of

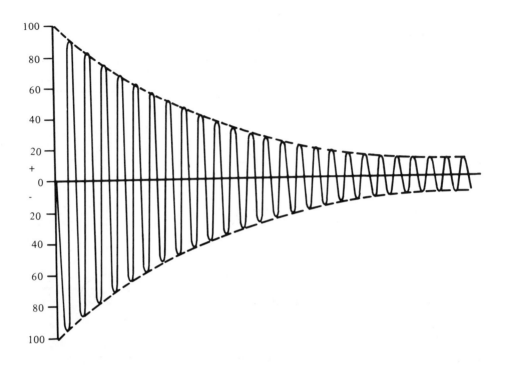

Fig. 9-9 A transient ringing waveform.

the load circuit accordingly, damping resistors R_1 and R_2
are connected across the vertical deflection coils. Note that
a small amount of damping is also provided by the collector
leakage current of transistor Q.

Various coupling methods are used between the collector
and the vertical deflection coils. For example, capacitive
coupling was employed in the configuration of Fig. 9-6. The
dc component of collector current does not flow through the
vertical deflection coils. On the other hand, direct coupling
is utilized in the arrangement of Fig. 9-7, and the dc component of collector current flows through the coils. That is,
the deflection coil current varies from nearly zero to a
maximum value during the rising slope of the current sawtooth,
but this current flow does not reverse its direction at any

time.   Consequently, the dc component increases the required

power dissipation of the coils.

To block the flow of dc through the vertical deflection

coils, either transformer or capacitive coupling may be uti-

lized.   With reference to Fig. 9-10(a), an isolation trans-

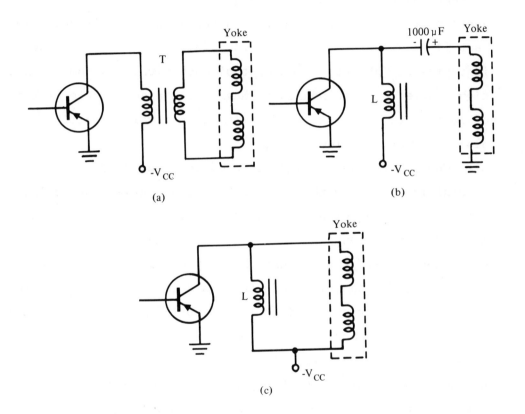

(a)   (b)

(c)

Fig. 9-10 Methods of coupling to the vertical deflection
coils: (a) transformer coupling, (b) capacitive coupling,
(c) direct coupling with shunt feed.

former is provided; a 1-to-1 turns ratio is typical.   The

chief disadvantage of a vertical output transformer is its

more or less nonlinear response.   That is, an iron core is

required in 60-Hz operation, and iron has an inherent nonlinear

magnetic characteristic.   This source of nonlinearity can be

minimized by using a comparatively large and heavy core. However, increased production costs are incurred.

A preferred method of blocking dc flow through the vertical deflection coils is shown in Fig. 9-10(b). A coupling
capacitor C provides a low-reactance path for ac current (about
3 Ω at 60 Hz), while inductor L presents a high reactance to ac
current and a low resistance to dc current. The chief disadvantage of a coupling capacitor is the large capacitance value
that is required. As noted in the diagram, a value of 1000 μF
is typical. The production cost of such a unit is comparatively
high. Note that the nonlinear magnetic characteristic of L is
of no concern, because its high-inductance value practically
blocks ac current flow.

The compromise design depicted in Fig. 9-10(c) serves
to minimize dc flow through the vertical deflection coils,
without incurring high-production costs. Although this is a
form of direct coupling, only a small fraction of the dc
collector current flows through the yoke winding. Inductor
L is designed with high inductance and low resistance. The
dc collector current divides in proportion to the resistance
values of the branch paths. Of course, this design does not
eliminate dc flow through the yoke entirely. However, it is
a practical solution to the production design problem. Centering magnets on the neck of the picture tube, mentioned
previously, are adjusted as required to offset the decentering
action of the small dc current flow through the yoke.

9.5 Linearity Control

Previous mention has been made of the vertical linearity
control. Its function is to correct any nonlinearity in the
vertical scanning process. An example of vertical nonlinearity
is shown in Fig. 9-11. Scanning linearity is often checked by

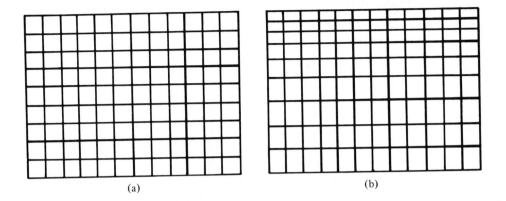

Fig. 9-11 Example of nonlinear vertical deflection:
(a) normal crosshatch patterns, (b) patterns compressed
at top and expanded at bottom.

means of a crosshatch pattern, obtained from a generator.
Although reasonably good linearity is inherent in a vertical
deflection system when transfer characteristics are matched in
the buffer and output stages, the problem of component tolerances must be contended with. This problem is eased considerably by employment of negative feedback. Nevertheless, there
remains a residual slow drift due to aging of semiconductors
and other components, and a maintenance wave shape control is
required.

There are two basic types of vertical linearity control.
One method, seen in Fig. 9-5, serves to shift the operating
point of output transistor Q2. Thereby, the transfer characteristic of Q2 can be matched more closely to that of Q1. The
other method that is employed utilizes a variable wave-shaping
network in the sawtooth signal path, or in a feedback loop.
This means of vertical linearity control is necessary when the
buffer transistor has a CC configuration. That is, nonlinearity
of the input sawtooth waveform cannot be corrected by exploiting
an opposing nonlinearity in the buffer and output circuits with

the CC configuration.

Figure 9-12 shows   an example of a   variable wave-shaping

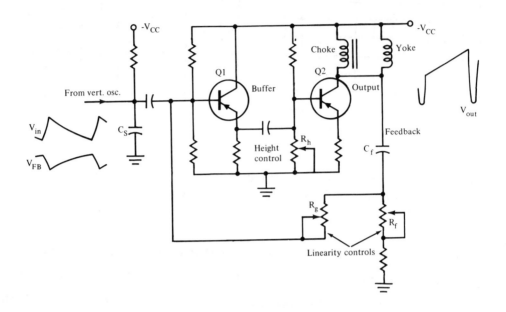

Fig. 9-12 An example of linearity control in a feedback loop.

network in a feedback loop.   Observe that the peaked sawtooth
voltage across the yoke is applied to a differentiating network comprising C_F and R_F. Differentiating action introduces
a concave curvature into the sawtooth component of the waveform.
This differentiated waveform is applied through R_G to the buffer
input, across the sawtooth-forming capacitor C_S. This capacitor
removes practically all of the peaking pulse from the feedback
waveform. As the feedback sawtooth has an opposite curvature
from that of the generated sawtooth, adjustment of R_F and R_G
results in production of a linear sawtooth at the base of the
buffer transistor Q1. Note that R_F determines the amount of
differentiation, and R_G determines the amplitude of the feedback
voltage. Thus, two vertical linearity controls are provided in

this arrangement. Height control is provided by R_H, which adjusts the bias voltage on Q2.

9.6 Multivibrator Vertical Sweep System

Another basic type of vertical sweep system is depicted in Fig. 9-13. This is a multivibrator arrangement in which

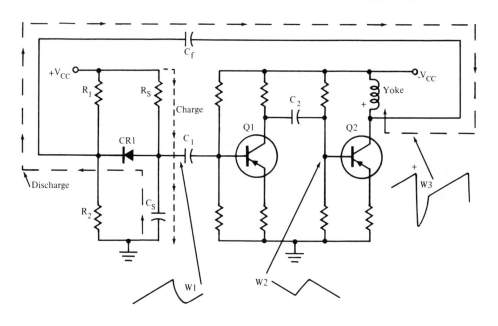

Fig. 9-13 Typical multivibrator sweep system.

a separate oscillator stage is not employed. Instead, positive feedback is utilized between transistors Q1 and Q2, with the load placed in the collector branch of Q2. Both transistors operate in the CE configuration. Note that diode CR is used as a switching device in the process of sawtooth waveform generation by capacitor C_S. The sequence of circuit action is as follows: When supply voltage is applied to the circuit in Fig. 9-13, capacitor C_S is uncharged; the rising slope of a sawtooth waveform is generated as C_S charges via R_S toward the supply voltage value. This forward-scanning interval is coupled

to Q1 through C_1, which operates as a buffer stage in this
process. In turn, Q1 drives Q2, which is a power transistor.
The output current from Q2 flows through the yoke winding.
Observe that feedback does not take place via C_F during this
time, because diode CR is reverse biased. However, this reverse
bias is less than V_{CC}, due to the voltage divider action of $R_1 R_2$.
Therefore, as soon as the amplitude of waveform W_1 equals the
voltage divider potential, diode CR goes into conduction,
which stops the charging of C_S and also connects feedback
capacitor C_F to the input circuit of Q1.

With the end of the charging interval of C_S in Fig. 9-13,
W_3 also ceases to rise, and the voltage across the yoke winding
starts falling rapidly. At the same time, C_S starts dis-
charging through diode CR. This rate of discharge is hastened
by feedback action via C_F. That is, collapse of the magnetic
field in the yoke winding produces a strong negative "kickback"
pulse, which is fed via C_F into C_S through diode CR. Note that
the end of the discharge and the width of the peaking pulse
in W_3 are determined by the period of the resonant circuit
consisting of the yoke-winding inductance, C_F, and C_S. At the
end of the peaking pulse, diode CR is again cut off, and C_S
starts to recharge through R_S. Thus, the scanning cycle is
repeated.

9.7 Vertical Retrace Blanking

Previous mention was made of the practical necessity
for blanking the vertical retrace lines. If an ac-coupled
video amplifier is used, if a picture tube is weak, or if
the brightness control is turned to high, vertical retrace
lines become visible as shown in Fig. 9-14, unless a vertical
blanking circuit is used. A typical configuration is depicted
in Fig. 9-15. The vertical output transistor Q energizes the

Fig. 9-14   Appearance of vertical retrace lines in an image.

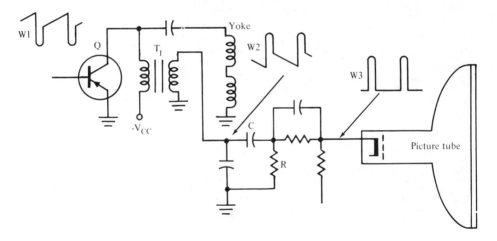

Fig. 9-15   Example of a vertical retrace blanking circuit.

yoke winding and also drives   the blanking   transformer T_1.
This transformer is utilized to change the collector waveform
into correct amplitude for cutting off the beam current in
the picture tube. Observe that the peaked sawtooth wave from
the secondary is differentiated by C and R. The result is to

remove the sawtooth component from W_2, so that a straight
baseline is obtained with positive blanking pulses that are
applied to the cathode of the picture tube. In turn, retrace
lines cannot appear in the image, because the beam current is
cut off during the vertical retrace interval.

9.8 Troubleshooting the Vertical Sweep System

Trouble symptoms encountered from defects in the vertical
sweep system include: no vertical deflection, inadequate vertical deflection, nonlinear deflection, picture rolling, poor
interlacing, and keystoned raster. When there is no vertical
deflection, a bright horizontal line is displayed on the screen,
as shown in Fig. 9-16. It is advisable to turn down the bright-

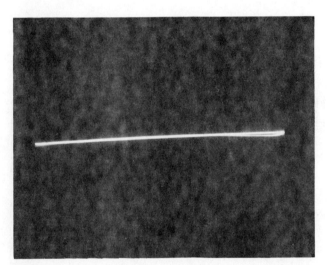

Fig. 9-16   Screen
symptom for loss of
vertical deflection.

ness control in this situation, to avoid burning the screen
phosphor. Common faults that result in no vertical deflection
are defective coupling or bypass capacitors, a worn size or
height control (open resistive element), open or shorted semiconductor diode, defective transistor, burned resistor, burned-
out coil winding, or broken printed circuit conductor.

When vertical deflection is inadequate, it is impos-

sible to fill the screen vertically, although the height control
has been advanced to its maximum setting. This trouble condition is often caused by a defective height control, leakage in
a bypass or coupling capacitor, burned resistors, or a faulty
transistor. Whenever a transistor is replaced (particularly a
power-type transistor), it is good practice to inspect the
associated resistors for possible damage due to overheating.

Nonlinear vertical deflection, as depicted in Fig. 9-17,

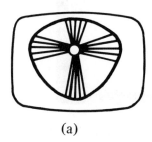 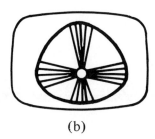

(a) (b)

Fig. 9-17 Examples
of vertical nonline-
arity: (a) top of
picture compressed,
bottom expanded,
(b) top of picture
expanded, bottom
compressed.

is generally caused by partial failure of a component in the
vertical output or vertical oscillator section. A convenient
quick check of vertical scanning linearity can be made by
rolling the picture downward on the screen by adjustment of
the vertical hold control. The vertical blanking bar and
"hammerhead" then move down the screen as illustrated in Fig.
9-18. If the width of the bar is observed as it travels down
the screen, scanning nonlinearity becomes evident as changes
in width of the bar. Note that it may be necessary to disable
the vertical blanking circuit in order to make the "hammerhead" visible; however, the bar is always visible, regardless
of vertical blanking circuit operation. The "hammerhead" is
a display of the vertical sync pulse and equalizing pulses on
the picture tube screen.

Most vertical nonlinearity trouble symptoms are caused

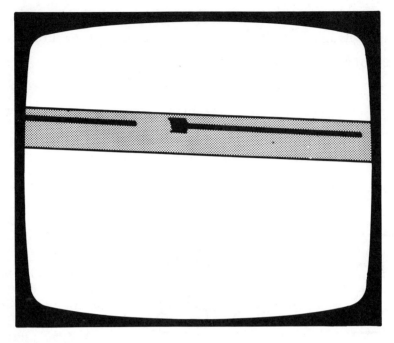

Fig. 9-18 Appearance of the vertical blanking bar with its
"hammerhead."

by open, short-circuited, or leaky capacitors in the vertical
scanning system.   However, a semiconductor diode with a poor
front-to-back ratio, or a transistor with collector leakage,
can also cause scanning nonlinearity.   In older receivers
that have been used for a number of years, electrolytic
capacitors are ready suspects; although they may appear to
be in normal condition otherwise, aged electrolytic capacitors often lose a substantial portion of their rated capacitance value.   A quick check can be made by shunting a capacitor
which is known to be good across the suspected unit to determine whether normal operation has resumed.

          Picture rolling results from the absence of or marginal
sync action.   Because this condition can be caused by either
sync section defects or vertical oscillator defects, it is
advisable to sectionalize the trouble location at the outset.

This test is made to best advantage with an oscilloscope.
For example, with reference to Fig. 9-3, the amplitude of the
vertical sync pulse would be checked at the left-hand terminal
of the 4.7-kΩ resistor. If the pulse amplitude is within $\pm 20\%$
of the peak-to-peak voltage specified in the receiver service
data, the sync section is cleared from suspicion. Accordingly,
attention is then turned to the vertical oscillator section.

Note in Fig. 9-3 that if the 4.7-kΩ resistor increases
considerably in value, the vertical sync pulse will be attenuated accordingly before it is applied to the base of transistor Q. Again, if R_5 decreases considerably in value, the
vertical sync pulse will become attenuated substantially.
These component defects result in marginal or "touchy" vertical locking. In case R_5 were short circuited, vertical sync
action would be absent. Another common cause of picture
rolling occurs when the free-running frequency of the vertical
oscillator is unstable and drifts in either direction. This
is generally caused by a worn and "noisy" vertical hold control.
It can also be caused by aging an electrolytic capacitor, such
as C_S in Fig. 9-3.

Poor interlacing (also called line pairing) is depicted
in Fig. 9-19. This is an undesirable operating condition,

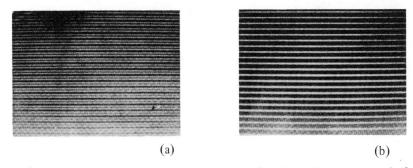

(a)   (b)

Fig. 9-19 Normal and abnormal interlacing: (a) partial loss
of interlace, (b) complete loss of interlace.

because picture detail is impaired. Note that in case of
complete loss of interlacing, practically half of the picture
definition is lost. Line pairing can be caused by an open
capacitor in the vertical integrator circuit, by an open
decoupling capacitor in the vertical oscillator section, or
by various defects in the horizontal sweep and high-voltage
sections. The horizontal system is discussed in a following
chapter. To summarize briefly, any component or operational
defect that permits entry of horizontal pulses into the vertical oscillator input circuit will result in poor interlace.

Keystoning is less common than other symptoms of vertical
system trouble, although it is encountered upon occasion. A
keystoned raster is not rectangular but trapezoidal in outline.
That is, when vertical keystoning is present, the left-hand
edge of the raster is shorter than the right-hand edge, or
vice versa. This trouble is almost always caused by a short
circuit or partial short circuit in one of the vertical deflection coils. For example, insulation breakdown between layers
can partially short-circuit a winding and cause a keystoning
symptom. Another possibility is a short circuit between a
pair of coil terminals due to a wire "whisker," solder splash,
or charred insulation.

Questions

Short Answer

1. What is the function of the vertical sweep section?
2. Discuss the operation of the circuit in Fig. 9-2 that
    produces the sawtooth waveform.

3. Discuss the operation of the blocking oscillator in Fig. 9-2.

4. What is the purpose of the vertical hold control in a television receiver?

5. What is the purpose of R_6 in the circuit in Fig. 9-3?

6. What is the purpose of the buffer amplifier in Fig. 9-4?

7. What are the waveform requirements to produce a linear current through the deflection coils?

8. What would cause ringing in the vertical deflection coils?

9. What is the disadvantage of direct coupling to the vertical deflection coils?

10. What is the disadvantage of using a vertical output transformer?

11. What is the purpose of the vertical linearity control?

12. Why is negative feedback used in the transistor circuits in the vertical section of a receiver?

13. Compare the two basic vertical linearity controls.

14. How does the network in Fig. 9-12 correct nonlinearity of sawtooth waveform?

15. Explain the operation of the vertical blanking circuit in Fig. 9-14.

16. List six vertical sweep troubles.

17. What are some of the problems that could occur in the vertical section of a television receiver?

18. What are some of the defective components that could make it impossible to fill the screen vertically?

19. How can you determine if the problem of picture rolling is located in the sync section or the vertical oscillator?

20. With reference to Fig. 9-3, what would the results be if resistor R_5 were shorted?

21. What are the symptoms of a worn vertical hold control?

22. Explain the effects of poor interlacing.

23. What are some of the causes of line pairing?

24. What is the keystone effect?

25. What are some of the causes of the keystone effect?

True-False

1. Electromagnetic deflection is almost always used for vertical deflection in a television receiver.

2. The vertical driver produces a differentiated waveform.

3. The blocking oscillator has a free-running frequency of slightly greater than 60 Hz.

4. The buffer section isolates the vertical oscillator from the output section.

5. The buffer section minimizes the interaction between the height and linearity controls and the hold control.

6. A low-impedance vertical output section uses a high impedance to supply the large driving current to the deflection coils.

7. A square wave of voltage is required to produce a saw-tooth current wave through a coil and a resistor.

8. The Q value of the deflection coils must be low to prevent ringing.

9. The purpose of connecting a damping resistor across the vertical deflection coils is to prevent ringing.

10. Either capacitive coupling or dc coupling may be used in a vertical deflection system.

11. The iron core in a vertical output transformer causes nonlinear operation.

12. Scanning linearity is often checked by a station-transmitted test pattern.

13. Negative feedback reduces the effect of component tolerance and aging.

14. Vertical linearity is sometimes controlled by changing the bias point of the output transistor.

15. Nonlinearity of the input waveform cannot be corrected by a buffer operating in the CC configuration.

16. The CRT beam current is cut off during retrace time by the blanking circuit.

17. No vertical deflection is indicated by a vertical line.

18. The vertical linearity can be checked by slowly rolling the vertical blanking bar down the screen and looking for a change of vertical size of the bar.

19. It may be necessary to disable the vertical blanking circuit in order to make the hammerhead visible on the screen.

20. A capacitor that is suspected of being faulty can be tested by placing a good unit in series with the suspected unit.

21. The problem of picture rolling can best be localized by the use of a TVM to measure voltages to ground in each section.

22. The keystone effect can be caused by a noisy vertical hold control.

23. Loss of interlace causes an effect called snow.

24. Poor interlace is caused by entrance of the IF picture carrier into the vertical oscillator section.

25. Keystoning is almost always caused by a shorted or partially shorted deflection coil.

Multiple Choice

1. The frequency of the vertical oscillator is:
    (a) 30 Hz.
    (b) 60 Hz.
    (c) 120 Hz.
    (d) 15,750 Hz.

2. Vertical sweep systems generally use a/an:
    (a) crystal-controlled oscillator.
    (b) blocking oscillator.
    (c) RC phase shift oscillator.
    (d) tuned oscillator.

3. The purpose of the low-impedance output stage in the vertical section of a receiver is to:
    (a) provide isolation between the oscillator and the deflection coils.
    (b) furnish the high current to the deflection coils.
    (c) provide isolation and furnish the high current to the deflection coils.
    (d) provide a load for the oscillator.

4. To produce a linear current through the deflection coils, the waveform must have a _____ shape.
    (a) sawtooth
    (b) square wave
    (c) pulse wave
    (d) trapezoidal

5. The purpose of placing damping resistors across the vertical deflection coils is to:
    (a) increase the linearity.
    (b) decrease the magnetic field.
    (c) prevent ringing.
    (d) reduce the heating effect of the coils.

6. The disadvantage of direct coupling to the vertical deflection coils is that:

   (a) ringing occurs.

   (b) more power dissipation occurs in the coils.

   (c) more transistors must be used.

   (d) an extra diode must be used for clamping.

7. The chief disadvantage of using a vertical output transformer is the:

   (a) extra cost.

   (b) nonlinearity caused by the iron core.

   (c) extra weight.

   (d) added inductance in the system.

8. A dc current through the vertical deflection coils causes a decentering action that is compensated for by:

   (a) centering magnets on the neck of the CRT.

   (b) the ion trap.

   (c) a curve in the neck of the CRT.

   (d) offsetting the screen.

9. Scanning linearity is often checked by a:

   (a) crosshatch pattern.

   (b) station-transmitted test pattern.

   (c) flying-spot scanner.

   (d) bar generator.

10. To overcome the effects of component tolerance and aging on the vertical waveform, manufacturers use:

   (a) negative feedback.

   (b) positive feedback.

   (c) a wave shape control.

   (d) both negative feedback and a wave shape control.

11. Retrace lines are prevented from being present on the CRT during retrace because the:

   (a) vertical deflection current is off.

(b) screen of the CRT is driven negative.

(c) vertical oscillator is cut off.

(d) CRT beam current is cut off.

12. The display of the vertical sync pulse and equalizing pulses on the picture tube screen is called the:

(a) footnote.   (c) hammerhead.

(b) blanking bar. (d) equalizing bar.

13. The quickest way to test a capacitor that is suspected of being open is:

(a) with an ohmmeter.

(b) with a capacitance bridge.

(c) by replacing the capacitor.

(d) by placing a good capacitor parallel to the suspected unit.

14. Keystoning is almost always caused by:

(a) an open deflection coil.

(b) a shorted deflection coil.

(c) horizontal pulses getting into the vertical oscillator section.

(d) nonlinearity of the vertical output sawtooth.

15. Any component defect that allows entry of horizontal pulses into the vertical oscillator input circuit will result in:

(a) keystoning.   (c) line pairing.

(b) snow.   (d) picture roll.

16. The keystone effect can be caused by:

(a) shorted or partially shorted deflection coils.

(b) noise in the vertical oscillator input.

(c) a noisy vertical hold control.

(d) horizontal pulses getting into the input of the vertical oscillator.

Chapter 10

FUNCTION OF THE HORIZONTAL OSCILLATOR AND AUTOMATIC FREQUENCY CONTROL SECTIONS

10.1   Function of the Horizontal Oscillator and AFC Sections

Horizontal motion of the scanning beam in a picture tube is basically determined by the horizontal oscillator and AFC sections.   Figure 10-1 shows a block diagram of the horizontal sweep system.   It consists of an automatic frequency control section, which effectively minimizes any disturbance from noise pulses and thereby stabilizes the horizontal scanning process.   A semisawtooth waveform is usually generated by the horizontal oscillator.   The driver section serves to step up and improve the output waveform from the oscillator and also isolates the oscillator section from the output section.   Finally, the horizontal deflection coils are energized by the output section.

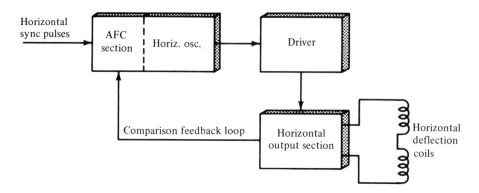

Fig. 10-1 Block diagram of a horizontal sweep system.

10.2 Oscillator AFC Circuitry and Operation

Blocking oscillators are generally used in horizontal oscillator arrangements. Configurations are basically the same as found in vertical blocking oscillators, except that component values are utilized to provide operation at 15,750 Hz, instead of 60 Hz. Observe in Fig. 10-1 that the horizontal sync pulses do not trigger the oscillator directly. Instead, indirect frequency control is employed, subsequently explained in detail. A typical horizontal blocking oscillator arrangement is depicted in Fig. 10-2. Disregarding the AFC circuitry at this time, observe that Q2 oscillates by means of positive feedback via transformer T_1.

Circuit operation of the blocking oscillator section in Fig. 10-2 is as follows: Transistor Q2 conducts during the brief horizontal retrace interval, thereby charging C_6. At the end of the charging interval, Q2 is cut off while C_6 discharges through R_7. Note that the time constant of the $C_6 R_7$ circuit determines when Q2 will go into conduction once more. Thus, this time constant (in combination with the operating point of Q2) establishes the oscillator fre-

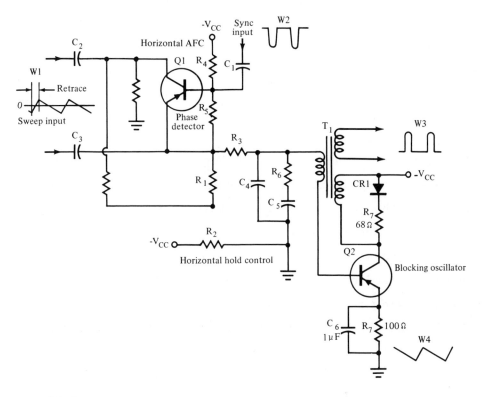

Fig. 10-2 A representative horizontal oscillator and AFC configuration.

quency. This operating point depends on the base bias of Q2. In turn, R_2 provides manual control of the oscillator frequency. Accordingly, R_2 is called the horizontal hold control. Note in passing that the base bias for Q2 is also obtained from the AFC section.

With reference to Fig. 10-2, the retrace interval starts when C_6 discharges to the same voltage as the bias on the base of Q2. Therefore, any variation in base bias will change the starting time of the retrace interval. Observe that a control voltage, produced by the AFC phase detector transistor Q1, appears across R_1. It is evident that this AFC voltage adds to or subtracts from the fixed bias voltage on the base of Q2, so that the oscillator frequency becomes faster or slower as the AFC voltage changes. Observe that the control voltage that drops across R_1 may be either positive or negative. That is, the phase detector transistor Q1 provides either direction of current flow through R_1, depending upon the applied waveform relations.

Note that transistor Q1 in Fig. 10-2 is a PNP type with practically identical collector and emitter regions. Therefore, the collector can operate as an emitter, and vice versa. Applied sync pulse W_2 is negative going and drives the base into conduction. In turn, capacitor C_1 is charged by base current flow. The discharge of C_1 is sufficiently slow so that Q1 is cut off between successive sync pulses. Now observe that the collector emitter sawtooth waveform W_1 is coupled from the output section. Thus, conduction of Q1 is determined by both W_2 and W_1, and the conduction condition changes if the phase relation (timing) of these waveforms changes.

Observe in Fig. 10-2 that the collector-to-emitter voltage is negative over the first half of the retrace interval. Thus, electrons flow out of the collector terminal. On the other hand, the collector-to-emitter voltage is positive over the last half of the retrace interval. Therefore, the collector now acts as an emitter, and the emitter acts as a collector--electrons now flow through R_1 in the other direction. The average voltage across R_1 is zero, provided that the free-running frequency of the oscillator is exactly correct. In other words, the sync pulse W_2 will then be timed so that it is applied to the base at the same time that the retrace portion of W_1 is going through zero. This means that current flows through R_1 first from emitter to collector and then flows from collector to emitter, with the result that the net current flow is zero for the duration of the sync pulse.

Now analyze the circuit action of Q1 in Fig. 10-2 in the situation where the oscillator starts to slow down its free-running frequency. This is just another way of saying that the oscillator period is lengthened, and the sync pulse arrives early. The sync pulse then occurs while the retrace interval is starting. That is, the collector is negative when the sync pulse drives Q1 into conduction, and the electron flow produces a negative voltage drop across R_1. There is little or no reverse current through R_1, because the sync pulse has passed by the time that W_1 goes positive. Because a negative control voltage is applied to the base of Q2, the free-running frequency of the oscillator speeds up accordingly. Thus, its frequency drift is corrected. It is evident that if the oscillator should speed up too much, the reverse control action would occur.

One of the essential features of the configuration depicted in Fig. 10-2 is the low-pass filter comprising R_3, C_4, R_6, and C_5. The integrating circuit R_3C_4 has a comparatively slow response, because it takes time for C_4 to charge through R_6. Consequently, a number of pulses must be applied from R_1 to the integrating circuit before their effect is evident as the dc control voltage on the base of Q_2. This "flywheel" action of the integrating circuit is important from the standpoint of noise suppression. In other words, successive noise pulses may be either positive going or negative going. If a negative-going noise pulse is followed by a positive-going noise pulse, for example, they tend to cancel out in the integrating circuit. This averaging-out process makes the

oscillator largely immune to noise disturbances, and the
picture remains steady on the screen although the noise
level might be high.

Observe in Fig. 10-2 that the oscillator output waveform W_3 is taken from a tertiary winding on transformer T_1.
This is a pulse-type waveform, and it is applied to a horizontal drive or buffer stage. Note that a series circuit
comprising R_6 and C_5 is connected between the primary of
T_1 and ground. This branch has a decreasing impedance at
higher frequencies and supplements the low-pass action of R_3
and C_4. The resistance and capacitance values are chosen
to provide optimum noise-rejection action. Also observe that
a series circuit comprising CR1 and R_7 is connected across
the secondary of T_1. As noted in the previous chapter, this
arrangement serves to dissipate "kickback" pulses and thereby
protects transistor Q1 against breakdown.

10.3 Duo-Diode AFC Circuitry

Another widely used horizontal AFC arrangement utilizes
a pair of semiconductor diodes instead of a transistor, this
being called a pulse height system. Several variations of
the basic configuration are employed by various manufacturers.
A representative circuit is depicted in Fig. 10-3. Note that
positive-going sync pulses are coupled to diodes CR1 and CR2.
Therefore, the two pulse voltages across C_1 oppose each other,
and the control voltage output would be zero, if it were not
for a sawtooth waveform that is also coupled into the AFC circuit. As seen in Fig. 10-3(b), separate sawtooth voltages are
coupled to diodes CR1 and CR2. These two sawtooth voltages
are 180° out of phase with each other. In other words, as the
first sawtooth wave is rising, the other is falling.

Circuit action in Fig. 10-3 takes place as follows:

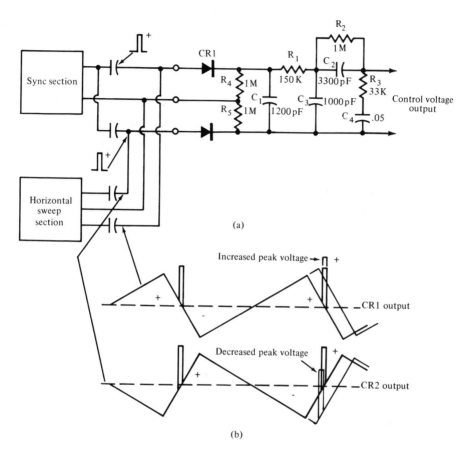

(a)

(b)

Fig. 10-3   One form of duo-diode AFC.

Because the input sawtooth waves are 180° out of phase, diodes
CR1 and CR2 conduct alternately, and the diode outputs oppose
each other   in charging C_1.   In turn, the   control voltage
output is zero, insofar as the sawtooth wave inputs are concerned.   Similarly, the combination pulse and sawtooth input
waveforms produce zero control voltage output, as long as the
oscillator is on frequency.   In other words, the positive peak
voltages of the two combination waveforms are equal, provided
the oscillator is on frequency. However, if the oscillator
"pulls" by tending to run too fast or too slow, circuit action
results in the increase of one positive peak voltage and in

the decrease of the other positive peak voltage. Therefore,
a residual charge builds up on C_1, and a control voltage output
is developed.

The foregoing process is depicted in Fig. 10-3(b). When
the oscillator tends to slow down, the effect is to lengthen
the period of the sawtooth wave. Because of the circuit configuration, the result is that the sync pulse rides up higher
on the CR1 sawtooth wave, whereas the sync pulse rides down
lower on the CR2 sawtooth wave. Consequently, the combination
CR1 waveform now has a higher positive peak voltage, whereas
the combination CR2 waveform now has a lower positive peak
voltage. It follows that the upper plate of C_1 charges to a
more positive potential than the lower plate, and a positive
control voltage output is developed. This positive control
voltage causes the oscillator to speed up, and the scanning
frequency is corrected as required.

Observe that the RC network following C_1 in Fig. 10-3
is basically a low-pass filter. As noted previously, low-
pass filter action serves to average out noise pulses that
might accompany the sync pulses. Although R_2C_2 and R_3C_4 are
not low-pass filter branches in the strict sense of the term,
they are needed to provide a suitable phase characteristic
for the AFC system. Technically, R_2C_2 and R_3C_4 are called an
antihunt network. An AFC system is an example of a servo
feedback system, and unless it has suitable transient response,
it will become unstable. When a servo system is in a condition
of instability, it will "hunt" instead of operating at a point
of equilibrium. For example, if C_4 becomes open circuited, the
AFC system will "hunt" and produce the "pie-crust" picture
symptom shown in Fig. 10-4.

Fig. 10-4 Pie-crust picture symptom.

10.4 Pulse Width AFC Circuitry

Another type of automatic frequency control circuit is called the pulse width design.   Its basic features are seen in Fig. 10-5.   Note that a comparison waveform is employed that has a fast fall time (in this example a comparison sawtooth wave with rapid flyback is utilized).   Part of the sync pulse is cancelled by the sawtooth flyback in the com-bination waveform, leaving a resultant pulse that is narrower than a sync pulse. Observe that the exact width of the resultant pulse depends on the phase relation of the sawtooth and pulse waveforms. For example, if the oscillator tends to run very fast, the resultant pulse may be reduced to zero. On the other hand, if the oscillator tends to run very slow, the resultant pulse may be as wide as a sync pulse. In normal operation, the resultant pulse is approximately half the width of a sync pulse.

Transistor Q in Fig. 10-5 operates with signal-developed bias, and only the resultant pulse extends into the conduction region. Therefore, the value of the control voltage output

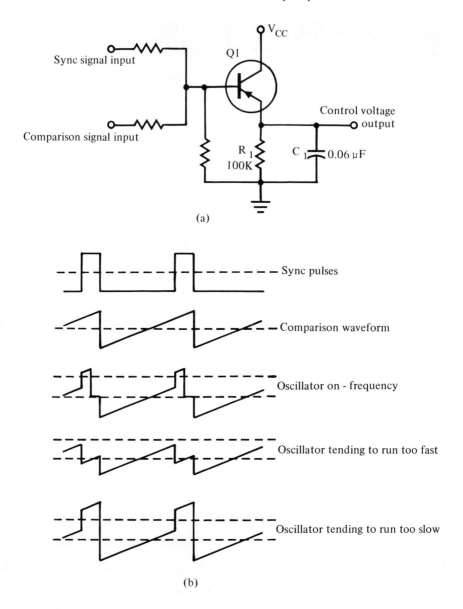

(a)

(b)

Fig. 10-5 Basic pulse width AFC arrangement.

depends upon the width of the resultant pulse. If the resultant pulse is wide, the control voltage output is high. On
the other hand, if the resultant pulse is narrow, the control
voltage output is small. As explained above, this variation
in AFC voltage with frequency keeps the oscillator on fre-

quency. The RC emitter circuit serves as a low-pass filter, in addition to providing signal-developed bias. However, because the AFC section operates in a servo system, stability of system operation is an added design consideration. Accordingly, the RC circuit is followed by an antihunt network, as explained previously.

When a sawtooth oscillator does not provide an output waveform with a rapid retrace interval, it becomes necessary to process the sawtooth wave before it is utilized as a comparison wave. For example, the sawtooth waveform may be passed through a differentiating circuit. Figure 10-6

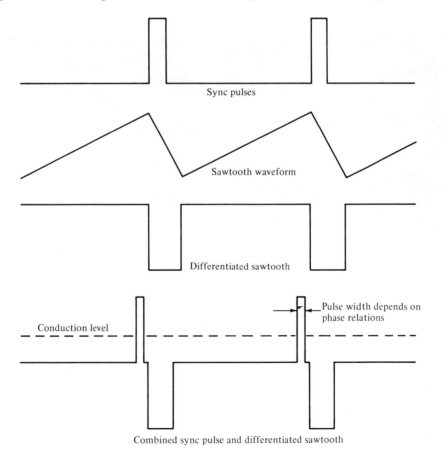

Sync pulses

Sawtooth waveform

Differentiated sawtooth

Combined sync pulse and differentiated sawtooth

Fig. 10-6 Rapid fall time is obtained by differentiating the sawtooth wave.

shows the result of differentiating a sawtooth waveform.
This process eliminates the rising slope of the sawtooth and
changes the flyback interval into a pulse. The pulse waveform
has a faster fall time than the sawtooth waveform. When this
pulse is used as a comparison waveform, it combines with sync
pulses as shown in Fig. 10-6. The end result is essentially
the same as if a comparison sawtooth with a rapid fall time
were utilized, as shown in Fig. 10-5.

It is instructive to note that when horizontal sync
lock is lost, the picture symptom indicates whether the
horizontal oscillator is running too fast or too slow.
Observe in Fig. 10-7   that loss of horizontal sync action

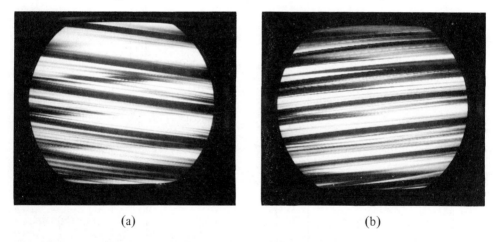

(a)   (b)

Fig. 10-7 Picture symptoms of horizontal sync loss:
(a) oscillator frequency too low, (b) oscillator frequency
too high.

results in a picture display that is "torn up" into diagonal
strips. If the strips slant uphill, the horizontal oscillator is running too slow. On the other hand, if the strips
slant downhill, the horizontal oscillator is running too
fast.   This guide is sometimes helpful in analysis of a
defective horizontal AFC system.   The exact operating frequency of the oscillator can be calculated from the number

of diagonal lines that appears in the picture trouble pattern; that is, each line corresponds to an error of 60 Hz.

As noted previously, various forms of duo-diode AFC circuits are in general use. For example, Fig. 10-8 depicts

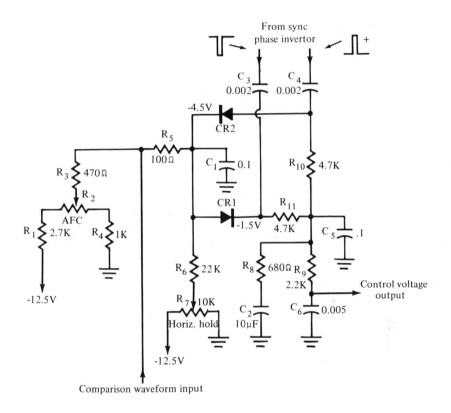

Fig. l0-8 Oppositely polarized diodes are used in this AFC arrangement.

an arrangement in which oppositely polarized diodes are employed. Basically, this develops a control voltage which ranges about zero through either positive or negative values. By way of comparison, when the diodes are operated in the same polarity, the control voltage output ranges about a reference positive value (or alternatively about a reference negative value). The end result is essentially the same, insofar as the control function is concerned,

and the choice of circuitry depends largely upon the preference of the designer.

   With reference to Fig. 10-8, the input sync pulses
are provided by a sync phase-inverter stage (not shown in
the diagram).   Thus, CR1 is driven by negative-going pulses,
and CR2 is driven by positive-going pulses.   The comparison
waveform is applied at the junction of the two diodes. Note
that when no sync pulses are applied, the control voltage
output depends on the settings of R_2 and R_7 and on the difference between the rectified comparison wave voltages.
The comparison waveform is rectified by CR1 and CR2, and the
control voltage output has a negative dc value that depends
upon the settings of R_2 and R_7.   This voltage establishes
the free-running frequency of the following horizontal oscillator.   Observe that R_7 is an operating control, identified
as the horizontal hold control. R_2 is a maintenance control,
identified as the AFC control. R_2 is adjusted to provide a
maximum pull-in range for the oscillator.

   With reference to Fig. 10-8, both of the diodes are
driven into conduction by the sync pulses. Conduction of
CR1 results in charging C_5 positively, whereas conduction of
CR2 results in charging C_5 negatively. In the reference
condition (with the oscillator on frequency) the net charge
applied to C_5 is zero, and the control voltage rests at its
reference negative value. As explained previously, the sync
pulses in the combination waveform "ride" up or down on the
flyback portion of the comparison sawtooth, depending upon
the tendency of the oscillator to run too fast or too slow.
Therefore, CR1 will conduct more heavily when the oscillator
tends to run too slow, whereas CR2 will conduct more heavily
when the oscillator tends to speed up.   Accordingly, the
rectified voltage output swings from zero to either positive

or negative values under these operating conditions.

From a functional viewpoint, R_2 and R_7 serve the same purpose in Fig. 10-8. Adjustment of either control shifts the reference negative voltage level of the control voltage output. However, R_2 changes the reference level rapidly through a wide range, whereas R_7 has a restricted range. Thus, R_7 operates as a vernier control for R_2. R_7 provides maximum convenience as an operating control. The setting of R_2 is chosen to make the normal operating point of R_7 fall at approximately the midpoint of its range.

Another form of duo-diode AFC arrangement is called an unbalanced configuration. Note that the arrangement described above is called a balanced configuration. Figure 10-9

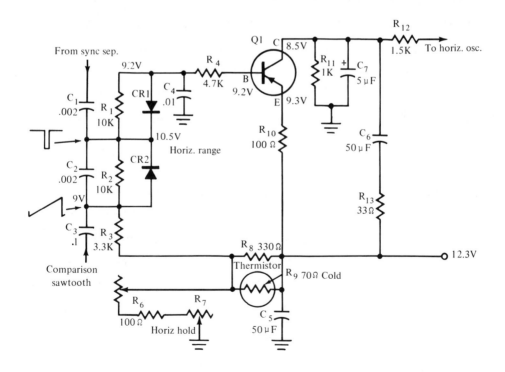

Fig. 10-9 An unbalanced AFC configuration.

depicts a typical unbalanced AFC circuit. From a theoretical viewpoint, a balanced network is more efficient in its noise-rejection process. The circuit action in the unbalanced configuration of Fig. 10-9 is as follows: Observe that the comparison sawtooth is applied to diode CR2 via C_3. This circuit branches through C_2 and R_2 with the result that a portion of the sawtooth voltage is also applied to CR1. Note that the sync pulse is coupled into the junction of CR1 and CR2, where it combines with the sawtooth waveform.

It follows that the charge on C_4 in Fig. 10-9 depends upon the comparative conduction of diodes CR1 and CR2. If CR1 conducts more than CR2, the net rectified output charges C_4 to a less positive potential than 9.2 V. On the other hand, if CR2 conducts more than CR1, the net rectified output charges C_4 to a more positive potential than 9.2 V. As explained previously, the relative conduction of the two diodes depends upon whether the sync pulse rides high or low on the flyback interval of the comparison waveform. In turn, this relative conduction depends on the tendency of the oscillator to run too fast or too slow. Because unequal sawtooth voltages are applied to CR1 and CR2, the latter operates at a higher reference level than the former. This is the reason that the configuration is called an unbalanced system.

Transistor Q1 in Fig. 10-9 is a dc amplifier that steps up the control voltage developed across C_4. Amplified AFC has the advantage of providing a greater hold-in range. Bias stability is an important consideration in the AFC amplifier section, because any drift in the operating point would tend to make the oscillator run above or below its normal free-running frequency. Therefore, thermistor R_9 is included in the bias network to compensate for changes in ambient operating temperature. Note that the horizontal hold control R_7 serves as a vernier for R_5. Thus, R_7 is an operating control, whereas R_9 is a maintenance control.

10.5 Ringing Coil Circuit Action

Any circuit has a residual noise-voltage level, although it may be very small. Accordingly, although the AFC section holds the horizontal oscillator on frequency, the residual noise voltages in the oscillator section have a tendency to produce slightly erratic operation. This small random jumping in frequency is called "jitter." To minimize jitter in the blocking oscillator configuration, a ringing coil is generally employed, as shown in Fig. 10-10. This coil is called the

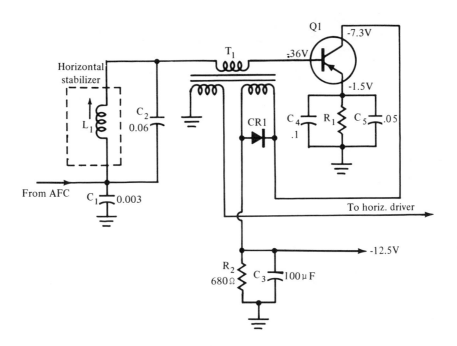

Fig. 10-10 Horizontal stabilizer coil minimizes jitter in oscillator operation.

horizontal stabilizer. Its operation is depicted in Fig. 10-11. Observe that when a ringing coil is not used, the oscillator comes out of cutoff gradually. In turn, a residual noise pulse will produce premature triggering, although the noise pulse might be very small.

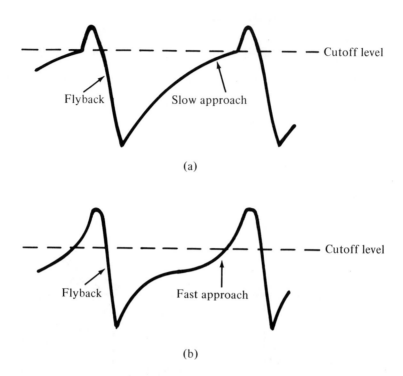

(a)

(b)

Fig. 10-11 Horizontal blocking oscillator waveforms:
(a) without ringing (stabilizer) coil, (b) with ringing
coil.

Now consider the circuit operation when a ringing coil
is employed.   Note that the coil is connected in series with
the base circuit of the oscillator transistor in Fig. 10-10.
When the flyback voltage change (Fig. 10-11) is applied to the
high Q ringing coil, it is shock excited into transient oscillation.   In turn, a sine wave variation is superimposed upon
the exponential decay waveform.   The result is that the transistor comes out of cutoff rapidly, as depicted in Fig.
10-11(b). This steep rise through the cutoff level minimizes
the jitter effect that can be produced by any residual noise
pulses.   Hence, the picture is framed more "solidly" on the
screen. Optimum stability is obtained when the phase of the

ringing waveform is as shown in Fig. 10-11(b). A slug is provided in coil L_1 for phase adjustment. This is a maintenance control and seldom requires attention.

10.6 Horizontal Phase Control

Another maintenance control, called the horizontal phasing control, is provided in many receivers. As shown in Fig. 10-12, this is typically an adjustable inductor connected

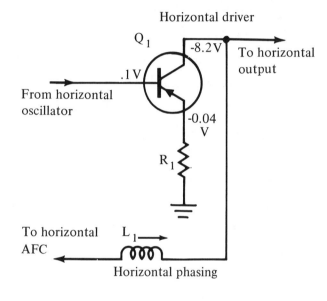

Horizontal driver

To horizontal output

From horizontal oscillator

To horizontal AFC

Horizontal phasing

Fig. 10-12 Example of a horizontal phase control inductor.

in series with the comparison waveform lead. This is a low Q coil, and it does not ring. Its purpose is merely to provide a phase shift control for the input comparison waveform to the AFC section. Thereby, the picture can be exactly framed on the raster by adjustment of the slug in the horizontal phasing coil. Introductory courses teach us that the current lags behind the voltage in an inductor. Therefore, by adjusting the inductance value of L_1, the phase of the comparison waveform can be shifted, as required.

10.7 Troubleshooting the Horizontal Oscillator and AFC Sections

Picture symptoms caused by circuit defects in the horizontal oscillator and AFC sections include dark screen, loss of horizontal sync action, horizontal pulling, horizontal picture displacement, pie-crust distortion, and subnormal picture width. A dark screen symptom can be caused by lack of output from the horizontal oscillator, or by a defect in the high-voltage section. Of course, this symptom can also be caused by a picture tube failure. Therefore, it is essential to check the output waveform from the horizontal oscillator with an oscilloscope for preliminary trouble localization. In case there is weak or no output from the oscillator, the suspicion of trouble in this section or its associated AFC section is confirmed.

When the amplitude of the oscillator output waveform is within normal tolerance (usually $\pm20\%$), it is highly probable that the dark screen trouble has occurred in the horizontal sweep or high-voltage section. However, this is not always a justifiable conclusion, inasmuch as the horizontal oscillator might be operating far off normal frequency. Therefore, it is good practice to measure the frequency of the waveform, in addition to its amplitude. To anticipate subsequent discussion, the horizontal sweep section is designed to operate at 15,750 Hz, and any substantial departure in frequency will result in little or no horizontal section output. When the horizontal oscillator is found to be operating far off its normal frequency, the trouble can be caused either by a defect in the oscillator section or in the AFC section.

Waveform checks are the important approach to trouble localization in the AFC section. Of course, a sync signal input must be present--this fact can be quickly verified with a scope test.   In case an input sync signal is absent, the trouble will be found in a section prior to the AFC network. Checks of dc voltage are often less useful than might be anticipated in analysis of AFC and horizontal oscillator circuitry. The reason for this impaired utility is abnormal conduction of diodes and transistors under trouble condi- tions.   Accordingly, technicians usually proceed with individual component tests, after a sectional localization has been made.   Statistically, faulty capacitors are prime suspects, followed by defective diodes and transistors.

Variable resistors or potentiometers are more likely to cause trouble than fixed resistors, due to wear of the resist- ance element. For this same reason, an operating control is more likely to be found defective than is a maintenance control. If a short-circuited capacitor has drawn excessive current through a fixed resistor, its value will be changed, or the resistor may be destroyed.   In case a transistor fails, it is good practice to check the associated bias and coupling circuits before inserting a new transistor into the circuit. For example, if the failure were due to coupling capacitor leakage, a new transistor will be immediately destroyed also.

A symptom of horizontal sync action loss (slanting diagonal lines on the screen) is approached in much the same way as a dark screen symptom. That is, the technician starts with waveform checks of the input sync pulse. If the pulse has subnormal amplitude, it can be concluded that the trouble will be found in a section prior to the AFC network. Again, loss of sync lock can be caused by a weak or absent compari- son waveform.   Attenuation of the comparison waveform is usually due to an open or leaky capacitor in the feedback loop.   Individual component tests of capacitors, controls, and semiconductors are commonly made after sectional locali- zation.

Horizontal pulling of the picture, or picture tearing, is caused by the same component failures that result in loss of horizontal sync lock.   However, the component failure is marginal instead of total in the case of a picture-pulling symptom.   The same considerations apply to horizontal pic- ture displacement (split picture symptom), with one excep- tion.   That is, a split picture symptom always points to a defect in the AFC section, inasmuch as the oscillator is operating on frequency by off phase.   As noted previously, a pie-crust symptom indicates a defective component in the antihunt network.   Finally, subnormal picture width has various possible causes, among which are weak output from the horizontal oscillator.   This possibility can be quickly checked with an oscilloscope.

Questions

Short Answer

1. What determines the horizontal motion of the electron beam in a picture tube?
2. What type of waveform is used for the development of the horizontal sweep?
3. What are the functions of the driver section of the horizontal section?
4. What is the frequency of the horizontal oscillator?
5. Why is the horizontal oscillator a free-running type of oscillator?

6. Explain the operation of the circuit shown in Fig. 10-2.

7. In Fig. 10-2, what is the purpose of transistor Q1?

8. In Fig. 10-2, what determines the starting time of the retrace interval?

9. In Fig. 10-2, explain the action of the AFC on the frequency of the horizontal oscillator.

10. How are noise pulses cancelled out in the circuit in Fig. 10-2?

11. What is the purpose of the series circuit, CR1 and R_7, in Fig. 10-2?

12. In the circuit in Fig. 10-3, what is the purpose of diodes CR1 and CR2?

13. What is the purpose of the RC network following C_1 in the circuit in Fig. 10-3?

14. What is a servo type of AFC circuit?

15. Discuss the operation of the pulse width AFC circuit.

16. How can the picture be used to determine if the horizontal oscillator is running too fast or too slow when the horizontal sync lock is lost?

17. What is the basic difference between the operation of the balanced and the unbalanced configuration of the duo-diode circuit?

18. What is the advantage of the balanced AFC circuit over the unbalanced circuit?

19. In Fig. 10-9, what is the purpose of the thermistor in the circuit?

20. How is jitter minimized in the circuit in Fig. 10-10?

21. What is the purpose of coil L_1 in the circuit shown in Fig. 10-10?

22. What are some of the picture symptoms that are caused by the horizontal oscillator and the AFC circuit?

23. Give three defects that could cause a black picture screen.

24. Which test instrument is the most important for locating problems in the AFC section or the horizontal oscillator section?

25. Why is it important to test bias voltages before replacing a damaged transistor with a new unit?

26. Why do split picture symptoms always point to the AFC circuit?

True-False

1. The horizontal deflection coils are located in a yoke around the neck of the picture tube.

2. The horizontal motion of the scanning beam in the picture is basically determined by the AFC section.

3. The frequency of the horizontal oscillator is 15,750 Hz.

4. In Fig. 10-2, the retrace interval starts when C_6 charges to the same voltage as the bias on the base of Q2.

5. Transistor Q1 is a phase detector transistor that provides either direction of current through resistor R_1.

6. When the oscillator frequency of the circuit in Fig. 10-2 is equal to the sync frequency, the average current through resistor R_1 is positive.

7. Components R_3, C_4, R_6, and C_5 (Fig. 10-2) form a high-pass filter.

8. The flywheel effect of the integrating circuit, R_6-C_4, is important for noise suppression.

9. The circuit-following capacitor C_1 in Fig. 10-3 is basically a low-pass filter.

10. The technical name for the RC network, made up of R_2C_2 and R_3C_4, is an "antihunting" network.

11. If capacitor C_4 in the circuit in Fig. 10-3 becomes open circuited, the AFC system will hunt and produce a pie-crust picture symptom.

12. In normal operation, the pulse out of the circuit in Fig. 10-5 is approximately equal to one-half of the sync pulse.

13. In Fig. 10-5, the RC circuit is followed by an antihunt network.

14. When the horizontal picture sync is lost, it is impossible to tell by observing the screen of the CRT whether the oscillator is running too fast or too slow.

15. When the oscillator tends to run too slowly, the output from CR2 will be greater, causing the oscillator to speed up.

16. In Fig. 10-8, resistors R_2 and R_7 serve the same purpose.

17. In Fig. 10-8, resistor R_7 operates as a vernier control for resistor R_2.

18. In Fig. 10-9, the comparison sawtooth is applied to diode CR2 through capacitor C_3.

19. The circuit configuration shown in Fig. 10-9 is called an unbalanced system.

20. In Fig. 10-9, resistor R_9 is a thermistor and compensates for changes in temperature.

21. When a ringing coil is used in a blocking oscillator (Fig. 10-10), the oscillator comes out of conduction rapidly.

22. The phasing control is usually a variable inductor.

23. A dark screen can be caused by lack of output from the horizontal oscillator or by a defect in the high-voltage section.

24. A dark screen problem is usually localized by making voltage checks.

25. When a sectional localization of the problem in the horizontal section has been made, the most probable component failure is one of the capacitors.
26. Waveform checks are an important approach in locating troubles in the horizontal oscillator or the AFC circuit.
27. Variable resistors are more likely to cause trouble than fixed resistors.
28. The best test for a problem that causes the burn out of a transistor is to replace the transistor.
29. Horizontal pulling of the picture is caused by the same component failure that results in loss of horizontal sync lock.
30. A split picture symptom always points to a defect in the vertical deflection coils.

Multiple Choice

1. The horizontal oscillator in a television receiver is usually a/an:
   (a) phase shift oscillator.
   (b) crystal oscillator.
   (c) blocking oscillator.
   (d) Weinbridge oscillator.
2. A horizontal AFC arrangement that uses a pair of semi-conductor diodes is called a _____ system.
   (a) pulse height
   (b) pulse width
   (c) phase shift
   (d) ringing coil
3. The flywheel effect of the integrating circuit in Fig. 10-2 is useful for:
   (a) pulse shaping.   (c) noise suppression.
   (b) signal generation.   (d) signal suppression.

4. The purpose of diode CR1 and resistor R_7 in Fig. 10-2 is:

    (a) to provide integration of the driving current.

    (b) to protect transistor Q2.

    (c) to shape the horizontal current waveform.

    (d) to eliminate noise pulses.

5. When the AFC circuit shown in Fig. 10-3 is in a condition of instability, it will:

    (a) hunt.

    (b) find a point of equilibrium.

    (c) give a peak positive output.

    (d) give a peak negative output.

6. The purpose of controls R_2 and R_7 in Fig. 10-8 is to:

    (a) adjust the AFC frequency.

    (b) adjust the AFC voltage.

    (c) set the AFC bias.

    (d) adjust the free-running frequency of the horizontal oscillator.

7. Jitter is prevented in the circuit in Fig. 10-10 by the action of the:

    (a) bias capacitor.   (c) transistor.

    (b) filter capacitor.   (d) ringing coil.

8. The horizontal phase control is normally a variable:

    (a) inductor.   (c) resistor.

    (b) capacitor.   (d) RC network.

9. If the input sync pulses to the horizontal oscillator are low in amplitude, the symptom is:

    (a) a dark screen.   (c) slanting lines on the screen.

    (b) a single vertical line. (d) a single horizontal line.

10. A split picture symptom points to trouble in the:

    (a) horizontal deflection coils. (c) blocking oscillator.

    (b) AFC circuit.   (d) picture tube.

Chapter 11

HORIZONTAL OUTPUT
AND
HIGH VOLTAGE SECTIONS

11.1   Function of the Horizontal Output and
       High-Voltage Sections

Horizontal motion of the scanning beam in a picture
tube is produced by deflection current output from the horizontal output section.   Electron travel from cathode to
screen in the picture tube is effected by high-potential
output from the high-voltage section.   Figure 11-1 shows a
block diagram for a horizontal output, high-voltage system.
The driver stage serves as a buffer between the oscillator
and output sections.   It also steps up the power output
from the oscillator in order to supply the drive requirement of the output section.   In turn, the output section
energizes the horizontal deflection coils, and also drives

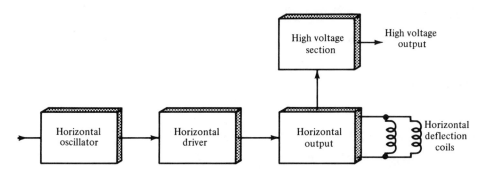

Fig. 11-1 Block diagram of the horizontal output and high-voltage system.

the high-voltage section. Because the output stage operates at a comparatively high-power level, its design entails one or more energy recovery subsections. That is, efficiency is a dominant operating consideration.

11.2 Horizontal Driver Circuitry and Operation

A typical horizontal driver stage must provide a pulse output waveform with a peak value of 100 mA. Figure 11-2

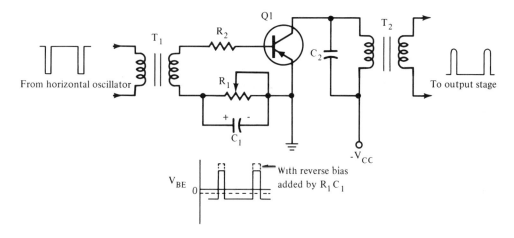

Fig. 11-2 Representative horizontal driver configuration.

shows a basic horizontal driver configuration. Observe

that the input pulse waveform switches transistor Q1 from
conduction during the forward-scanning interval into cutoff
during the flyback interval. Coupling transformer T_1 has a
step-down turns ratio to match the horizontal oscillator
output impedance to the base input impedance of Q1. Transformer T_2 also has a step-down turns ratio to match the
driver output impedance to the input impedance of the following horizontal output transistor.

When Q1 is suddenly driven into cutoff (Fig. 11-2),
the stored magnetic energy in T_2 induces a primary current
that charges C_2. This capacitor charge, in turn, discharges
back through the primary of T_2, producing a sharp flyback
pulse.   In other words, T_2 and C_2 ring for one-half cycle
as Q1 is cut off.   This ringing action is desirable to gen-
erate a fast rise and fall pulse for operation of the
horizontal output stage.   Rapid rise and fall are also
obtained by minimizing storage delay in the driver transistor.   Thus, R_2 is used to limit the base current drawn
by Q1 while it is saturated during the forward-scanning
interval.   Similarly, R_1C_1 is employed to apply an adjustable
amount of reverse signal-developed bias to the base of Q1.
In effect, this reverse bias attenuates the amplitude of
the drive signal, and R_1 is adjusted to minimize the storage
delay that results from too much forward current during
saturation.

11.3 Horizontal Output Circuitry and Operation

A horizontal output circuit operates basically as an
electronic switch.   As depicted in Fig. 11-3, the essential
elements of this circuit are a voltage source, a parallel
RC load, and the on-off switch.   In this ideal configuration,
any circuit resistance is neglected.   The inductance of the

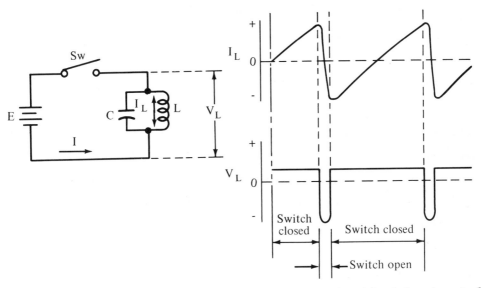

Fig. 11-3 Sequence of circuit action in the ideal horizontal deflection system.

horizontal deflection coils is effectively shunted by the distributed capacitance of the windings. As was noted previously, a linear sawtooth current flow through a pure (lossless) inductance is produced by a pulse voltage waveform. In other words, when switch Sw is closed, C is charged instantly to potential E, and current starts to rise linearly through L. However, this increase in current stops abruptly at the end of the forward-scanning interval.

Now let us follow the circuit action that occurs when switch Sw is opened. The foregoing current rise through L in Fig. 11-3 is accompanied by the build-up of a magnetic field. That is, there is magnetic energy stored in the inductor at the instant that switch Sw is opened. Therefore, when the switch is opened, this magnetic fields collapses, and current continues to flow through L in the same direction. Because the switch is open, this inductive current can flow only into capacitor C. Thus, the capacitor charges up in reverse polarity and stores potential energy. Note that the

rate of charge depends on the LC product.   That is, this is
basically an LC resonant circuit, and the capacitor charges in
accordance with its resonant frequency.   For the same reason,
the charge-current waveform is sinusoidal.   At the instant
that the magnetic field energy in L reaches zero, the capacitor
starts to discharge back through the inductor.   That is, current
now flows through L in the opposite direction, with the charged
capacitor acting as a voltage source.   In this manner, a half-
sine wave of transient oscillation occurs.

Note that the foregoing transient oscillation does not
proceed for more than one-half cycle in Fig. 11-3, because
switch Sw is closed again at the instant that the half-cycle
is completed.   Therefore, the stored magnetic energy in the
coil cannot charge the capacitor at this time.   Instead,
discharge takes place as the first half of a sawtooth wave
through the battery circuit.   It is important to note that
the energy which was previously taken from the battery has
now been returned to the battery.   In other words, in this
lossless system, all the energy which was initially supplied
by the battery has been recovered, and the operating efficiency is 100%.   The sequence of circuit action in this ideal
arrangement is summarized by the I_L and E_L waveforms shown in
Figure 11-3.

It follows that the switch in Fig. 11-3 is required to
pass current first in one direction, and then in the other
direction.   Because a transistor is used as an electronic
switch, this requirement might seem to be an impossible
condition of operation.   However, a transistor is a unilateral
(one-way) device only when it is operated out of its collector
saturation region.   That is, if a transistor is held in its
saturated mode, the emitter can be operated as a collector and
the collector can be operated as an emitter.   In turn, a single

transistor can be used as switch Sw in Fig. 11-3, when the
transistor is driven successively between cutoff and saturation.

As is usual, a pulse waveform is employed to drive the
transistor between cutoff and saturation. A basic arrangement
is depicted in Fig. 11-4. Transformer T operates as an ac-

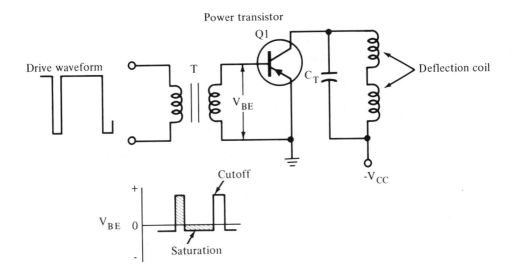

Fig. 11-4 Basic horizontal deflection arrangment.

coupling device. In turn, the driving pulse is applied to the
base of transistor Q with alternate positive and negative
polarity, as shown in the diagram. The area of the positive
excursion is necessarily equal to the area of the negative
excursion. Accordingly, the drive signal provides a highly
positive peak during retrace, with a sufficiently negative
peak value to maintain the saturated mode for Q during the
forward-scanning interval.

With reference to Fig. 11-5, the collector output
waveform rises linearly until the cutoff pulse is applied
to the base of Q. At this instant, the collector current
falls at a rate determined by the delay time of the tran-

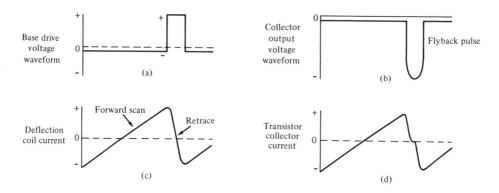

Fig. 11-5 Basic voltage and current waveforms in the horizontal deflection system.

sistor. As explained above, the magnetic field in the deflection coils starts to collapse, and current continues to flow. Inasmuch as Q is cut off, this current must charge C_T. Note that because the deflection coils have inductive reactance, the peak voltage across the coils occurs as the coil current passes through zero. As shown in the diagram, this means that the collector voltage increases to a negative peak at the instant that the coil current passes through zero during the flyback interval.

Observe in Fig. 11-5 that the cutoff voltage pulse falls to zero at the end of the flyback interval, and current starts to flow in the reverse direction through the transistor and deflection coils (Fig. 11-4). The transistor is driven into saturation at this time, and the stored magnetic energy in the coils produces a linear decay of current flow. Because the system is not lossless (100% efficient), the negative peak of the current sawtooth has somewhat less amplitude than the positive peak. This difference represents energy supplied to the system by the drive waveform at the base of transistor Q. The basic arrangement depicted in Fig. 11-4 is elaborated in various ways to meet practical require-

ments of a horizontal deflection system. It is instructive
to consider the chief requirements that are involved.

11.4 Deflection Power Levels

A typical large screen receiver employs a horizontal
deflection system that operates at a peak power level of more
than 1000 VA (more than 1 kW of apparent power). Silicon
transistors are generally used in the output circuit and can
withstand a peak reverse voltage of approximately 100 V.
Accordingly, the peak-to-peak current value in this example
is over 10 A. As mentioned before, the peak voltage across
the deflection coils depends upon their inductance value and
the current rate of change (roc) during the forward-scanning
interval. A larger inductance can be used without increasing
the peak voltage, if a suitable ringing circuit is employed
to cancel out part of the flyback pulse.

With reference to Fig. 11-6, a ringing circuit consisting of a parallel LC circuit is coupled to the collector
of the output transistor. The circuit is resonant at three
times the flyback frequency and is called a third-harmonic
ringing circuit. As shown in the diagram, the phase relations of the flyback pulse and the ringing voltage are such
that the peak of the pulse is cancelled out and the resultant
modified pulse has an inverted peak with reduced amplitude.
In summary, this circuit elaboration avoids transistor breakdown while permitting more turns to be used in the deflection
coils, so that more ampere turns are provided at a given
current level.

11.5 High-Voltage and Booster-Damper Subsections

All modern receivers obtain accelerating voltage for the
picture tube from a subsection of the horizontal deflection

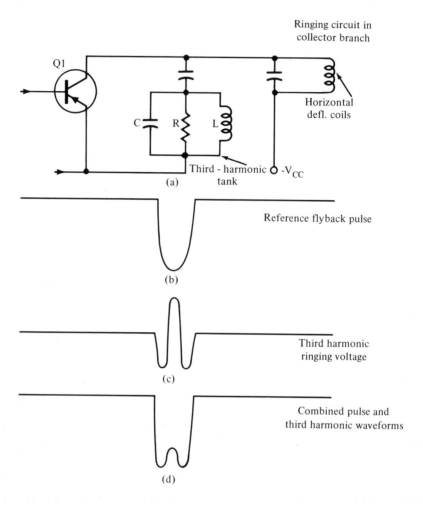

Fig. 11-6 Reduction in peak amplitude of flyback pulse by inclusion of a third harmonic ringing circuit.

system. This high-voltage arrangement is energized by the horizontal flyback pulse. In addition, a booster subsection is provided for generation of dc potentials of 200 or 300 V. This supply is necessary because the video amplifier and picture tube require operating potentials considerably greater than the V_{CC} source. A damper subsection is also included, which operates as a switch between the deflection and booster sections. Its switching action not only controls booster circuit operation, but also reduces the Q of the deflection system during the flyback interval so that ringing does not persist into the forward-scanning period.

Figure 11-7 exemplifies a basic configuration. Observe

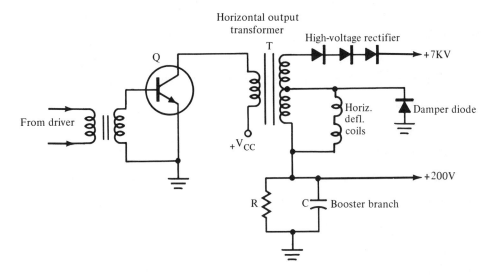

Fig. 11-7 Basic deflection arrangement with high voltage and booster-damper subsections.

that a horizontal output transformer is employed to match the output impedance of the transistor to the deflection coil impedance. The complete secondary winding serves to step up the potential of the flyback pulse to 7 kV for supply of high voltage to the picture tube. Note that the horizontal deflection coils are shunted by a damper diode. This diode conducts only during the flyback interval. Similarly, the high-voltage rectifier diodes conduct only during the flyback interval. A number of diodes are necessarily connected in series in order to avoid peak inverse voltage breakdown.

The circuit action in the configuration of Fig. 11-7 takes place as follows. During the time that transistor Q is held in saturation by the drive waveform, and while the for-

ward scan is in progress, the damper diode and the high-voltage
rectifier diodes are nonconducting. At the instant that the
cutoff pulse is applied to the base of Q, the flyback pulse
appears across the horizontal deflection coils into the damper
diode, and a stepped-up pulse is applied to the high-voltage
rectifier diodes. Insofar as high-voltage circuit action is
concerned, a positive-pulsating dc potential is supplied to
the ensuing high-voltage filter section. Operation of the
booster-damper circuitry is somewhat more involved and is
explained as follows.

When the flyback pulse is applied to the damper diode,
electrons flow from the deflection coils to ground and back up
through R, thereby charging booster capacitor C to +200 V.
Thus, the booster operates effectively as a dc power supply.
However, it has an additional important function in preventing
system ringing except during the retrace interval. That is,
the horizontal deflection system has a high Q value during the
forward-scanning period and rings for one-half cycle as flyback
is initiated. The damper diode also switches into conduction
during the flyback period, and at the end of retrace has
diverted sufficient energy into the booster circuit so that
transient ringing is suppressed at the start of the next forward-scanning interval.

11.6 Hybrid Horizontal Output and High-Voltage System

A considerable proportion of receiver designers prefers
a hybrid configuration in which a high-voltage rectifier
tube is utilized instead of a stack of semiconductor diodes.
Figure 11-8 exemplifies this arrangement and includes another
basic circuit wherein the horizontal deflection coils are
energized directly by the horizontal output transistor. The
operating features of this configuration are as follows.

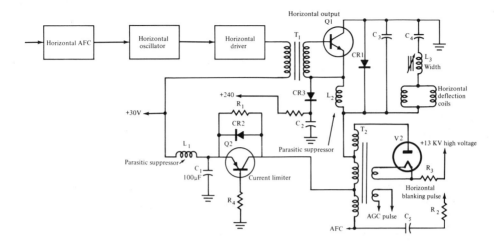

Fig. 11-8 A complete horizontal output and high-voltage configuration.

Transistor Q1 operates in an emitter follower configuration in the horizontal output stage. The high-voltage transformer T_2, deflection coils, and damper CR1 are the load circuit for Q1. It is instructive to follow the circuit-action sequence in this load arrangement.

With reference to Fig. 11-9, the output transistor Q1 starts conduction at about the center of the forward-scanning interval, as shown in the yoke current waveform. In turn, the sawtooth current continues to rise linearly until the instant that Q1 is cut off by the driving pulse from T_1, as shown in Fig. 11-8. This pulse is depicted in the driving voltage waveform in Fig. 11-9. In turn, the collapsing magnetic field in the horizontal deflection coils produces a half-sine wave flyback pulse as shown in the yoke voltage waveform. As explained previously, the flyback pulse switches damper diode CR1 into conduction (Fig. 11-8). Stored magnetic energy thereupon decays, and CR1 conducts for approximately the first half of the forward-scanning

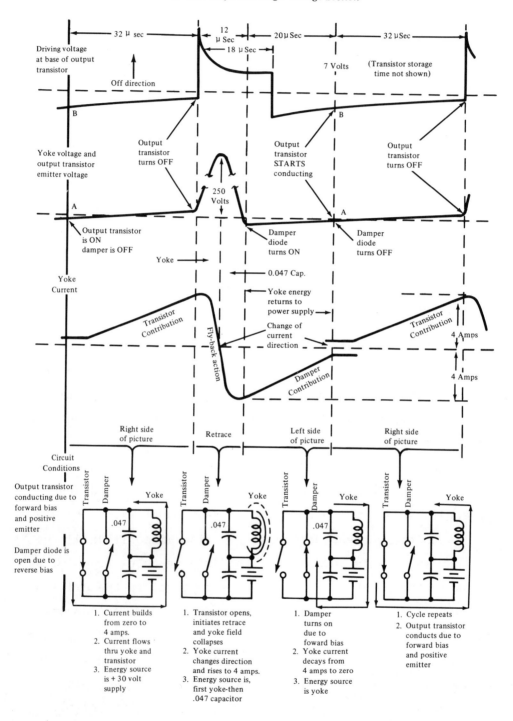

Fig. 11-9 Sequence of circuit action in the configuration of Fig. 11-8. (Courtesy, RCA Electronic Components Division)

interval. This action is seen in the yoke current waveform in Fig. 11-9. The foregoing operating cycle is then repeated.

Because transistor Q1 in Fig. 11-8 would be damaged by excessive current flow, transistor Q2 is employed as a current-limiting device. If Q1 tends to draw excessive current, Q2 is biased to a higher potential, and its collector current remains practically constant. Note that Q2 is in the path of flyback pulses and would be damaged unless these pulses were bypassed. This is the function of diode CR2, which conducts during the flyback interval. Inductor L_3 places an inductive reactance in series with the deflection coils, thereby serving as a width coil to provide the correct horizontal size of raster on the screen. L_3 is also called an efficiency coil because its adjustment also affects the current demand of Q1.

Autotransformer T_2 in Fig. 11-8 operates as a high-voltage transformer and steps up the amplitude of the flyback pulse. The resulting high-voltage pulse is rectified by V2, thereby developing +13-kV dc potential for accelerating the electron beam in the picture tube. Note that booster diode CR3 rectifies the flyback pulse from the emitter of Q1 and charges C_2. Thereby an intermediate dc voltage source of +240 V is provided. Observe that CR1 and C_3 are also part of an energy recovery system, in that C_3 is charged by conduction of CR1 during the flyback interval. This potential energy provides the second half of the retrace in the yoke current waveform. In other words, C_3 forms part of an LC resonant circuit in combination with the deflection coils.

Note also in Fig. 11-8 that T_2 supplies a comparison waveform for the horizontal AFC section. A horizontal

blanking pulse for the picture tube is also provided by T_2
via C_5 and R_2.   Two supplementary secondary windings on T_2
are utilized to energize the filament of V2 and to supply a
pulse voltage of suitable amplitude to the AGC section.
Resistor R_3 serves as a filter component in the high-voltage
filter circuit, which is terminated by the input capacitance
of the accelerating anode in the picture tube. R_3 also provides a protective current-limiting function, in event of
short-circuit failure in the picture tube.

11.7   Troubleshooting the Horizontal Output and High-Voltage Sections

Various picture symptoms occur as a result of defects
in the horizontal output and high-voltage sections. Some of
these symptoms provide definite localization, and others
indicate a probability or possibility of trouble in these
sections.   In turn, localization tests are often required.
The chief test instruments employed in these tests are the
high-voltage dc voltmeter, oscilloscope, pattern generator,
and specialized instruments such as the television analyst.
As explained in greater detail subsequently, analyst-type
instruments are basically specialized generators which
supply complex waveform signals for injection into various
circuits.

Picture trouble symptoms include an absence of raster,
called a dark screen condition; inadequate raster width,
often called a narrow picture symptom; excessive height and
width, with reduced brightness, called blooming; cramped
image at the left, right, or in the central region of the
screen, called horizontal nonlinearity; one or more bright
vertical stripes with associated overlap of the image,
called horizontal foldover; trapezoidal raster instead of

rectangular raster shape, called keystoning; impaired AGC action with resulting abnormal or subnormal picture contrast; and defective sync lock with symptoms ranging from "touchy" horizontal sync to picture pulling, or complete loss of sync lock. In the majority of cases, a dark screen symptom results from a complete or partial failure of the high-voltage supply.

However, there are various other possibilities, such as a defective picture tube or incorrect bias voltages at the cathode and grid in the picture tube input circuit. Consequently, it is helpful to first measure the high-voltage value at the accelerating anode of the picture tube. This measurement is made with a conventional VOM, VTVM, or TVM, supplemented by a suitable high-voltage probe, as illustrated in Fig. 11-10. The probe is essentially an external multi-

Fig. 11-10 A high-voltage dc probe. (Courtesy, B & K Manu-facturing Co.)

plier resistor that extends the scale indication to 15 kV,
for example.

High-voltage failure can result from component defects
in either the high-voltage section or in the horizontal
deflection section.   For example, a semiconductor rectifier
stack can become short circuited or open circuited.   In such
a case, there is no dc output, although the high-voltage ac
input is normal.   If a high-voltage capacitance-divider probe
is available, the ac input voltage can be measured with a
voltmeter or oscilloscope.   However, capacitance-divider
probes are generally regarded as lab-type equipment and
are not in wide use by service technicians.   In most situations, a substitution test is made when rectifier failure is
suspected.

It is evident that high-voltage failure can also be
caused indirectly by drive failure from the horizontal oscillator.   Accordingly, one of the basic localization tests is
a waveform check at the input of the horizontal deflection
section.   The drive waveform should have the approximate
amplitude specified in the receiver service data and should
also have the correct wave shape.   One of its most important
characteristics is rapid rise and fall, so that the switching
action of the horizontal output transistor takes place defi-
nitely and quickly.   As noted previously, measurement of rise
and fall time requires the use of a triggered sweep oscilloscope.   This has become standard equipment in the majority of
the large service shops.

Some technicians prefer to make signal substitution
tests, instead of making waveform checks.   For example,
when failure of drive voltage is suspected, a suitable drive
substitution voltage can be applied from a television analyst, which is a specialized signal injector designed for

troubleshooting procedures. Then, if a raster reappears on
the picture tube screen, the suspicion of drive failure is
confirmed. Another approach in this situation consists of
the substitution of a high voltage to the picture tube. That
is, an analyst-type instrument may provide a 15-kV dc output,
which can be applied to the picture tube. If the raster
reappears when high voltage is provided, the conclusion can
be made that a defect is present in the high-voltage circuitry. Note that picture tube testers are sometimes
employed, but that a substitution test is usually made
when there is suspicion of picture tube failure.

A narrow picture symptom as exemplified in Fig. 11-11

Fig. 11-11 Example
of insufficient hori-
zontal width.

can be caused by defects in sections other than the horizontal
output circuit. For example, low-supply voltage often becomes
first evident as subnormal picture (raster) width. Again, an
attenuated or distorted drive waveform can also produce this
picture symptom. Therefore, these possibilities should be
checked at the outset. In case the trouble is localized to
the horizontal output section, the defective component may be

in the damper circuitry, or in the output circuitry. It
follows from the yoke current waveform depicted in Fig. 11-9
that reduction in width (nonlinearity) in the left-hand portion of the image is likely to be caused by damper circuit
defects.   On the other hand, if the cramping or nonlinearity
occurs in the right-hand portion of the image, the trouble is
likely to be found in the output circuitry.

Neither dc voltage measurements nor waveform checks are
as useful as trouble clues in the horizontal output section as
in various other receiver sections. The reason for this lack
of utility is due to the interaction of the subsections, and
to the nonlinear operating characteristics of the horizontal
output system.   However, the usual statistical considerations
apply to component failures.   Thus, fixed capacitors are prime
suspects. It has been noted previously that electrolytic
capacitors may appear to be in good condition, although they
have lost a substantial portion of their rated capacitance
value, due to aging processes.   Semiconductor diodes and
transistors rank next in failure frequency, followed by inductors and transformers.   Resistors are the least likely trouble-
makers, although occasional failure is possible.

Blooming is denoted by an enlarged and dim picture,
which is expanded both horizontally and vertically with the
outer portions of the image off screen, as exemplified in
Fig. 11-12. This picture symptom almost invariably indicates
a subnormal value of high-voltage supply to the picture tube.
Accordingly, the output from the high-voltage section is
measured at the outset.   Note that this measurement should
be made under load.   That is, reduction in the high-voltage
value is sometimes caused by an abnormal current demand as
a result of picture tube defects.   In turn, if an open-circuit
measurement is made, the operating voltage will seem to be

Fig. 11-12 Raster and image abnormally enlarged, due to blooming.

correct, although it is actually subnormal when the high-voltage lead is connected to the picture tube.

The most common cause of blooming is a defective high-voltage filter capacitor. If a high value of leakage resistance develops, substantial current will be drained by the defective capacitor, because of its high operating potential. Note that a test of a high-voltage filter capacitor with a conventional capacitor tester is almost meaningless. In other words, leakage that is serious at 15 kV is often undetectable at a test potential of several hundred volts. Therefore, a substitution test is made by most technicians in this situation. Some service shops have high-voltage test equipment available, and in such cases capacitors and other high-voltage components can be tested directly.

Horizontal nonlinearity, in the absence of accompanying symptoms, is generally caused by marginal component defects in the damper or output circuitry. Nonlinearity can also be caused by mismatched or out-of-tolerance replacement components. For example, if the horizontal output transformer becomes defective in the configuration of Fig. 11-7, it is essential to employ a replacement transformer that has the

correct turns ratios, correct impedance values, and suitable
power rating. Otherwise, horizontal nonlinearity is likely
to result. Also note that various types of yokes are utilized in different receivers. Horizontal deflection coils
are wound with specified inductance and resistance values,
and with certain geometries. Therefore, the reciever service data should be consulted for suitable types or replacement yokes.

Horizontal foldover, shown in Fig. 11-13, is basically

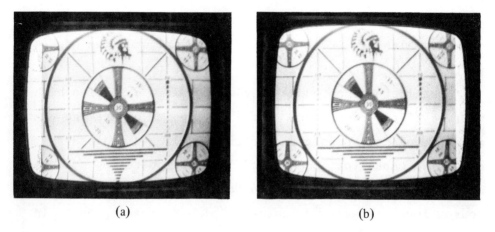

(a)   (b)

Fig. 11-13 Examples of foldover at left side and at right
side of the picture.

caused by excessive flyback time. The trouble may be located
in either the horizontal output or oscillator section--in some
situations, a component defect in the driver section can cause
a foldover symptom. It is advisable to check the "on" and
"off" times of the drive waveform with a triggered sweep oscilloscope that has a calibrated time base. As depicted in Fig.
11-9, the "on" time is typically 18 μsec, with an "off" time
of 46 μsec. If the switching time is incorrect, the trouble
will be found in the oscillator or driver sections. Otherwise,
the cause of foldover is located in the output section. Note

that a slow rise or fall time in the drive waveform can also contribute to a foldover symptom.

An unexpected cause of foldover is encountered when close tolerance components are replaced with wider tolerance components. For example, receiver service data often specify a 10% tolerance on certain sweep system capacitors. In case a 20% replacement capacitor is used, and the particular unit has too high capacitance, foldover can be expected. The same general considerations apply to replacement transformers, yokes, and width coils.

When horizontal deflection coils are series connected, and one of the coils becomes partially or completely short circuited, a keystoned raster results, as shown in Fig. 11-14.

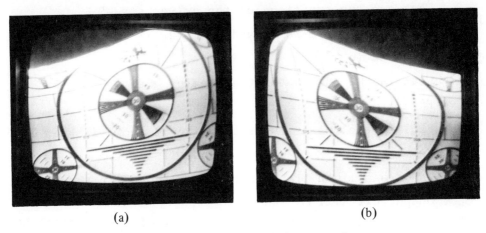

(a)   (b)

Fig. 11-14 Examples of horizontal keystoning.

Short circuits occur from breakdown between layers in a yoke winding, mechanical damage, bent terminal lugs, solder splashes, and so on. Any abnormal operating condition in the horizontal output section can cause associated malfunctions in the AGC and sync sections, because of sectional interaction. Sometimes an AGC trouble symptom is caused by a defective AGC winding on the horizontal output transformer. In this situa-

tion, there is negligible disturbance of the horizontal deflection function, and the trouble symptom is limited to upset in
the AGC function.

Questions

Short Answer

1. How is the horizontal motion of the scanning beam produced
    in a picture tube?
2. Draw a block diagram of a horizontal output, high-voltage
    stage, and label each block.
3. What are the functions of the driver stage?
4. Why do transformers T_1 and T_2 (Fig. 11-2) have a step-down
    turns ratio?
5. What is the purpose of the ringing action of T_2 and C_2 in
    Fig. 11-2?
6. Explain the operation of the circuit shown in Fig. 11-3.
7. How is a transistor used so that it functions as a switch?
8. Why are silicon transistors usually used in the horizontal
    output circuit?
9. In Fig. 11-6, what is the frequency of the parallel LC
    circuit in respect to the flyback frequency?
10. How does the circuit design in Fig. 11-6 prevent tran-
    sistor breakdown?
11. In Fig. 11-7, why are there a number of diodes connected
    in series?
12. When does the damping diode in Fig. 11-7 come into con-
    duction?
13. At what point of the forward-scanning interval does
    transistor Q1 (Fig. 11-9) begin conduction?

14. In Fig. 11-8, what is the purpose of transistor Q2?

15. In Fig. 11-8, what is the purpose of the autotransformer T_2?

16. In Fig. 11-8, what is the purpose of resistor R_3?

17. List four picture tube symptoms that are associated with failure of the horizontal sweep section of a television receiver.

18. What is the purpose of a high-voltage probe?

19. What picture tube symptoms would be present if there were an opening in the high-voltage rectifier stack?

20. Why is it that a failure in the horizontal oscillator section can cause the loss of output from the high-voltage section?

21. What is the function of a television analyst?

22. What are some of the troubles that can cause a narrow picture symptom?

23. Why are dc voltage tests and waveform checks less useful in the horizontal output section than in other parts of the receiver?

24. What is picture tube blooming?

25. What is the most common cause of the blooming effect?

26. Why is it necessary to use an exact replacement for the high-voltage output transformer?

27. What causes horizontal foldover?

True-False

1. The driver stage serves as a power amplifier and as a buffer between the oscillator and the output sections.

2. In Fig. 11-2, coupling transformer T_1 has a step-down turns ratio so that it gives voltage amplification.

3. In Fig. 11-2, transformer T_2 and capacitor C_2 form a low-pass filter.

4. A horizontal output circuit operates basically as an electronic switch.

5. The LC product of capacitor C in Fig. 11-3 determines its charge rate.

6. A transistor can be operated as a switch by operating it between cutoff and saturation.

7. In Fig. 11-5, the maximum coil current occurs at the instant that the collector voltage reaches a maximum positive value.

8. A large screen receiver employs a horizontal deflection system that operates at a peak power level of more than 1000 VA.

9. Germanium transistors are usually used in the horizontal output circuit.

10. The peak voltage across the deflection coils depends upon their inductance value and the current rate of change during the forward-scanning interval.

11. In Fig. 11-6, the frequency of the LC circuit is equal to the flyback frequency.

12. The accelerating voltage for the picture tube is developed from a subsection of the horizontal deflection system.

13. The damping diode in Fig. 11-7 comes into conduction during cutoff of transistor Q.

14. Transistor Q2 in Fig. 11-8 is used as a current limiter for transistor Q1.

15. In Fig. 11-8, coil L_2 is called an efficiency coil.

16. In Fig. 11-8, resistor R_3 limits the current in case there is a short circuit in the picture tube.

17. Failure of the high-voltage section will not cause a dark screen symptom.

18. A high-voltage capacitor probe is used to extend the ac

range of an oscilloscope or voltmeter.

19. A substitution test is usually made when rectifier failure is suspected.

20. High-voltage failure cannot be caused by failure of the horizontal oscillator.

21. A triggered sweep oscilloscope must be used to measure the rise and fall time of the horizontal output transistor.

22. A television analyst may provide a 15-kV dc output for the picture tube.

23. A narrow picture symptom can only be caused by the horizontal output circuit.

24. Measurements of dc voltage and waveform checks are less useful clues in the horizontal output section than in other sections of the receiver.

25. Picture tube blooming is usually associated with a low value of high voltage.

26. The output from the high-voltage section should be measured without a load.

27. Reduction in high voltage may be caused by a picture tube defect.

28. A high-voltage filter can be tested for defects with an ordinary capacitor tester.

29. Horizontal linearity can be caused by marginal component defects in the damper or output circuit.

30. Horizontal foldover is caused by too short a flyback time.

31. A keystoned raster is caused by a partially short-circuited deflection coil.

Multiple Choice

1. A typical horizontal driver stage provides a pulse
    output waveform with a peak value of:
    (a) 1 mA.
    (b) 10 mA.
    (c) 100 mA.
    (d) 1 A.

2. A horizontal output circuit operates basically as a/an:
    (a) electronic switch.
    (b) sawtooth generator.
    (c) wave shaper.
    (d) pulse generator.

3. The rate of charge into capacitor C_1 in Fig. 11-3 is
    determined by the:
    (a) RC time constant.
    (b) LR time constant.
    (c) LC product.
    (d) frequency of the horizontal oscillator.

4. A large screen receiver uses a horizontal deflection
    system that operates at a peak power of:
    (a) less than 10 W.
    (b) less than 100 VA.
    (c) more than 1000 VA.
    (d) approximately 40 W.

5. The transistors used in the horizontal output circuit
    are usually of the _____ type, with a reverse
    breakdown voltage of approximately _____ V.
    (a) silicon, 1000
    (b) germanium, 1000
    (c) silicon, 100
    (d) germanium, 100

6. The circuit in Fig. 11-6 has a resonant frequency of three times the flyback frequency. This design is used to:

    (a) prevent oscillation of the output.

    (b) avoid transistor breakdown.

    (c) cancel feedback.

    (d) increase the pulse time.

7. The accelerating voltage for the picture tube is developed from a/an:

    (a) section of the horizontal deflection system.

    (b) section of the vertical deflection system.

    (c) oscillator that takes its output from the IF stages.

    (d) voltage multiplier.

8. Transistor Q2 in Fig. 11-8 is used as a/an:

    (a) current limiter for Q1.

    (b) voltage limiter for Q2.

    (c) voltage boost for L_3.

    (d) amplifier for Q1.

9. In Fig. 11-8, capacitor C_5 and resistor R_2 in conjunction with transformer T_2 provide:

    (a) the sweep signal.

    (b) damping.

    (c) filter components.

    (d) retrace blanking.

10. With reference to Fig. 11-8, in case of a short in the accelerating anode of the picture tube:

    (a) R_3 would limit the current.

    (b) transistor T_2 would have excessive current.

    (c) V2 would probably short-circuit.

    (d) V2 would draw excessive current.

11. High-voltage failure can result from component failure

in the:

    (a)   video section.

    (b)   IF section.

    (c)   horizontal deflection section.

    (d)   horizontal deflection section or the high-voltage section.

12. A high-voltage probe is used to extend the:

    (a)   ac voltage range of a voltmeter.

    (b)   dc voltage range of a voltmeter.

    (c)   voltage range of an oscilloscope.

    (d)   frequency range of a VOM.

13. A high-voltage capacitor probe is used to extend the:

    (a)   dc voltage range of an oscilloscope.

    (b)   ac range of an oscilloscope.

    (c)   ac range of a TVM.

    (d)   ac range of an oscilloscope or voltmeter.

14. A short in the high-voltage rectifier stack would cause:

    (a)   excessive brightness on the screen of the CRT.

    (b)   a black CRT.

    (c)   excess width in the picture.

    (d)   a narrow horizontal line.

15. A high-voltage failure can be caused by a failure in the _____ section.

    (a)   IF

    (b)   video

    (c)   horizontal oscillator

    (d)   all the above.

16. A television analyst is a/an:

    (a)   special type of technician.

    (b)   computer tester.

    (c)   instrument that can be used to inject a signal.

    (d)   special type of oscilloscope.

17. The most useful method of determining a faulty part in the horizontal output section of a television receiver is by:

    (a) waveform analysis with an oscilloscope.

    (b) dc voltage measurement.

    (c) resistance measurement.

    (d) part replacement.

18. The least likely parts to go bad in the horizontal output section are:

    (a) capacitors.

    (b) transistors.

    (c) diodes.

    (d) resistors.

19. The problem of picture tube blooming is usually caused by a:

    (a) low value of high voltage.

    (b) high value of high voltage.

    (c) shorted picture tube.

    (d) shorted output transistor.

20. The most common cause of the blooming effect is a:

    (a) shorted picture tube.

    (b) weak output transistor.

    (c) low-horizontal oscillator output.

    (d) defective high-voltage filter capacitor.

21. A partially short-circuited deflection coil can cause:

    (a) a keystoned raster.

    (b) foldover.

    (c) loss of brightness.

    (d) blooming.

Chapter 12

INTERCARRIER SOUND
AND
AUDIO SECTIONS

12.1 Function of the Intercarrier Sound and Audio Sections

A conventional television receiver comprises a picture signal channel and a sound signal channel. The first processing circuits are common to both the picture and sound signals. After the signals have been stepped up to an appreciable level, branch circuits are employed to process the picture and sound signals separately. The plan of a typical signal system is depicted in Fig. 12-1. Observe that the picture signal is processed through an ordinary superheterodyne system. It is instructive to follow the progress of the sound signal through the various receiver sections.

The sound signal at the antenna input terminals falls

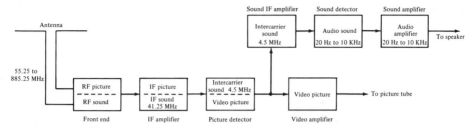

Fig. 12-1 Plan of a typical television picture and sound system.

in the range from 55.25 to 885.25 MHz. After amplification through the RF amplifier, the sound signal is converted to a typical intermediate frequency of 41.25 MHz. Next, the 41.25-MHz signal is stepped up through the IF amplifier and fed to the picture detector. Note that the sound signal undergoes a second conversion in the picture detector where it is heterodyned with the picture carrier to produce the 4.5-MHz intercarrier sound signal. Although picture sideband frequencies are also present in the picture detector circuit, the picture carrier frequency is the strongest component, so that in effect the IF sound signal is being heterodyned with the picture carrier signal.

With reference to Fig. 12-1, the picture and sound signals branch from the picture detector into separate channels. A 4.5-MHz tuned circuit at the output of the picture detector "picks off" the intercarrier sound signal and feeds it to the sound detector. In turn, the intercarrier sound signal is demodulated by the sound detector and applied to the audio amplifier. This audio amplifier is conventional and has a frequency response from approximately 20 Hz to 10 kHz. (The television sound signal is a frequency-modulated transmission. Therefore, the sound detector is an FM configuration, as explained in greater detail subsequently.) It is instructive

to note that the 4.5-MHz intercarrier sound signal is actually
available first at the mixer output in the front end.   In
other words, it is one of the heterodyne conversion products.
However, since the 4.5-MHz signal has a very low level at this
point, it is not "taken off" here but is rejected by the IF
tuned circuits.   Thus, the 41.25-MHz conversion product is
stepped up through the IF amplifier, and the 4.5-MHz intercarrier sound signal becomes available next as a conversion
product from the picture detector.

It was noted previously that the sound-IF signal must
be maintained at a comparatively low level through the IF
amplifier, to avoid objectionable amplitude modulation of the
FM sound signal by the AM picture signal.   That is, unless
the sound-IF level is restricted to 10% or less of the picture-
IF level, the vertical sync pulses are likely to modulate the
FM sound signal to such an extent that the limiter in the
sound-IF section cannot remove the resulting 60-Hz "notches"
in the FM signal.   The practical consequence of this difficulty is a rasping 60-Hz "buzz sound" from the speaker when
picture signals with white backgrounds are being transmitted.
Because the IF amplifier can provide only limited gain for the
sound-IF signal, a 4.5-MHz sound-IF amplifier is employed
prior to the FM sound detector, as is shown in Fig. 12-1.

12.2 Intercarrier Sound and Audio Circuitry

Either a tuned coil or a tuned transformer may be utilized in the sound takeoff circuit, as shown in Fig. 12-2.
Sound takeoff may be located at the picture detector output
or the video-driver output.   The video-driver stage provides
some additional amplification for the intercarrier sound
signal.   Although sound takeoff could be located at the out-

put of the video section, this is seldom done because of the problem of controlling intercarrier buzz. That is, suppression of buzz requires that the intercarrier signal be amplified by class A amplifiers. Because the video-output stage would need an excessively great dynamic range to avoid occasional momentary overload, it is impractical to pass the intercarrier signal through the video-output stage.

Observe in Fig. 12-2 that the sound takeoff coil or

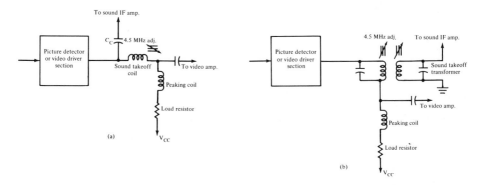

Fig. 12-2 Sound takeoff arrangements: (a) tuned coil and coupling capacitor circuit, (b) tuned transformer circuit.

transformer serves more than one purpose. In addition to picking off the 4.5-MHz sound signal, it also operates as a sound trap. That is, a takeoff coil or the primary of a takeoff transformer inserts a substantial 4.5-MHz impedance in series with the video-signal path. Thereby, the 4.5-MHz signal is prevented from passing into the video-output stage. If the sound takeoff circuit is mistuned, the intercarrier sound signal can gain entry into the output stage, with the result that 4.5-MHz dot (grain) interference appears in the picture. Note that because the bandwidth of the intercarrier sound signal is approximately 50 kHz, the sound takeoff circuit has a fairly high Q value, typically around 80.

It follows that sound-IF amplifiers operate at much less

bandwidth than video-IF amplifiers. Otherwise, the circuitry
is much the same in both receiver sections. A typical intercarrier sound-IF configuration is depicted in Fig. 12-3. Two

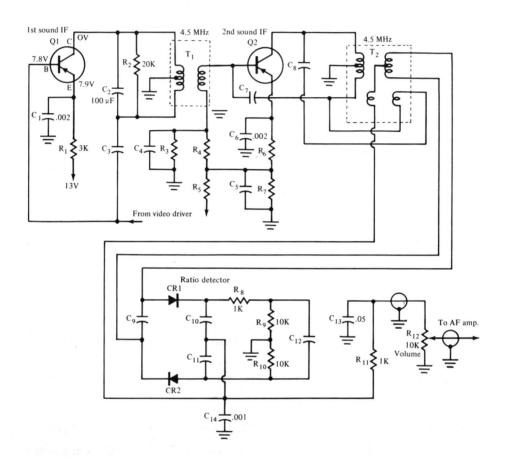

Fig. 12-3 Example of an intercarrier sound-IF configuration
with ratio detection.

stages are employed in the common emitter configuration, followed by an FM detector. Bifilar-tuned transformers are used
in this example, although single-tuned coupling circuits are
utilized in some receivers. To obtain a 50-kHz bandwidth
the primary of T_1 is loaded by R_2, a 20-kΩ resistor. Neutralization of Q1 and Q2 is required to prevent regeneration and

possible oscillation. This is the function of neutralizing capacitors C_3 and C_7. Regeneration would result in greatly subnormal bandwidth and distorted sound output, whereas oscillation would block the signal passage and produce a no-sound symptom.

12.3 FM Detection

Ratio detectors, as exemplified in Fig. 12-3, are widely used as intercarrier FM demodulators. Discriminators are also employed in various receivers. Although the basic operation of both types of FM detectors is essentially the same, a discriminator requires a separate limiter, whereas a ratio detector has inherent limiting action. However, because a ratio detector cannot completely limit high percentages of AM signal, designers occasionally provide a separate limiter for a ratio detector also. The fundamental action of a limiter is seen in Fig. 12-4. That is, amplitude modulation variations are

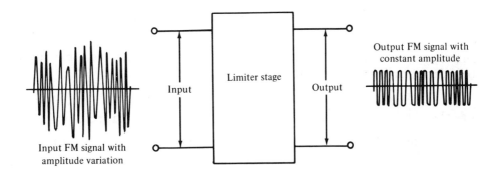

Fig. 12-4 Fundamental action of a limiter stage.

clipped by a limiter stage. Clipping is accomplished by overdriving the limiter transistor into saturation and into collector current cutoff.

It is instructive to analyze the circuit action of a

conventional discriminator type of FM detector, as shown in
Fig. 12-5. Signal voltage E_1 is applied to the primary L_1

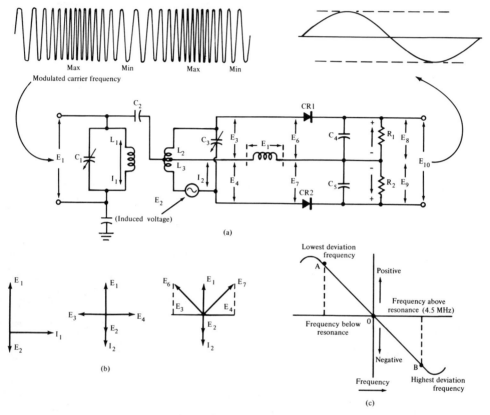

Fig. 12-5 Discriminator type of detector: (a) basic circuitry, (b) reference voltage and current phase relations,
(c) discriminator frequency response curve.

of the discriminator transformer. In turn, signal voltage
E_2 is induced in the secondary winding L_2L_3. Note that
signal voltage is also coupled from the primary to the center
tap on the secondary by capacitor C_2. From the center of
L_2L_3, this coupled signal voltage is applied to diodes
CR1 and CR2. RF choke L_4 provides a dc return circuit and
prevents thecoupled signal voltage from being applied to
the junction of C_4 and C_5. That is, the input voltage E_1
is, in effect, dropped across L_4.

It follows from tuned-transformer theory that E_2 in Fig. 12-5 is 180° out of phase with E_1. Also, both E_1 and E_2 are 90° out of phase with the primary current I_1. This relationship is shown in vector form in Fig. 12-5(b). Observe that E_3 and E_4 are 180° out of phase with each other, and that both E_3 and E_4 are 90° out of phase with the input voltage E_1. Accordingly, the signal voltages applied to diodes CR1 and CR2 are the vectorial resultants of E_1 and E_3, and of E_1 and E_4, as seen in Fig. 12-5(b). When the instantaneous frequency of the FM signal is 4.5 MH$_3$, the resultants have a 90° phase difference, as depicted in Fig. 12-6(a). On

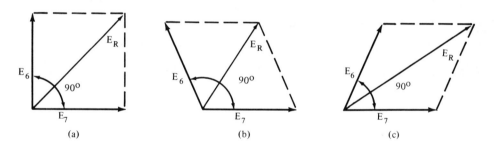

Fig. 12-6 Vector phase variations produced by frequency swing above or below 4.5 MHz: (a) at 4.5 MHz, (b) below 4.5 MHz, (c) above 4.5 MHz.

the other hand, when the instantaneous frequency decreases, the vectorial resultants have a greater phase difference, as seen in Fig. 12-6(b). Again, when the instantaneous frequency increases, the vectorial resultants have a lesser phase difference, as shown in Fig. 12-6(c). For clarity, Fig. 12-6 presents vectors E_6, E_7, and E_R only.

Observe that the total resultant signal voltages applied to diodes CR1 and CR2 in Fig. 12-5 have equal amplitudes when the signal frequency is 4.5 MHz. However, these amplitudes become unequal as the intercarrier signal frequency swings

above or below 4.5 MHz.   Note that the rectified output voltages E_8 and E_9 oppose each other and cancel at 4.5 MHz.   On
the other hand, when E_8 is greater than E_9 , the discriminator
output voltage is positive, and when E_9 is greater than E_8 ,
the output voltage is negative. The amplitude of this audio
output voltage becomes greater as the intercarrier signal
swings farther from the 4.5-MHz center frequency. To repeat
a basic point, the input signal to the discriminator has constant amplitude, which is ensured by prior passage through a
limiter stage. Thus a discriminator operates solely to recover
the audio-modulating component from the FM signal.

Now consider the circuit action of a ratio detector, in
which the audio-modulating component is recovered from the FM
signal with simultaneous limiting action. With reference to
Fig. 12-7, diodes CR1 and CR2 are oppositely polarized, com-

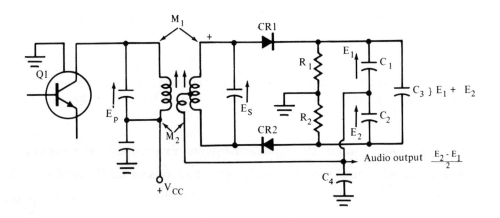

Fig. 12-7 Basic ratio detector configuration.

pared with the previous discriminator configuration. However,
the demodulation process is essentially the same in both
arrangements. In the ratio detector circuit, the input FM
signal is not capacitively coupled to the center point of the
diode branch. Instead, a tertiary winding is employed on the

ratio detector transformer. Thus, mutual inductance M_2 serves the same purpose as the coupling capacitor in a discriminator circuit. Inherent limiting action is provided in Fig. 12-7 by C_3 by means of capacitive storage. It is instructive to follow the sequence of limiting operation.

Observe in Fig. 12-7 that the demodulated voltages E_1 and E_2 across R_1 and R_2 (and across C_1 and C_2) will be equal when the FM signal frequency is 4.5 MHz. In turn, the audio output signal will be zero, because it is developed in a bridge circuit that is balanced at 4.5 MHz. Then, if the FM signal swings away more or less from 4.5 MHz, the demodulated voltages E_1 and E_2 become unequal, as was depicted in Fig. 12-6. For example, E_1 might become greater than E_2, and the audio output voltage is then equal to half the difference between E_1 and E_2. Note that because C_3 in Fig. 12-7 has a large capacitance value, its terminal voltage cannot change appreciably nor rapidly when the FM signal amplitude changes. This is just another way of saying that any envelope variation in the applied FM signal will be effectively limited by capacitive storage action. Under most reception conditions, this inherent limiting action of the ratio detector is satisfactory. However, in the event that the incoming FM signal has been amplitude modulated 80%, for example, by the vertical sync pulses, the limiting action will be incomplete and sync buzz will be audible in the sound output. Therefore, a ratio detector may be preceded by a limiter in a deluxe type of receiver.

12.4 Audio Signal Deemphasis

Both discriminators and ratio detectors require a deemphasis circuit in the audio output branch. As in broad-

cast FM transmission, the higher audio frequencies are preemphasized at the television transmitter, in order to provide
an optimum signal-to-noise ratio at the receiver. Accordingly,
the higher audio frequencies must be deemphasized at the
receiver to restore the normal tonal balance. Figure 12-8(a)

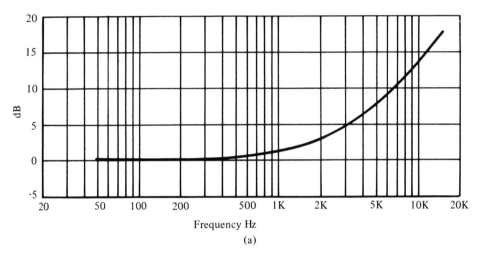

(a)

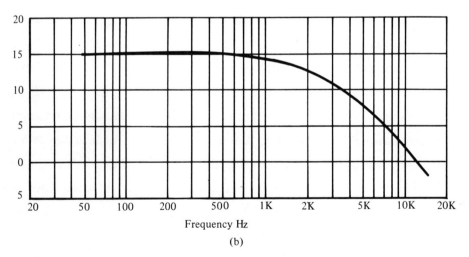

(b)

Fig. 12-8 Preemphasis and deemphasis frequency characteristics: (a) preemphasis curve used at FM transmitter,
(b) deemphasis curve used at receiver.

shows the standard preemphasis frequency characteristic, with the corresponding deemphasis characteristic in (b). It is evident that the combination of these responses results in uniform audio frequency characteristic. An RC integrating circuit with a time constant of 75 μsec is generally employed for deemphasis, as exemplified in Fig. 12-9. This arrangement

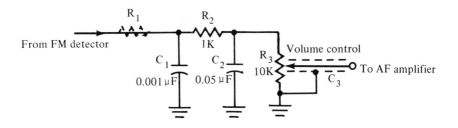

Fig. 12-9 Typical deemphasis network.

consists of three RC sections; the first section consists of the internal resistance of the FM detector and C_1, followed by R_2 and C_2, and completed by R_3 and C_3 (where C_3 is the capacitance of the shielded audio lead). The effective time constant of this network is approximately 75 μsec.

When limiting is employed prior to an FM detector, a transistor may be supplemented by a diode for improved limiting action, as exemplified in Fig. 12-10. Note that Q2 operates with a comparatively low collector-to-emitter potential of 1.4 V. Also, the collector load for Q2 includes a 2200-Ω resistor R_9. In turn, Q2 is driven into saturation on negative peaks of the base input signal. Thus, limiting is provided on negative peaks. To obtain limiting on positive signal peaks, diode CR1 is shunted across the primary winding of T_2. This diode starts to conduct on a positive peak potential of approximately 0.3 V. Thereafter, its shunting action increases rapidly, so that limiting is provided on positive peaks. In combination with the inherent limiting of the radio detector employed in this system, intercarrier

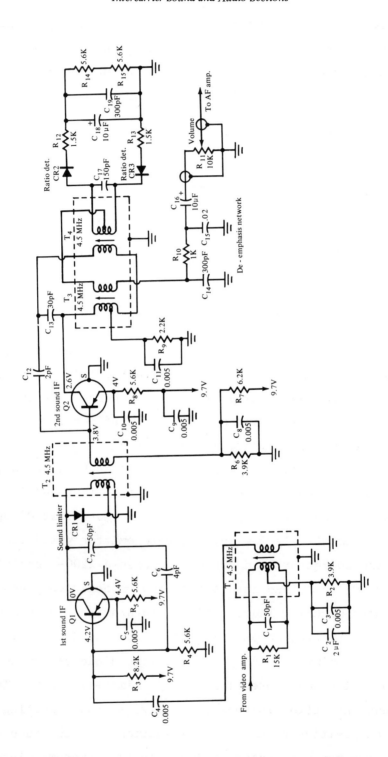

Fig. 12-10 Transistor-and-diode limiting configuration.

buzz is never audible unless a circuit defect occurs.

12.5 Audio Amplifier Circuitry and Operation

Audio amplifiers in most television receivers are of
the conventional type, although deluxe receivers employ
high-fidelity amplifiers. The configuration shown in Fig.
12-11 is typical of general practice. It utilizes two

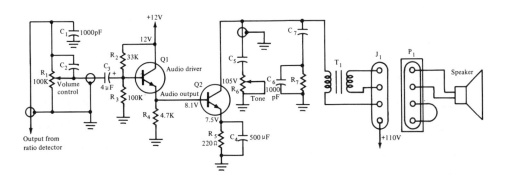

Fig. 12-11 Typical audio amplifier section for a television
receiver.

stages that operate in single-ended class A, with an output
transformer to couple the output stage to the speaker.
Observe that C_1 is a deemphasis capacitor in the ratio detector section. C_2 is a small compensating capacitor that provides improved high-frequency response at lower settings of
the volume control R_1. Driver transistor Q1 operates in the
common collector mode to provide a suitable impedance match
between the ratio detector output and transistor Q2. Direct
coupling is utilized from Q1 to Q2.

Note in Figure 12-11 that the audio output transistor
Q2 is a low-current high-voltage type, similar to transistors
used in video-output stages. Thereby, a substantial power
output with economical circuit design is realized. Potentiometer R_6 operates as a tone control by providing a trebel cut

(bass boost) action. Optimum overall audio frequency response is provided by the equalizing network comprising R_6, C_6, and C_7. Observe that the speaker plug P_1 has four terminals, two of which are arranged as a supply voltage interlock. Accordingly, if the speaker is disconnected from the amplifier, the collector supply voltage for Q2 is removed. This is an essential safety precaution, because operation of the output stage without a normal speaker load would result in an excessive peak-inverse collector voltage that would damage Q2.

12.6 Integrated Sound Section Circuitry

There has been a marked trend toward utilization of integrated circuitry in the intercarrier sound system. Figure 12-12 exemplifies a configuration in which the sound-IF amplifier, FM detector, and audio amplifier are built around a single IC chip. A block diagram is depicted in (a), and the external-internal plan is seen in (b). Observe that the 4.5-MHz signal is coupled into the chip via external tuned transformer T_1. The first IF stage comprises Q1, Q2, and Q3 and is directly coupled to the second IF stage. This second stage consists of Q4, Q5, and Q6. In turn, the amplified-IF signal is fed to the limiter stage comprising Q7 and Q8. The limiter output in turn energizes the primary of external ratio detector transformer T_2. Note that all of the IF selectivity is provided by these two tuned transformers.

Observe in Fig. 12-12 that the ratio detector section consists of detector diodes CR3 and CR4, with an unconventional load resistance arrangement. That is, the load comprises resistors R_{11}, R_{12}, and reverse-biased diodes CR5, CR6, and CR7. These diodes operate simply as capacitors to filter out the 4.5-MHz component from the demodulated audio signal. An audio preamplifier circuit is also provided, consisting of

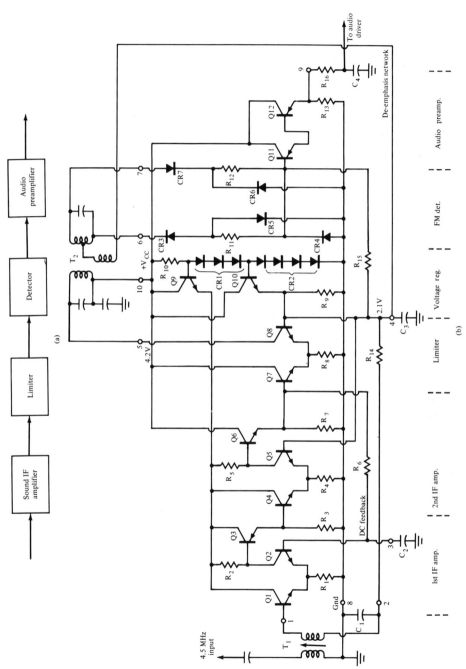

Fig. 12-12 An integrated sound-IF amplifier, FM detector, and audio preamplifier. (Courtesy, Radio Corporation of America)

transistors Q11 and Q12. As would be anticipated, a deemphasis network is required; this includes the external resistor R_{17} and capacitor C_4. Finally, note that diodes CR1 and CR2 with transistors Q9 and Q10 operate as a voltage regulator to stabilize IC operation.

12.7 Troubleshooting the Intercarrier Sound and Audio Sections

Intercarrier sound or audio defects seldom produce any picture symptoms. Sound output symptoms include no sound, weak sound with or without buzz or background noise, normal sound with objectionable buzz level, and various forms of distorted audio output. Preliminary sectionalization is directed to location of the faulty receiver section. For example, if sync buzz is accompanied by a negative or partially negative picture, it indicates that a component defect has occurred prior to the sound takeoff point. On the other hand, if picture reproduction is normal and there is no sound output, we would conclude that the trouble will be found between the sound takeoff point and the speaker.

Signal tracing is the most useful method of closing in on a defective stage. Although various types of instruments can be used for this purpose, a wide-band scope with a low-capacitance probe is most informative. Of course, the receiver must be tuned to a television station, or a suitable generator signal must be provided when signal-tracing tests are made. In normal receiver operation, a 4.5-MHz sine wave pattern will be displayed on the scope screen when the probe is applied to the input terminal of the intercarrier sound-IF amplifier (see Fig. 12-13). The normal signal amplitude at this point is on the order of 0.2 V. This 4.5-MHz sine wave can be checked at each stage up to the FM detector. If

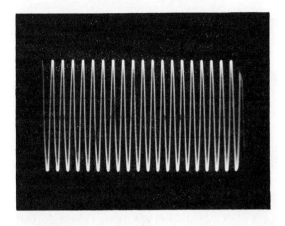

Fig. 12-13 A 4.5–MHz intercarrier signal display.

the signal is absent or substantially attenuated at a particular stage, it indicates that a defective component will be
found in this area.

Note that the amplitude of the 4.5–MHz sine wave will
remain constant only if the receiver is energized by a generator. That is, the amplitude will vary to some extent if the
receiver is energized by a television station signal. When
there is substantial sync buzz in the sound channel, the
intercarrier signal will display an amplitude modulation by
the vertical sync pulse, as illustrated in Fig. 12-14. This
is an example of least modulation, which places the upward
demand on the limiting function of a ratio detector. In other
words, a ratio detector limits upward modulation more effi-
ciently than downward modulation.

When sync-buzz modulation is excessive, look for a stage
(usually a video-amplifier stage) which is operating in a nonlinear mode. In any case, buzz modulation will occur in a
circuit that passes both the video signal and the 4.5–MHz
intercarrier signal with a nonlinear transfer characteristic.
Thus, buzz modulation can occur in an overloaded video–IF

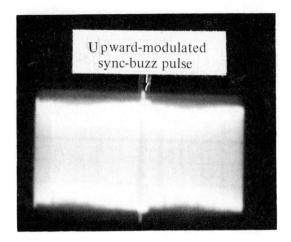

Fig. 12-14 An example of downward modulation in the intercarrier signal by the vertical sync pulse.

stage, or even in an overloaded RF stage. Nonlinear operation
is usually caused by incorrect bias as a result of a leaky
capacitor.   However, nonlinear operation can also be caused
by a transistor defect. An AGC fault can apply incorrect bias
voltage to one or more stages and thereby produce buzz modulation.   In some cases, the sound-IF limiter develops a defect
that impairs its clipping action.   This condition becomes
apparent in a waveform check; observe that the output waveform
from the limiter has almost as much envelope variation as the
input waveform.

A no-sound symptom is also localized to best advantage
with an oscilloscope. The 4.5-MHz signal can be traced from
the sound takeoff point to the stage where the signal is
stopped. In most cases, the difficulty is due to a defective
capacitor. For example, a leaky capacitor can bias a transistor out of its operating range, and an open neutralizing
capacitor often results in stage oscillation and signal
blocking. After the defective stage has been localized, dc
voltage measurements are generally most effective to close

in on the faulty component. As noted previously in discussion of the video-IF section, oscillation results in an abnormal dc voltage output from the detector. In other words, if an intercarrier-IF stage is oscillating, you should measure a high dc voltage output from the FM detector.

Note that a no-sound symptom can result from a defect in the audio amplifier section, up to and including the speaker. Again, an oscilloscope is the most useful signal-tracing instrument. Weak sound symptoms are generally caused by marginal defects in the same components that are responsible for a no-sound symptom. For example, if a coupling capacitor has marginal leakage, the operating point of the following transistor will be shifted with resulting attenuation of the output signal. In high-level stages particularly, such as the output or driver stage, such signal attenuation is likely to be accompanied by audio distortion. If a capacitor defect is not the cause of attenuated and/or distorted audio signals, usually a transistor is suspect. Resistors seldom cause trouble symptoms, with the exception of the volume control, which may become excessively worn after extended service.

Noisy sound output is commonly caused by insufficient limiting. Of course, the sound system develops considerable noise when no input signal is present, because the signal-to-noise ratio is then zero. When noise becomes objectionable under normal reception conditions, the most likely cause is an open electrolytic capacitor at the output of the ratio detector circuit. As noted previously, electrolytic capacitors may lose a substantial portion of their rated capacitance after extended use. A similar sound symptom can be caused by a defective limiter stage that fails to clip the incoming 4.5-MHz intercarrier signal. Defective transistors sometimes

develop excessive noise.   This condition is generally associated with low gain and abnormal or subnormal dc terminal
voltages.

Questions

Short Answer

1. Draw a simple block diagram of a television receiver and
    state the function of each block.
2. What is the frequency range of the sound signal at the
    antenna input terminals of a television receiver?
3. What is the intermediate frequency of the sound signal in
    the IF amplifier section of the receiver?
4. How is the sound taken from the picture detector?
5. What is the approximate bandwidth of the audio amplifier?
6. Because the 4.5-MHz sound signal is present at the front
    end of the television receiver, why is it not taken off
    at that point?
7. What two purposes does the sound trap in Fig. 12-2 serve?
8. Explain the terms "deemphasis" and "preemphasis" as they
    are used in conjunction with FM sound.
9. In reference to Fig. 12-9, what type of circuit is the
    deemphasis network?
10. How can a transistor be used as a limiter?
11. In Fig. 12-10, how is the positive-limiting action
    performed?
12. Discuss each of the important parts of the circuit in
    Fig. 12-11.
13. In Fig. 12-12, what is the purpose of resistor R_{17} and
    capacitor C_4?

14. In Fig. 12-12, what is the function of the network, R_{11}, R_{12}, CR5, CR6, and CR7?

15. In Fig. 12-12, which components perform the function of a voltage regulation?

16. What are some of the symptoms that indicate sound output troubles?

17. Where is the trouble located if there is no sound and the picture is normal?

18. Discuss the method of using an oscilloscope to trouble-shoot the sound section of a television receiver.

19. Why is it more desirable to use a generator rather than a television station when testing for sound problems?

20. What are some of the problems that can produce buzz modulation?

21. How can a no-sound symptom be best localized?

22. What effect does a leaky coupling capacitor have on a transistor stage?

23. What is the most likely cause of a noisy sound output?

True-False

1. A conventional television has a picture signal channel and a sound signal channel.

2. The sound signal at the antenna terminals is usually at a frequency of 41.25 MHz.

3. The sound signal undergoes two conversions: one at the input to the IF amplifier, and another at the picture detector.

4. In the picture detector circuit, the sound signal is usually the strongest component.

5. The 4.5-MHz sound carrier is picked off at the picture detector by a tuned circuit.

6. Unless the picture-IF level is kept at approximately
    10% of the sound signal level, a buzz will be produced
    in the sound.

7. The signal applied to the sound detector is a 4.5-MHz
    sound-IF signal.

8. Sound takeoff may be located at either the picture
    detector output or the video-driver output.

9. Buzz in the audio output is usually caused by modulation
    of the audio FM signal by the vertical sync pulses.

10. Sound-IF amplifiers operate with much less bandwidth than
    video amplifiers.

11. The purpose of neutralizing capacitors in transistor Q1
    and Q2 (Fig. 12-3) is to prevent buzz in the sound section.

12. The bandwidth of the intercarrier sound signal is approxi-
    mately 50 kHz.

13. Dot or grain interference on the picture tube is usually
    caused by the presence of sound signal in the video stages.

14. Both discriminators and ratio detectors require a
    deemphasis circuit in the audio output section.

15. The higher audio frequencies are preemphasized at the
    television transmitter.

16. Deemphasis is usually accomplished by an RC circuit
    with a time constant of 75 msec.

17. The audio amplifier in Fig. 12-11 uses RC coupling
    between stages Q1 and Q2.

18. The four-pin plug (P_1) protects transistor Q2 from
    excessively high collector voltage when the speaker is
    removed.

19. The overall frequency response of the circuit in Fig.
    12-11 is determined by the equalizing network.

20. The major advantage of using an IC in the sound
    section is manufacturing cost.

21. Diodes CR5, CR6, and CR7 in Fig. 12-12 are used as limiters for the incoming FM signal.

22. In Fig. 12-12, CR1, CR2, Q9, and Q10 operate as a voltage regulator to stabilize IC operation.

23. If sync buzz is accompanied by a partially negative picture, it indicates that a defect has occurred past the sound takeoff point.

24. When testing for a sound problem, it is more desirable to use a television station, rather than a generator, as a signal source.

25. A ratio detector has difficulty in limiting downward modulation.

26. Noisy sound output is usually caused by poor limiting action of the FM signal.

Multiple Choice

1. The first processing circuit in a television receiver is:
   (a) common to both the sound signal and the picture signal.
   (b) used to process only the picture signal.
   (c) used to process only the sound signal.
   (d) used to process only the sync signals.

2. After amplification through the RF amplifiers, the sound signal is converted to a typical intermediate frequency of _____ MHz.
   (a) 30   (c) 55.25
   (b) 4.5   (d) 41.25

3. The sound signal is picked off at the output of the picture detector by a/an:
   (a) RC circuit.   (c) diode detector.
   (b) LR circuit.   (d) tuned circuit.

4. The sound signal is maintained at a low level through the IF amplifier to prevent:

   (a) AM modulation of the sound signal by the picture signal.

   (b) FM modulation of the sound signal by the picture signal.

   (c) AM modulation of the picture signal by the sound signal.

   (d) FM modulation of the picture signal by the sound signal.

5. Unless the sound signal is restricted to 10% or less of the picture-IF signal level, the vertical sync pulses will modulate the sound signal and cause:

   (a) sound in the picture.   (c) loss of vertical sync.

   (b) buzz in the sound.   (d) loss of horizontal sync.

6. The sound takeoff transformer (Fig. 12-2) serves the function of:

   (a) takeoff for the sound signal.

   (b) preventing the sound signal from entering the video section.

   (c) preventing the sound signal from entering the video section and serves as a takeoff for the sound signal.

   (d) a sound takeoff and sound detector.

7. The function of capacitors C_3 and C_7 in Fig. 12-3 is to:

   (a) filter the IF signal from the sound section.

   (b) filter the video from the sound section.

   (c) filter the vertical sync pulses from the sound section.

   (d) prevent possible oscillations in transistors Q1 and Q2.

8. Both discriminators and ratio detectors require:

    (a) a separate limiter in the input circuit.

    (b) a deemphasis circuit in the audio output branch.

    (c) a preemphasis circuit at the audio output branch.

    (d) preemphasis at the FM input.

9. Deemphasis in an FM detector is usually a/an:

    (a) RC integrating circuit with a time constant of 75 msec.

    (b) LC tuned circuit.

    (c) LR circuit with a short time constant.

    (d) diode clipper.

10. In Fig. 12-10, negative limiting is obtained by:

    (a) the clipping action of diode CR1.

    (b) driving transistor Q2 into cutoff.

    (c) driving transistor Q2 into saturation.

    (d) the action of CR1 and T_2.

11. The purpose of the four-terminal plug (P_1) in Fig. 12-11 is:

    (a) to assure safe operation of the speaker.

    (b) to prevent damage to the power supply.

    (c) to prevent damage to Q2 due to an open speaker.

    (d) to prevent damage to Q2 due to a shorted speaker.

12. IC's are used in the sound section primarily for:

    (a) easier maintenance.

    (b) better sound reproduction.

    (c) their smaller size and weight.

    (d) lower manufacturing cost.

13. In Fig. 12-12, all the IF selectivity is provided by:

    (a) Q4, Q5, and Q6.   (c) Q1, Q2, and Q3.

    (b) T_1 and T_2.   (d) R_{17} and C_4.

14. In Fig. 12-12, diodes CR1 and CR2 with transistors Q9 and Q10 operate as a/an:

    (a) voltage regulator.

    (b) FM detector.

    (c) deemphasis network.

    (d) sync filter.

15. If picture buzz is accompanied by a negative picture, it is an indication that a component defect has occurred:

    (a) prior to the sound takeoff point.

    (b) after the sound takeoff point.

    (c) in the vertical amplifier.

    (d) in the CRT.

16. Excessive sync modulation is usually caused by a/an:

    (a) video stage operating in a nonlinear mode.

    (b) audio stage operating in a nonlinear mode.

    (c) shorted deflection coil.

    (d) open IF amplifier.

17. A high value of dc voltage output from the FM detector is usually caused by oscillations in a/an _____ stage.

    (a) IF

    (b) RF

    (c) detector

    (d) audio

18. Noisy sound output is commonly caused by:

    (a) a noisy transistor.

    (b) a defective IF amplifier.

    (c) a defective video amplifier.

    (d) insufficient limiting.

Chapter 13

COLOR TELEVISION TRANSMISSION PRINCIPLES

13.1 System Survey

In the first analysis, color television transmission and reception can be described as a system that reproduces color images as depicted in Fig. 13-1.   That is, a color

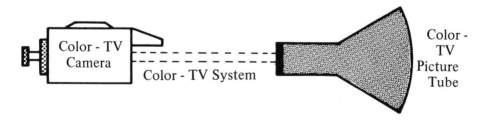

Fig. 13-1   Fundamental plan of the color television system.

scene is scanned and converted into a corresponding video

signal by a color television camera.   In turn, this signal
is processed through the color television system   and is
finally applied to a color television picture tube.   Thus,
the original color scene is reproduced as a similar color
image on the screen of the picture tube.   Of course, there
are numerous steps in the processing of the signal, and
these steps are not necessarily quite the same in various
countries, nor even in the same country as in the United
States where the NTSC system has been standardized.   For
example, France employs different standards in VHF and UHF
transmission.   However, the end result is always the same.
NTSC is an abbreviation for National Television Systems
Committee, a group that establishes federal standards for
color television transmission in the United States.

Over 30 years of experiment and development were
required to bring color television technology to its present
status.   Various approaches were investigated and progressively abandoned because of limitations that became apparent.
Because color television was not commercially launched until
after black and white television standards had been firmly
entrenched, it was also necessary to design the color television system in such a manner that operation would be practical in the established black and white channel allocations.
The technical difficulties that were encountered were success-
fully overcome by the use of a system that transmits color
information with a multiplexed quadrature signal which is
modulated on a subcarrier encoded in the conventional black
and white signal.   A three-color picture tube is utilized to
reproduce the color image.   This NTSC system was adopted by
the FCC in 1953.

In its most general aspect, a color television receiver
can be regarded as a conventional black and white receiver,

plus a chroma section and a color picture tube, as depicted in Figure 13-2.   One of the prominent advantages of the NTSC

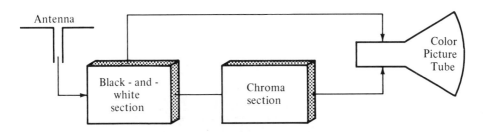

Fig. 13-2 Basic arrangement of a color television receiver.

system is its *compatibility*. A color television receiver can reproduce either color or black and white broadcast programs, and a black and white receiver can reproduce either black and white or color broadcast programs, without any change in adjustments. Of course, when a color receiver is tuned to a black and white transmission, the image is reproduced without any color. Similarly, when a black and white receiver is tuned to a color transmission, the color signal is reproduced as a black and white image.

13.2 Principles of Color Vision and Color Signal Formation

Although there are many hundreds of different hues and shades of color that can be perceived by the eye, almost any hue and saturation that occurs in nature can be duplicated by blending suitable amounts of three *primary* colors. Color television employs the *additive* primaries, whereas color printing utilizes the *subtractive* primaries. The additive primaries are red, green, and blue, whereas the subtractive primaries are used when colored light sources are blended,

as in a color picture tube. On the other hand, the subtractive primaries are used when a picture or print is viewed by
reflected light from a white source. White light is produced
by a suitable blend of the red, green, and blue primary hues.

    Figure 13-3 illustrates the basic laws of color

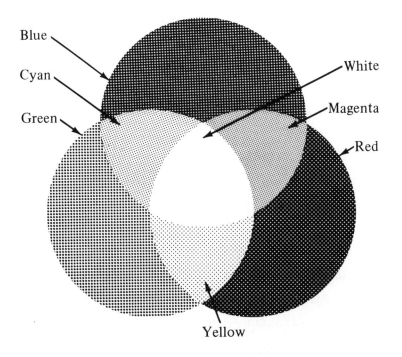

Fig. 13-3 Basic blends of the three primary colors.

blending from primary light sources. That is, a blend of
red and green produces yellow, a blend of green and blue
produces cyan, and a blend of red and blue produces magenta.
Note that yellow, cyan, and blue are called the additive
complementary colors. It is evident that none of the three
primary hues can be obtained by blending of the other two
primary hues.   The blending of red, green, and blue in
suitable proportions produces white.   However, white is not
strictly a color, but a brightness characteristic of light,
as explained in greater detail subsequently. Black is also

not a color in the technical sense, but simply an absence
of light.

Each color, or hue, has a certain wavelength. A color
also has a certain *saturation*, or how much white light is
blended with the hue. For example, a red sports car may
approximate a 100% saturated red hue, whereas a pink baby
bonnet represents perhaps a 15% saturated red hue. If the
pink hue fades into white, it then has 0% saturation. Brightness is another basic characteristic of a color. For example,
a saturated green appears brighter to the eye than a saturated
red, and a saturated red appears brighter than a saturated
blue. The total brightness of a color blend is equal to the
sum of the brightnesses of all of the hues comprising the
particular blend. It is important to note that when primary
hues are blended to obtain a color match at an arbitrary
brightness level, the color match will remain true over a
wide range of brightness.

The foregoing facts are summarized to good advantage by
means of a chromaticity diagram, such as shown in Fig. 13-4.
Observe that as we go around the outer boundary of the "horse-
shoe," we pass through a complete spectrum of colors. These
are pure or 100% saturated colors. If we move inside the diagram and go around one of the intermediate boundaries, we pass
again through a complete spectrum of colors, which are now
unsaturated (locus of medium saturation). Then as we move
farther into the diagram and go around the innermost boundary,
we pass once again through a complete spectrum of colors with
low saturation. Finally, if we move into the center of the
diagram (spot C), we are at a point of 0% saturation, or
white.

Figure 13-5 shows a chromaticity diagram in the

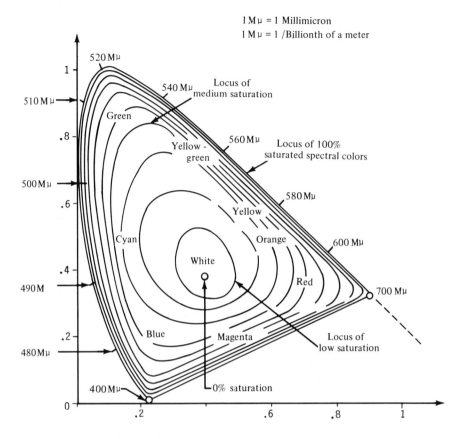

Fig. 13-4 A chromaticity diagram.

general form of a color "map," with the approximate areas
occupied by various hues. Note that as we move out from
white (C) along a straight line in any direction, the basic
hue along this line remains essentially the same, although
it increases the saturation up to the outer boundary of the
diagram. This is just another way of saying that hue and
saturation are essentially independent variables. Figure
13-6 shows two separate hues, with variation in saturation
from 0% to 100%. Thus, colors A and B possess the same
hue, but this hue contains much more white light at B than
at A. Color A has the same saturation as color a (100%),

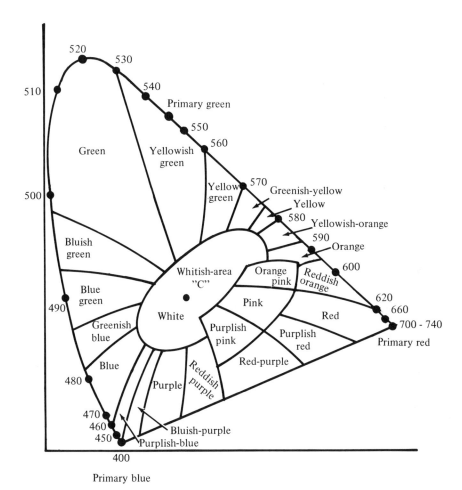

Fig. 13-5 Hue and saturation relations in the chromaticity diagram.

but differs in hue.   Again, colors A and B have the same hue, but differ considerably in saturation.

Referring back to Fig. 13-3, recall that the three complementary colors are formed by blends of various pairs of primary colors.   For example, yellow is formed by a blend of red and green, whereas cyan is formed by a blend of blue and green.   The diagram depicted in Fig. 13-7 summarizes these relations to good advantage.   It shows that a blend of red and green produces yellow and that if

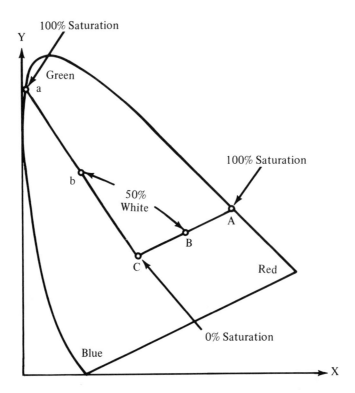

Fig. 13-6 Saturation loci of two hues on the chromaticity diagram.

more red is utilized, the resulting hue becomes yellowish orange, orange, or reddish orange, depending upon the proportions of red and green hues. Or, if more green is utilized, the resulting hue becomes greenish yellow or yellowish green, again depending upon the proportions of the two primary hues. The same general variation holds true on the other side of the diagram for blends of green and blue. These are examples of comparatively high saturations of the various hues. In any case, when two primary colors are blended, the resulting hue must fall somewhere along a straight line connecting these two primary colors.

In view of the foregoing facts, it follows that a color television camera will contain three camera tubes, and

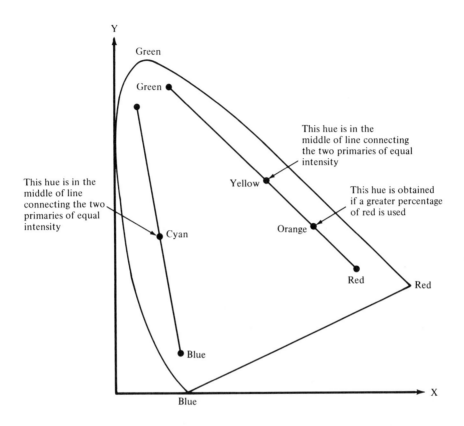

Fig. 13-7 Use of the chromaticity diagram to analyze blends of two primary colors.

a color picture tube will contain three electron guns, as depicted in Fig. 13-8. As indicated in the diagram, a red transmission filter is placed in front of the red camera tube, a green transmission filter is placed in front of the green camera tube, and a blue transmission filter is placed in front of the blue camera tube. The same image, of course, is focused upon each of the camera tubes. In turn, the color television camera separates the primary hues from the televised scene. Each primary hue is converted into a corresponding electrical signal, and these three signals are applied to the television transmitter. At the

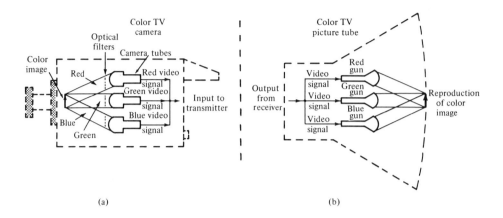

Fig. 13-8 A color television camera separates the primary hues from the televised scene, and the color picture tube recombines them.

receiver, the three color signals are processed and applied individually to three electron guns in the color picture tube. Each gun, of course, is focused upon the same screen area. Thereby, the color picture recombines the primary hues and reproduces the original televised scene in true colors.

13.3 Compatibility Considerations

As noted previously, the NTSC standards are devised in a manner that permits the inclusion of a color signal with a conventional black and white signal and FM sound signal within a 6-MHz television channel. In other words, the color television system is designed in such a way that addition of the chroma (color information) signal to a conventional black and white signal results in formation of a color image, as shown in Fig. 13-9. This is an essential point in the achievement of compatibility, inasmuch as a black and white receiver responds in the usual manner to the black and white signal component, while rejecting the chroma signal component of the

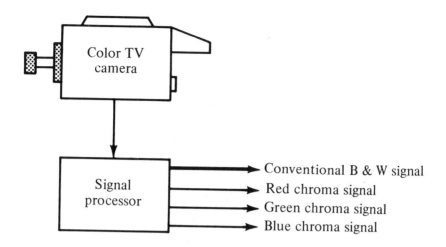

Fig. 13-9 The complete color signal comprises an ordinary black and white video signal, plus three chroma signals.

complete color signal. That is, a black and white receiver automatically processes the complete color signal as if no chroma component were present.

Another basic aspect of compatibility concerns the characteristics of the chroma signal with respect to black and white signal. Before the advent of color television, engineers were aware of the fact that the spectrum of a conventional black and white video signal is not continuous. In other words, the sidebands of an ordinary black and white signal are distributed in groups along the video-frequency axis, as shown in Fig. 13-10. Thus, it was feasible to "fit" the chroma signal groups between the groups of black and white signal energy. This technique is called *frequency interleaving* and is realized when the chroma signal is modulated on a subcarrier (subsidiary carrier) which has a frequency that coincides with an odd multiple of half the line frequency. This staggering of black and white groups with chroma groups of energy along the frequency axis minimizes interference between the black and white and chroma

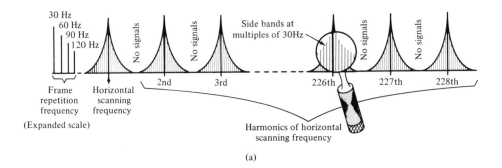

30 Hz
60 Hz
90 Hz
120 Hz

No signals No signals

Side bands at multiples of 30Hz

No signals No signals

2nd 3rd 226th 227th 228th

Frame repetition frequency

Horizontal scanning frequency

(Expanded scale)

Harmonics of horizontal scanning frequency

(a)

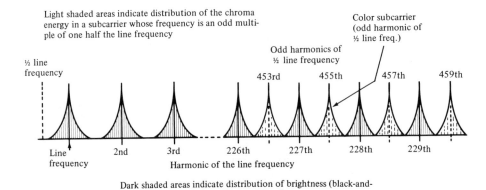

Light shaded areas indicate distribution of the chroma energy in a subcarrier whose frequency is an odd multiple of one half the line frequency

Color subcarrier (odd harmonic of ½ line freq.)

Odd harmonics of ½ line frequency

½ line frequency

453rd 455th 457th 459th

Line frequency 2nd 3rd 226th 227th 228th 229th

Harmonic of the line frequency

Dark shaded areas indicate distribution of brightness (black-and-white) energy at whole multiples of line frequency

(b)

Fig. 13-10 Video signal spectra: (a) conventional black and white signal, (b) black and white and chroma signals.

signal components.

Figure 13-11 depicts the process whereby the chroma signal automatically cancels out on the screen of a black and white picture tube. Observe that even harmonics of half the line frequency reinforce each other on successive scans. Accordingly, the black and white picture signal does not "cancel itself out" on the screen of the picture tube. On the other hand, odd harmonics of half the line frequency cancel each other on successive scans. Because this is the frequency spectrum of the chroma signal, the color information "cancels itself out" on the picture tube screen. This process is not quite complete for two reasons: first, when

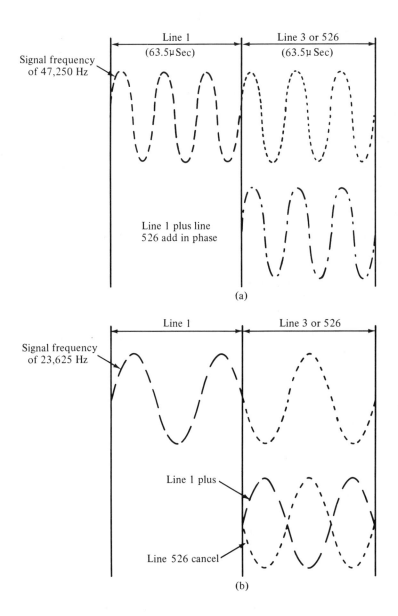

Fig. 13-11 Process of frequency interleaving: (a) even harmonics of half-line frequency reinforce on successive scans, (b) odd harmonics of half-line frequency cancel on successive scans.

motion takes place in the image, the second scan is not identical with the first scan; secondly, because the second scan occurs slightly later than the first scan, persistence of vision is involved in the process, and this is somewhat less than perfect.

Inasmuch as the chroma signal cancels itself out on the screen of a black and white picture tube, we may ask at this point how it is possible to reproduce a color picture. The basic answer to this question is seen in Fig. 13-2--that is, a color receiver is designed in two principal sections. One section processes the black and white component of the complete color signal, while the other section processes the chroma component of the signal. Because chroma processing takes place prior to application of the signal to the picture tube, frequency interleaving does not affect display of the chroma signal. Any chroma signal that might happen to feed through the black and white section of the color receiver will produce negligible interference on the picture tube screen due to the frequency-interleaving cancellation process.

Another basic aspect of compatibility concerns the bandwidths required for satisfactory transmission of color information as compared with black and white information. A 4-MHz video channel is required to transmit a black and white picture with normal detail. On the other hand, satisfactory transmission of color information can be accomplished in a 1-MHz video channel. In practice, the chroma signal is broadcast in a 2-MHz band, although most color receivers process the chroma signal in a 1-MHz band. These bandwidth relations are depicted in Fig. 13-12. This comparatively narrow chroma-system bandwidth is based on the characteristics of color vision. That is, the eye perceives a complete spectrum of hues in large areas of an image. However, it becomes impossible to distinguish blue from gray in small

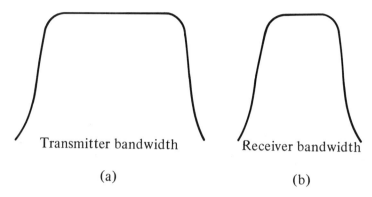

Transmitter bandwidth   Receiver bandwidth

(a)   (b)

Fig. 13-12 Comparison of (a) broadcast bandwidth to
(b) receiver bandwidth.

areas of the image, and green merges into gray in still
smaller areas.   Orange hues are the last to become indis-
tinct, but even they merge with grays in very small areas
of the image.   This is just another way of saying that the
orange hues (which also correspond in a general way to
flesh tones) require more chroma bandwidth than blue hues.
Restriction of chroma-circuit bandwidth is helpful in
achieving compatibility, because residual interference
effects (dot patterns and line crawl) are thereby minimized,
as explained in greater detail subsequently. With reference
to Fig. 13-13, note that the color subcarrier is placed
3.579545 MHz (nominally 3.58 MHz) above the picture carrier.
The chroma signal has two components, called the I signal
and the Q signal. These abbreviations stand for "in phase"
and "quadrature phase" and are described more extensively
subsequently. Both the I signal and the Q signal are modulated on the color subcarrier. However, the I signal has a
vestigial sideband form, while the Q signal has a double
sideband form.   Thus, the I signal can be compared in a
general way with the black and white signal because both are

transmitted in vestigial sideband form.

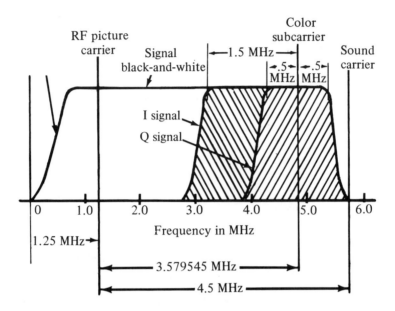

Fig. 13-13 Bandwidths occupied by the black and white and chroma signals in a color receiver.

13.4 The Basic Color Television Transmitter

Color television transmission employed an R - Y/B - Y system prior to adoption of the I/Q system. The I/Q system is compatible with the R - Y/B - Y system. Most color television receivers operate either on the R - Y/B - Y system, or on related variations. In other words, the R - Y/B - Y system is basic, and it is instructive to start with a description of this system. To understand the meaning of the terms R - Y and B - Y, look back at Fig. 13-8. Observe that the color television camera contains red, green, and blue camera tubes and that the color television picture tube contains red, blue, and green guns. If a closed-circuit system were being used, and if compatibility were not a prime consideration, three transmission channels could be utilized for transmission of the red, green, and blue video signals. However, it is evident that some form of signal processing is necessary to provide compatibility between color television and black and white television receivers.

This requirement has been briefly noted previously, and with reference to Fig. 13-9 recall that the output signal from the color television camera is processed to form a conventional black and white video signal plus three chroma signals. These are basically color information signals which contain no black and white information. (Remember that black and white are not colors in the technical sense of the term.) With the general signal relations depicted in Fig. 13-9, a color television receiver can accept all the signals and reproduce a complete color picture. On the other hand, a black and white television receiver accepts only the black and white signal and rejects the chroma signals. In turn, the black and white receiver reproduces a black and white picture. Now designate the black and white video signal as the Y signal. It is sometimes called the monochrome signal.

Because the chroma information must be fitted into the established black and white transmission channels, this chroma information is modulated on a 3.58-MHz color subcarrier. With reference to Fig. 13-10, recall that this is the logical way to minimize interference between the Y signal and the chroma signal, because the subcarrier falls in "empty spaces" that are present in the Y signal spectrum.

Now the basic question arises, which will be asked essentially as follows: "If a chroma signal contains no Y information, and contains only color information, how is this chroma signal to be described technically?" Although the answer seems to be very puzzling at first glance, it is actually quite simple

and logical. The description of a chroma signal with respect
to signal voltages is as follows: the red signal is designated
as an R signal; it is the video-signal output from the red
camera.   Similarly, the green signal is designated as a G
signal; it is the video-signal output from the green camera.
Again, the blue signal is designated as a B signal; it is the
video-signal output from the blue camera. Observe carefully,
that because the red chroma signal contains no brightness information, it is an R - Y signal.   That is, it is the *difference*
between the red video signal and the black and white signal.
Accordingly, an R - Y signal is often called a *color-difference*
signal. Recall that white is formed by a certain blend of red,
green, and blue hues.   Conversely, a white signal (Y signal)
can be subtracted from a red signal (R signal) to form an R - Y
chroma or color-difference signal.   Similarly, G - Y and B - Y
chroma signals can be formed.

Considering the full meaning of the foregoing logic, it
is evident that transmission of Y and color-difference signals
will provide the necessary system compatibility for color
television and black and white television receivers. At this
point, it is helpful to apply some simple arithmetic to the
foregoing video-signal relations. First, a Y signal is formed
by combining the following proportions of red, green, and blue
signal outputs from the color television camera:

$$Y = 0.30R + 0.59G + 0.11B \qquad\qquad (13.1)$$

Equation 13.1   states that a Y signal voltage can be
obtained by adding three color signal voltages in the stated
proportions.   Next, subtract Y from R to obtain the formula
for the R - Y signal voltage:

$$R - Y = 1.00R - 0.30R - 0.59G - 0.11B \qquad (13.2)$$

or, $\qquad$ R − Y = 0.70R − 0.59G − 0.11B $\qquad$ (13.3)

In the same manner, obtain the formulas for the G − Y and B − Y signal voltages:

$$G − Y = − 0.30R + 0.41G − 0.11B \qquad (13.4)$$

$$B − Y = − 0.30R − 0.59G + 0.89B \qquad (13.5)$$

An interesting and important fact appears when the formulas for the R − Y, G − Y, and B − Y signal voltages are considered. Because all three formulas contain terms involving various proportions of R, G, and B voltages, it follows that transmission of three color-difference signals is not really necessary. If any two of the color-difference signals are transmitted, these two signals can be processed at the receiver to recover the third color-difference signal. Inasmuch as this technique further reduces any residual inter-ference between the Y signal and the color-difference signals, it has been incorporated in the NTSC standards. In practice, the basic color television transmitter radiates the Y signal, an R − Y signal, and a B − Y signal. Subsequently, the G − Y signal is recovered at the receiver by means of circuitry that processes the R − Y and B − Y signals.

It is now pertinent to consider a block diagram for the basic R − Y/B$_1$ − Y color television transmitter, as depicted in Fig. 13-14. Three color cameras are employed. Follow the operation of the transmitter while color stripes are being scanned, as shown in Fig. 13-15. Stipulate that the red, green, and blue stripes have 100% saturation and full brightness in this example. Each of the color cameras pro-duces full output while scanning one color stripe but pro-

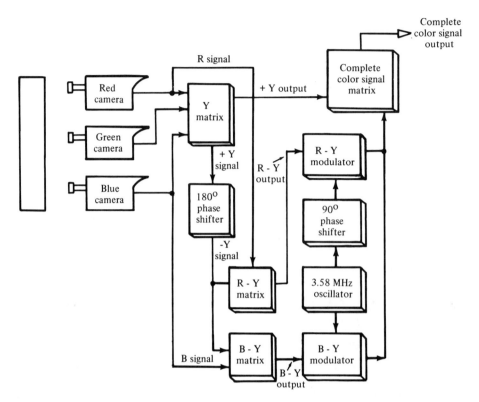

Fig. 13-14 Basic R-Y/B-Y color television transmitter.

duces zero output while scanning the other two color stripes. Note in Fig. 13-14 that the R, G, and B outputs are applied first to the Y matrix. Here, the Y signal is formed from the R, G, and B signals, as depicted in Fig. 13-16. The matrix is simply a resistive mixer which forms a Y signal in accordance with Equation 13-1.

  With reference to Fig. 13-16, the Y matrix consists of a resistive mixing network that combines the outputs from the red, green, and blue cameras in the proportions required to form a Y signal. This Y signal output from the matrix is the standard black and white video signal which will operate a black and white receiver normally. The output from the Y matrix is the same as the output from a black and white tele-

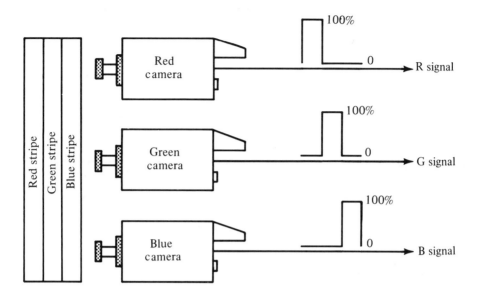

Fig. 13-15 R, G, and B camera outputs while scanning color stripes.

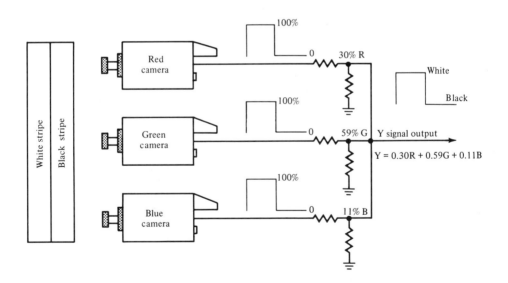

Fig. 13-16 Operation of the Y matrix.

vision camera. Next, consider the operation of the transmitter when a red stripe is being scanned.   Figure 13-17

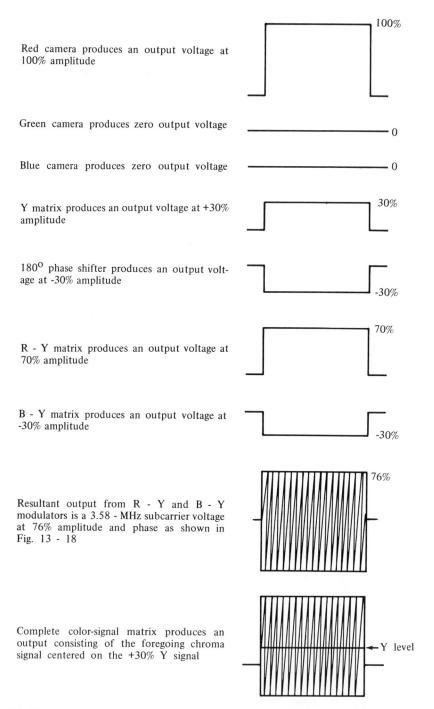

Red camera produces an output voltage at 100% amplitude — 100%

Green camera produces zero output voltage — 0

Blue camera produces zero output voltage — 0

Y matrix produces an output voltage at +30% amplitude — 30%

180° phase shifter produces an output voltage at -30% amplitude — -30%

R - Y matrix produces an output voltage at 70% amplitude — 70%

B - Y matrix produces an output voltage at -30% amplitude — -30%

Resultant output from R - Y and B - Y modulators is a 3.58 - MHz subcarrier voltage at 76% amplitude and phase as shown in Fig. 13 - 18 — 76%

Complete color-signal matrix produces an output consisting of the foregoing chroma signal centered on the +30% Y signal — Y level

Fig. 13-17 Operation of transmitter sections in Fig. 13-14 while scanning a red color stripe at full saturation and brightness.

summarizes the signal-processing sequence, the end result
of which is a chroma signal of 76% amplitude centered on a
Y signal of 30% amplitude. Follow this sequence step by
step.

With reference to Fig. 13-15, recall that the red
camera has 100% output while scanning a red stripe. On the
other hand, the green camera and the blue camera have zero
outputs while scanning a red stripe. These signal levels
are noted in Fig. 13-17. The output from the Y matrix in
Fig. 13-14 will be 30%, and the output from the 180° phase
shifter will be -30%. The R - Y matrix is a resistive
network which combines the -Y signal with the R signal.
Therefore, the output from the R - Y matrix will be 70%.
Note that the B - Y matrix is a resistive network which combines the -Y signal with the B signal. Accordingly, the
output from the B - Y matrix will be -30%. These R - Y
and B - Y signal voltages are applied to R - Y and B - Y
modulators before final combination with the Y signal.

Note in Fig. 13-14 that the 3.58-MHz subcarrier
voltages are separated by a phase difference of 90° in the
R - Y and B - Y modulators. The result is *quadrature
modulation*, which was mentioned previously. Quadrature
modulation in the example under consideration can be represented vectorially as shown in Fig. 13-18. Therefore, the
complete color signal consists of a 76% chroma signal
centered on a 30% Y signal, as depicted in Fig. 13-17. A
fully saturated red hue at full brightness is represented
by this complete color signal, with the resultant subcarrier
in the phase shown in Fig. 13-18. Hue corresponds to the
resultant subcarrier phase, brightness corresponds to the
amplitude of the Y signal, and saturation corresponds to the
resultant subcarrier amplitude.

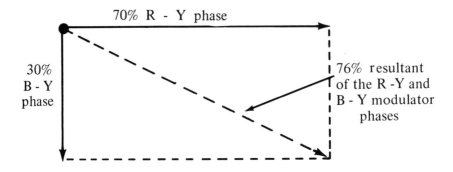

Fig. 13-18 Quadrature modulation of the subcarrier forms a 76% resultant from 70% R-Y and 30% B-Y signals.

These facts are summarized in the chroma phase diagram shown in Fig. 13-19. The vectors show the phases and com-

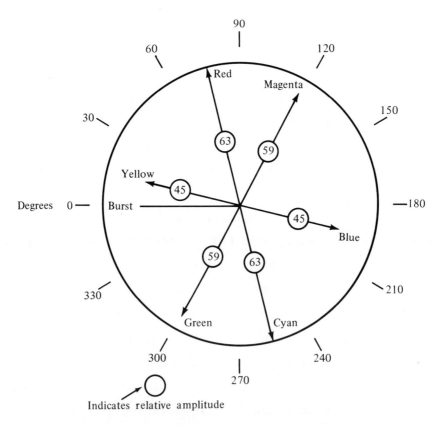

Indicates relative amplitude

Fig. 13-19 Comparative phases and amplitudes of the color subcarrier for the fully saturated primary and complementary colors.

parative amplitudes of the color-subcarrier signal for fully
saturated primary and complementary colors.   Phase angles
are referenced with respect to *burst* phase.   Note that the
color burst is a sample of the unmodulated color subcarrier,
located on the back porch of the horizontal sync pulse, as
depicted in Fig. 13-20.   This color burst is a synchronizing

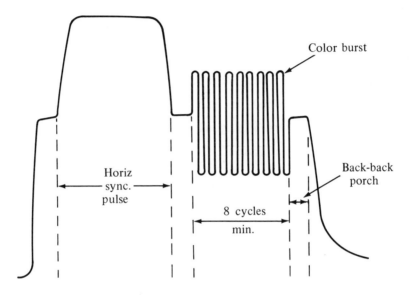

Fig. 13-20 Horizontal sync pulse with 3.58-MHz color burst
inserted.

signal, utilized in the chroma circuits of the color television receiver.   Note that the vectors in Fig. 13-19 become
shorter when unsaturated colors are being transmitted.   If
a color fades out to a gray or white or black in a scene, the
chroma voltages disappear entirely, and only the Y signal is
left.   This fact becomes obvious in view of the following
relations.

Operation of the R - Y matrix in Fig. 13-14 is described
by Equation 13.2.   Similarly, operation of the B - Y matrix is
described by Equation 13.5.   Observe that when black is being

scanned, all terms in these formulas are zero. When white is
being scanned, we write:

$$R - Y = 1.00 - 0.30 - 0.59 - 0.11 = 0$$

and $$\qquad B - Y = 1.00 - 0.30 - 0.59 - 0.11 = 0$$

That is, when black and white or grays are being
scanned, there is no chroma signal produced at the transmitter. This is just another way of saying that a black
and white image has no color-difference component. Dis-
appearance of the chroma signal while scanning black and
white scenes is helpful in minimizing residual chroma
interference with the Y signal. The principal chroma
signal phases are indicated in Fig. 13-21. In this example,

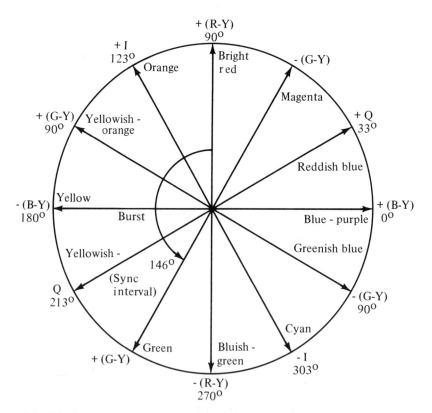

Fig. 13-21 Chroma signal phases with identifying hues at
30° intervals.

another phase-angle reference is utilized, wherein 0° is taken as the B - Y phase (opposite to burst). It makes no difference what reference is used, as long as we are consistent in our calculations.

13.5 Color-Bar Signals

A basic point is that there is no brightness (Y) information in a chroma signal. Therefore, the chroma signals depicted in Fig. 13-21 might appear to be invisible on the screen of a color picture tube. However, if the brightness control is advanced, an artificial Y signal can be added to such chroma signals, and a display such as illustrated in Fig. 13-22 will be seen. As explained in greater detail subsequently, this is termed a rainbow color-bar signal. It is widely used in color television servicing procedures. The more elaborate color-bar generators provide primary and complementary colors at full saturation and full brightness, as illustrated in Fig. 13-23. This is called an NTSC color-bar pattern and has the signal proportions depicted in Fig. 13-24.

The NTSC color-bar signal is particularly instructive. As shown in Fig. 13-24, each of the color bars consists of a Y component and a 3.58-MHz chroma component. The Y amplitudes are in accordance with Equation 13.1. Note that the chroma amplitudes are in accordance with the relations depicted in Fig. 13-19. The chroma signal for a red bar in Fig. 13-17 was calculated to have an amplitude of 76%, instead of 63%. The reason for this seeming discrepancy is that chroma values are readjusted prior to actual transmission, to avoid over-modulation of the picture carrier. The unadjusted chroma values produced by the simplified arrangement in Fig. 13-14

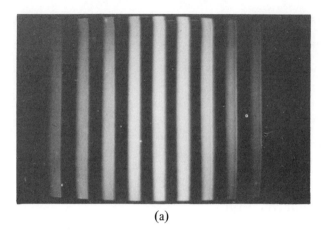

(a)

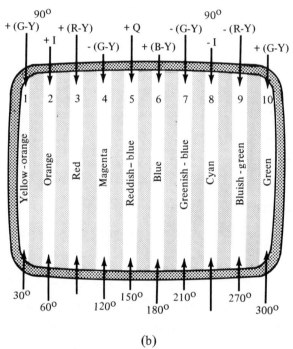

(b)

Fig. 13-22 A chroma-bar display, with the hues shown in
Fig. 13-21: (a) pattern on screen of color picture tube,
(b) chroma-bar identification.

are readjusted in practice by reducing R − Y to 0.877, and
reducing B − Y to 0.493.   In turn, the readjusted chroma
values are changed back to unadjusted values at the color
receiver.

Fig. 13-23 Display of the primary and complementary colors at full saturation and brightness.

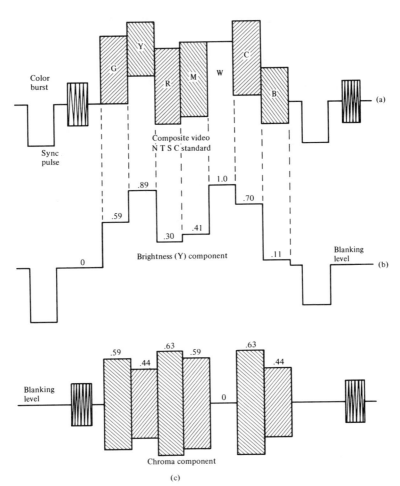

Fig. 13-24 Signal proportions in an NTSC color-bar signal.

A color-bar generator is necessarily designed to provide readjusted chroma values, and the chroma amplitudes are
accordingly indicated in Fig. 13-24.   The chroma phases are
indicated in Fig. 13-19.   The chroma signal is *encoded* into
the black and white (Y) signal to form the complete color
signal.   That is equivalent to saying that a color-bar signal
is a multiplexed signal.   At the receiver, the complete color
signal is *decoded* or processed to recover its individual Y,
R - Y, and B - Y components.   Details are discussed in Chapter
14.

13.6 Basic I/Q Color Television Transmitter

As noted previously, color television transmission in
the United States employs the I and Q chroma axes, rather
than the R - Y and B - Y axes.   On the other hand, nearly
all color television receivers operate on the R - Y and
B - Y chroma axes or related variations.   It follows that
transmission may be effected on any chosen pair of chroma
axes, and reception may be accomplished on any other pair
of chroma axes.   However, there is an advantage to transmission on the I and Q axes, inasmuch as maximum color detail
in the flesh-tone region is made possible, provided that
reception is accomplished on the I and Q chroma axes.   With
reference to Fig. 13-21, recall that the I chroma phase
corresponds to orange hues.   In I and Q transmission, these
hues are processed in a 1.5-MHz video channel, whereas the
hues corresponding to the Q chroma phase are processed in a
0.5-MHz video channel.
Quadrature modulation is utilized in I/Q transmission,
just as in R - Y/B - Y transmission.   That is,   the I and Q
axes are in quadrature because they have a 90° phase differ-

ence between them, just as the R - Y and B - Y axes are in quadrature. A block diagram for the basic I/Q color television transmission system is shown in Fig. 13-25. Its essen-

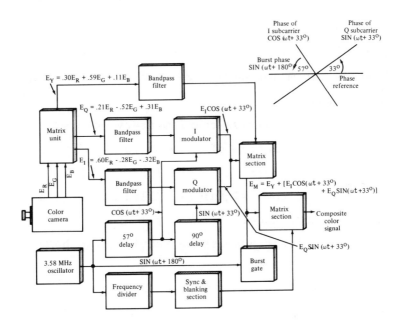

Fig. 13-25 Basic I/Q color television transmitter arrangement.

tial similarity to the R - Y/B - Y system is evident. The I signal consists of 0.74(R - Y) and -0.27(B - Y). The Q signal consists of 0.48(R - Y) and 0.41(B - Y). The I signal is an "in-phase" signal, which means that the I axis falls along the line of maximum color vision acuity. The Q signal is a "quadrature-phase" signal, which means that the Q axis is at right angles to the I axis. As would be anticipated, the Q axis falls along the line of minimum color vision acuity. That is, because maximum color vision acuity occurs along the I axis, it is reasonable to suppose that minimum color vision acuity would occur along the Q axis.

Questions

Short Answer

1. Describe the color transmission by drawing a block diagram of the system.
2. What is the major advantage of the NTSC system of color television?
3. What are the additive complementary colors?
4. Draw a block diagram of a color television transmission system and discuss the operation of each block.
5. How is the chroma signal cancelled out on a black and white picture tube?
6. Why does color transmission require less bandwidth than black and white?
7. What is a monochrome signal?
8. What is the difference between the red video signal and the black and white signal?
9. How is the G - Y signal transmitted?
10. What is the Y matrix?
11. What is the relationship between hue and the amplitude of the Y signal?
12. What is the color-burst signal?
13. How is brightness developed in a chroma signal by a color-bar generator?
14. What is the advantage of the NTSC color-bar generator?
15. Why do we say that a color bar is a multiplexed signal?
16. Along which axis, I or Q, does the maximum and minimum color vision acuity occur?

True-False

1. The NTSC color system is compatible with black and white television.

2. A four-color picture tube is used in a color television receiver.

3. The blending of red, green, and blue colors can be used to produce white.

4. A color television camera contains three camera tubes.

5. The same image is transmitted by each camera tube in a color television camera.

6. At the receiver, each basic color is processed separately to a particular electron gun.

7. Frequency interleaving is the process of fitting the chroma signal between the black and white signal.

8. The color picture cancels itself out on the screen of a black and white picture tube.

9. The transmission of color information takes about one-fourth the bandwidth that is required for black and white transmission.

10. The chroma information is modulated on a 3.58-MHz color subcarrier.

11. A black and white receiver reproduces both color and black and white signals.

12. The black and white video signal is designated as the Y signal.

13. The black and white video signal is sometimes called the monochrome signal.

14. An R - Y signal is often called a color-difference signal.

15. A basic color television transmitter radiates the Y signal, an R - Y signal, and a B - Y signal.

16. The G - Y signal is recovered at the receiver.

17. Each of the color cameras produces full output while scanning one color stripe of either red, blue, or green, and no output while scanning the other two color stripes.

18. The Y matrix is a video detector made up of a diode and resistors.

19. The output from the Y matrix is the chroma signal.

20. Brightness corresponds to the amplitude of the Y signal, and hue corresponds to the resultant subcarrier phase.

21. The color burst is a sample of the unmodulated color subcarrier.

22. The color-burst signal is a horizontal sync pulse.

23. When black and white or grays are being scanned, there is no chroma signal produced at the transmitter.

24. There is no brightness information in a chroma signal.

25. A color-bar signal is a multiplexed signal.

26. Color television transmission in the United States uses the I and Q chroma axes.

27. Maximum color vision acuity occurs along the Q axis.

Multiple Choice

1. The three basic colors are detected by the three pick-up tubes in a color television camera because:
   (a) each tube has a color-sensitive cathode.
   (b) the scene is transmitted to each tube through a filter that rejects the other two basic colors.
   (c) of the time-sharing color scanner in the camera.
   (d) each pick-up tube operates in turn as the other two are cut off.

2. The bandwidth required for color transmission is about _____ that required for black and white transmission.
   (a) the same as (c) one-fourth
   (b) one-half   (d) twice

3. The black and white video signal is designated as the:

    (a)   Y signal, or the monochrome signal.

    (b)   composite video signal.

    (c)   chroma video signal.

    (d)   NTSC video signal.

4. An R - Y signal is often called a/an:

    (a)   color-difference signal.   (c)   color signal.

    (b)   monochrome signal.   (d)   brightness signal.

5. The Y matrix is comprised of a:

    (a)   diode resistance network. (c)   resistive network.

    (b)   diode detector.   (d)   transister amplifier.

6. The output from the Y matrix is the:

    (a)   chroma signal.

    (b)   red and green signal.

    (c)   green signal.

    (d)   black and white video signal.

7. Brightness corresponds to the:

    (a)   hue.   (c)   duration of the Y signal.

    (b)   subcarrier phase.   (d)   amplitude of the Y signal.

8. Phase angles are referenced in respect to:

    (a)   the Y signal.   (c)   the B - Y signal.

    (b)   the G signal.   (d)   burst phase.

9. The color-burst signal is a/an:

    (a)   synchronizing signal.

    (b)   horizontal sync pulse.

    (c)   vertical sync pulse.

    (d)   level reference signal to set up the AGC circuits.

10. A color television test signal that requires the insertion of an artificial Y signal is called a/an:

    (a)   NTSC generator.   (c)   Y signal generator.

    (b)   chroma generator. (d)   encoder generator.

Chapter 14

COLOR TELEVISION
RECEIVER PRINCIPLES

14.1 Color Television Receiver Functions

Basically, a color television receiver has two functions. It reproduces a color image when tuned to a color
television broadcast signal, and it reproduces a black and
white image when tuned to a black and white television
broadcast signal.   This changeover in response is accomplished automatically, as explained in greater detail in
the following sections. A block diagram for a color television receiver is shown in Fig. 14-1.   The shaded blocks
indicate stages used only in color receivers. Some of the
shaded blocks are used during both black and white and color
reception, whereas others of the shaded blocks are used only
during color reception. Those colored blocks which are used

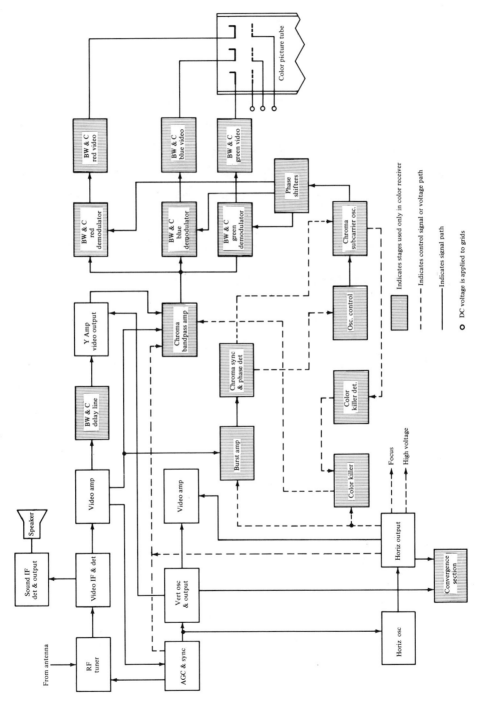

Fig. 14-1 Block diagram of a color television receiver.

during both black and white and color reception are marked
"BW and C."

Observe that the plain blocks in Fig. 14-1 comprise
the sections utilized in a conventional black and white receiver. As these sections have been discussed in previous chapters, we will now turn our attention to the shaded blocks and
the color picture tube. It is useful to start with an explanation of the structure and function of the color picture tube,
and then to follow the progress of a color television signal
through the various receiver sections. Thereby the signal-
processing requirements are clarified, and the functioning of
the *chroma circuitry* is perceived in a logical form.

14.2 Color Picture Tubes

Most color picture tubes contain three electron guns,
as depicted in Fig. 14-2. The screen is formed with trios of

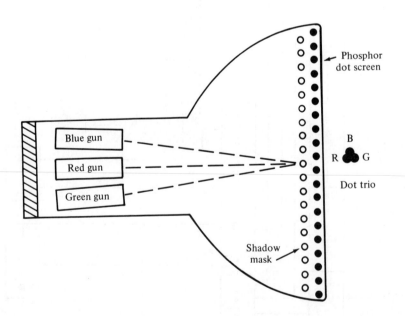

Fig. 14-2 Plan of the shadow-mask type of color picture
tube.

three phosphors, which are scanned simultaneously by three
electron beams. In turn, the screen glows white when all three
electron guns are operating. If the blue gun is cut off, the
screen glows yellow; if both the blue and red guns are cut
off, the screen glows green, and so on. The shadow mask, or
aperture mask, is a very fine "sieve" that assists in directing
each of the electron beams upon its associated phosphor dot, as
shown in Fig. 14-3. A representative color picture tube

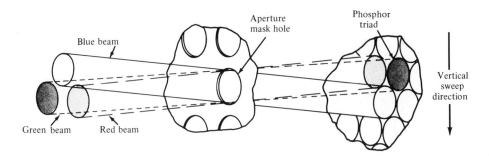

Fig. 14-3 Relations of the phosphor dots, aperature mask,
and electron beams in a color picture tube.

employs 200,000 trios, or triads, comprising 600,000 phosphor
dots. An individual dot has a diameter of approximately 0.009
in.

Figure 14-4 shows the general appearance of a color
picture tube. A deflection yoke is mounted on the tube
neck, as in the case of a black and white picture tube.
In addition, magnet assemblies are mounted behind the yoke.
These magnets are adjusted to make the three electron beams
pass through the aperture mask at correct angles, as
depicted in Fig. 14-3. When these *convergence* adjustments
are correct, a black and white image is reproduced without
any color fringing. If the convergence adjustments are incorrect, objects in a black and white image will be displayed

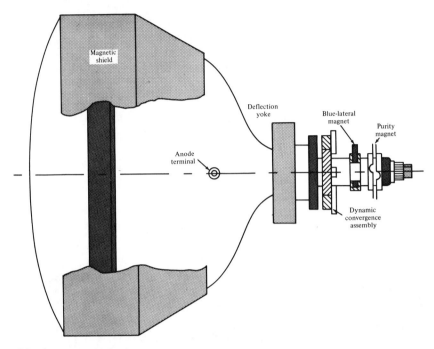

Fig. 14-4 External appearance of a shadow-mask type of color
picture tube.

with colored borders, and the background areas will be tinted
with various colors.   Both permanent magnets and electromagnets are provided for the adjustment of convergence.   The
permanent magnets are called *static* convergence adjustments,
and the electromagnets are called *dynamic* convergence adjustments.   Note that the electromagnets are energized by the
convergence section in Fig. 14-1.

Another type of color picture tube, called the
Trinitron, is manufactured by the Sony Corporation.   As
depicted in Fig. 14-5, red, green, and blue phosphors are
utilized, which are deposited side by side in vertical
stripes to form the picture tube screen.   Note that the
shadow mask, or aperture grille, is formed with slots,
instead of holes.   Each slot has the same width as a color

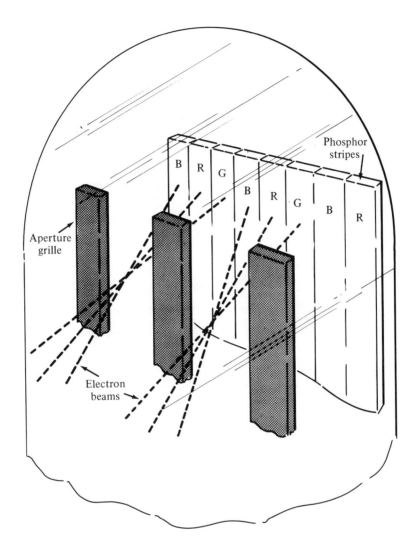

Fig. 14-5 Screen and aperature-grille relations in a Sony Trinitron color picture tube.

strip.   Figure 14-6 shows the structure of the electron gun in a Trinitron tube. Three cathodes are used in line horizontally to produce three electron beams which pass first through the control grid G_1.   The next grid, G_2, is a screen grid or accelerating anode.   It speeds up the electrons and provides initial focus action.   Next, the beams pass through the focus electrodes, and then through

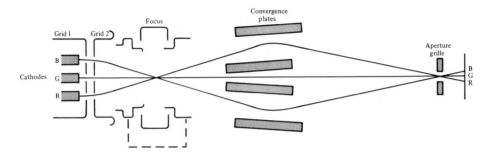

Fig. 14-6 Cross section of the electron beam path in a
Trinitron color picture tube.

the convergence electrodes or plates.   When the convergence
voltages are correctly adjusted, the three electron beams
come to a sharp focus at the aperture grille. Figure 14-7
shows how each electron beam strikes its associated color
stripe as a result of the angle at which it passes through
the aperture grille.

Observe in Fig. 14-7 that each of the electron beams
actually strikes two of its associated color stripes simultaneously. If a smaller beam were used, only one stripe
would be struck. However, the light output from the screen
would be reduced by one-half. To obtain maximum practical
excitation of the phosphors, an accelerating voltage of
approximately 20 kV is employed. The chief advantage of the
Trinitron color picture tube is its comparative simplicity.
Only six picture tube adjustment controls are required, compared with the two dozen controls utilized by the typical
shadow-mask tube.

14.3 Color Television Receiver Operation

When a color television receiver is tuned to a color
broadcast signal, the waveform applied to the video detector
consists of the composite color signal modulated on the

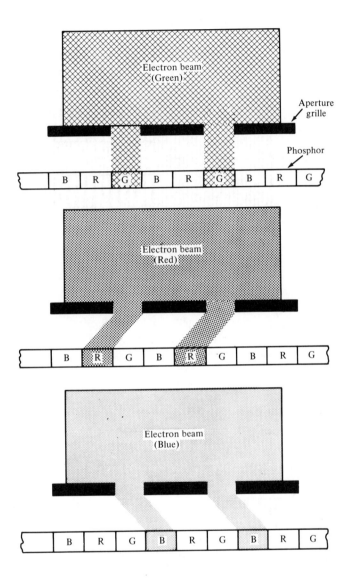

Fig. 14-7 Scanning action or green, red, and blue phosphor stripes by the electron beams.

picture-IF carrier, as shown in Fig. 14-8.   This composite color signal is demodulated through the video detector to develop the envelope information, as depicted in Fig. 14-9. Note that the 3.58-MHz component of this composite color

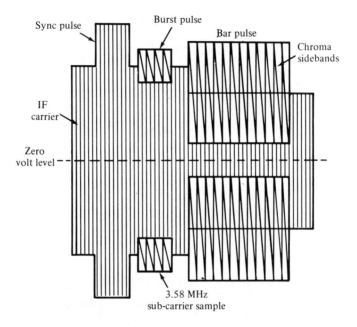

Fig. 14-8 Waveform of the IF signal when the color receiver is tuned to a color television broadcast station.

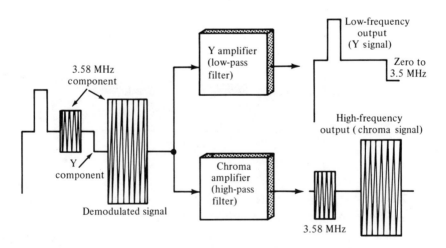

Fig. 14-9 Output waveform from the video detector is passed through the Y amplifier and the chroma amplifier.

signal is encoded into the Y component.   The first step in signal processing consists in passing the composite color signal through low-pass and high-pass filters to separate the Y information from the chroma information.

Observe in Fig. 14-9 that the low-pass filter (Y amplifier) passes the Y signal but rejects the chroma signal. Conversely, the high-pass filter (chroma amplifier) passes the chroma signal but rejects the Y signal. Although this filter processing is not complete, the residual chroma signal that feeds through the Y amplifier is practically invisible because of frequency-interleaving action. Similarly, the residual Y signal that feeds through the chroma amplifier is practically invisible because of this frequency-interleaving action. Figure 14-10 shows how the Y and chroma amplifier frequency responses are related to provide the foregoing filter action. The chroma amplifier, also called a bandpass amplifier, has its response peaked at the high-frequency end of the video channel. In turn, the chroma demodulators responds to a band of video frequencies from 3.0 to 4.2 MHz. Thus, most of the Y signal is rejected by the chroma amplifier. Conversely, the Y amplifier has a falling response above 3 MHz. In turn, much of the chroma signal is rejected by the Y amplifier.

Because the chroma section has a considerably narrower bandwidth than the Y section, the chroma signal is comparatively delayed in its arrival at the color picture tube. Therefore, a delay line is inserted in the Y channel, as depicted in Fig. 14-1. The delay time provided is typically 1 μsec. This delay provides optimum "color fit" in the black and white image. Figure 14-11 shows the construction of a typical delay line. In addition to the delay line, a color-subcarrier trap in the Y channel is used to attenuate the response at 3.58 MHz, as seen in (e) of Fig. 14-10. This

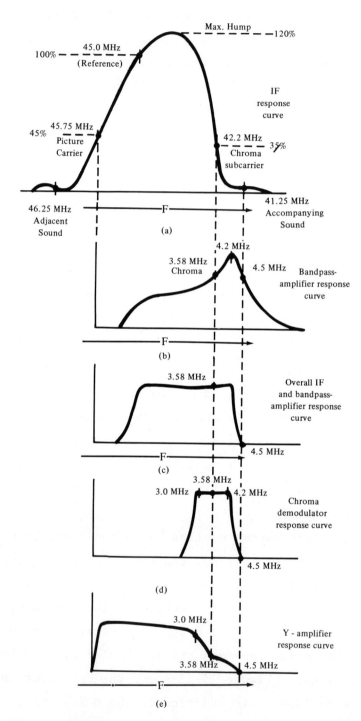

Fig. 14-10 Frequency responses of typical IF, bandpass, chroma-demodular, and Y circuit sections.

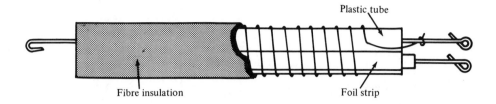

Fig. 14-11 Construction of a delay line.

trap is simply a parallel resonant circuit tuned to 3.58 MHz.

Next, let us consider the operation of the chroma bandpass amplifier. In the example of Fig. 14-1, the approximate input and output signal amplitudes are 1.5 V and 4 V, respectively. Figure 14-12 shows the circuit arrangement that is utilized. The bandpass amplifier works in association with the color-killer section; that is, the bandpass amplifier channel is switched "on" when the receiver is tuned to a color signal. On the other hand, the bandpass amplifier is switched "off" by the color killer when the receiver is tuned to a black and white signal. This electronic switch is employed to reject possible interference that could produce color streaks during black and white reception. Also, the color-killer circuit in Fig. 14-12 operates as an automatic chroma control (ACC) arrangement during color reception. In turn, the output chroma signal is held at about the same level whether the input signal is weak or strong.

Observe in Fig. 14-12 that the output from the video amplifier is fed to the input of the bandpass amplifier. The bandpass amplifier has a rising frequency response with a peak at 4.2 MHz, as depicted in Fig. 14-10(b). Note that the base emitter bias voltage for Q1 in Fig. 14-12 is determined by the ACC voltage from Q4. To provide maximum bandpass amplifier gain on weak signals, delay diode CR1 is

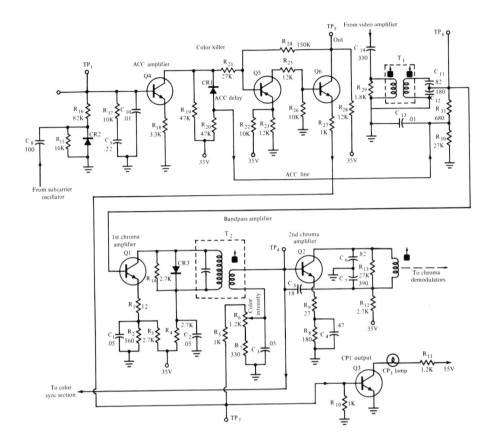

Fig. 14-12 Bandpass amplifier and color-killer configuration.

included in the ACC line.   If the incoming chroma signal
increases in amplitude, the color burst increases in amplitude proportionally.   As explained in greater detail subsequently, the stronger burst produces a greater output from
the subcarrier oscillator.   Conversely, if there is no
incoming color burst, there is no output from the subcarrier
oscillator.

Diode CR2 in Fig. 14-12 rectifies the   3.58-MHz output
from the subcarrier oscillator, and thereby applies a positive

bias voltage to the base of Q4. As Q4 conducts more current, its collector potential becomes less positive. If this negative-going bias overcomes the threshold of CR1, it proceeds to the base of Q1 and reduces the stage gain by biasing the transistor toward cutoff. Therefore, the gain of Q1 remains practically constant although the incoming chroma signal has increased in amplitude. The gain of Q2 is constant whenever there is an incoming chroma signal. When there is no incoming chroma signal, Q2 is automatically cut off. Note that while Q2 is operating, its gain is set by adjusting the color-intensity control R_6. As would be anticipated, the dc voltages at aarious points in the network change when the receiver is tuned from a black and white signal to a color signal. For example, the base voltage of Q4 operates at 0.08 V on an incoming black and white signal but rises to 3.2 V on an incoming color signal.

Note that test points are provided in the foregoing example for convenient voltage and signal checks. Thus, TP_1 in Fig. 14-12 is provided for measurement of the base bias voltage on Q4. The switching voltage for Q2 is measured at TP_4. Observe that this switching voltage has the same source as the ACC voltage--that is, the switching voltage is developed by Q4. However, it is greatly increased in amplitude in passage through dc amplifiers Q5 and Q6. Accordingly, even a weak output from the subcarrier oscillator suffices to saturate Q6 and switch Q2 into conduction. Note also that Q3 is an additional dc amplifier that switches into conduction whenever the receiver is tuned to a color signal. In turn, the control-panel lamp CP_1 is illuminated.

14.4 Chroma Demodulators

From the bandpass amplifier, the 3.58-MHz signal pro-

ceeds to the chroma demodulators, as depicted in Fig. 14-1.
Although various demodulator arrangements can be utilized,
the end result is always the same. That is, the chroma signal is decoded to recover the original color information.
This decoding process involves two processes. First, the
subcarrier is inserted into the chroma signal. Recall that
the subcarrier is suppressed at the color television transmitter, and only the chroma sidebands are contained in the
radiated color signal. The reason for this suppression is
to minimize interference between the chroma signal and the
Y signal. Therefore, a local subcarrier oscillator must be
employed at the receiver in order to reconstitute the complete
chroma signal.

Secondly, the subcarrier must be inserted into the
chroma sidebands in suitable phase. Thus, if the subcarrier
is inserted in the red phase (Fig. 14-13), the red chroma
signal is recovered. If the subcarrier is reinserted in
the green phase, the green chroma signal is recovered.
With reference to Fig. 14-1, the subcarrier is passed
through three phase-shifting circuits in order to recover
the red, blue, and green chroma signals. A third requirement is also involved, which may or may not involve the
chroma demodulators. It is that the Y signal must be combined with the complete chroma signals to form the complete
color signals. This may be done via the chroma demodulators,
as depicted in Fig. 14-1, or it may be done subsequently to
chroma demodulation. Because the processing arrangement in
which the Y signal is combined with the chroma signal in the
demodulators is most instructive, this method will be
explained in basic detail.

A typical chroma demodulator configuration is shown
in Fig. 14-14. Because the Y signal is applied at the demodu-

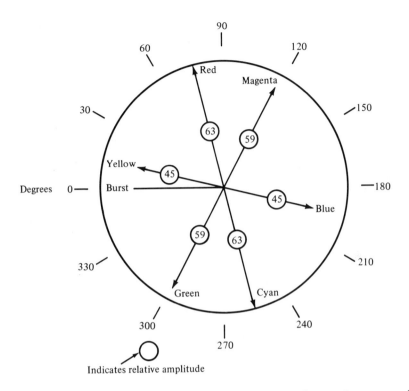

Fig. 14-13 Chroma-subcarrier phases for the primary and complementary colors.

lator inputs, the term *color demodulator* is more descriptive. Three demodulators are employed, each of which processes a primary color signal. Basically, a color demodulator is a *phase detector* and an *amplitude detector*. The demodulator circuitry in Fig. 14-14 bears obvious similarity to a ratio detector configuration, without a limiting capacitor. The Y signal is introduced with the chroma signal at the center tap of the bandpass transformer secondary. On the other hand, the subcarrier voltage is introduced at the center tap of the demodulator output circuit. As noted previously, three phase-shifting circuits are employed to provide demodulation of the red, blue, and green chroma axes.

One circuit feature that appears puzzling at first

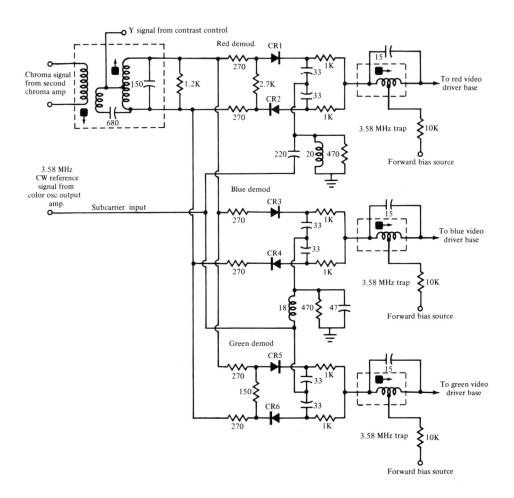

Fig. 14-14 Typical chroma demodulator configuration.

glance is the lack of symmetry in the green demodulator circuit of Fig. 14-14. That is, diode CR5 is oppositely polarized
with respect to CR1 and CR3. Similarly, CR6 is oppositely
polarized with respect to CR2 and CR4. Thus, it might seem
that there would actually be a magenta output (Fig. 14-13)
from the green demodulator. However, a subcarrier phase
shifter is employed which provides the requisite phase for
obtaining a green signal output. This asymmetry is utilized
in the chroma demodulator system to provide cancellation of

spurious demodulation products called "blips." If these
spurious voltages were permitted to remain in the output
signals, they would interfere with and distort the color
picture.

Another spurious demodulator product that appears in
the demodulator output signal is the 3.58-MHz subcarrier feedthrough voltage. Therefore, a 3.58-MHz trap is placed in each
of the demodulator output leads. In turn, only the envelope
of the decoded color signal is passed on to the following
video amplifier. Figure 14-15 shows the principle of chroma

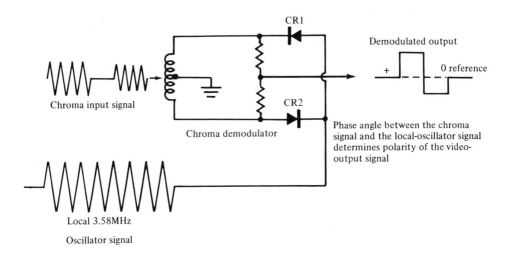

Fig. 14-15 Chroma demodulation involves both phase detection
and amplitude detection.

demodulation from the waveform viewpoint. As would be anticipated, the red, blue, and green video amplifiers are similar
in all essential respects to the video amplifiers used in
black and white receivers. Therefore, explanation of the
video-amplifier circuitry is not repeated here.

14.5 Color Sync Section

Now consider the operation of the color sync section.
With reference to Fig. 14-1, this comprises the oscillator
control and chroma-subcarrier oscillator sections. We will
find that color sync is a subfunction of black and white
sync action.   In other words, the receiver can lose color
sync without losing black and white sync action, as illustrated in Fig. 14-16(a). On the other hand, if black and

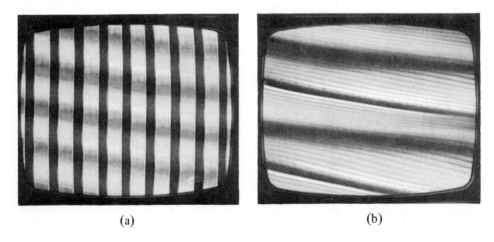

(a)   (b)

Fig. 14-16 Two conditions of color sync loss: (a) loss of
color sync only, (b) loss of both black and white and color
sync.

white sync is lost, color sync action is also lost, as seen
in Fig. 14-16(b).   The reason for this relation becomes
apparent when we analyze the operation of the color sync
section.

Various color sync arrangements are utilized to keep
the subcarrier oscillator precisely on frequency. One of
the widely used configurations is depicted in Fig. 14-17.
Observe that the chroma signal output from the bandpass
amplifier is fed to base of Q1, a gated color sync ampli-

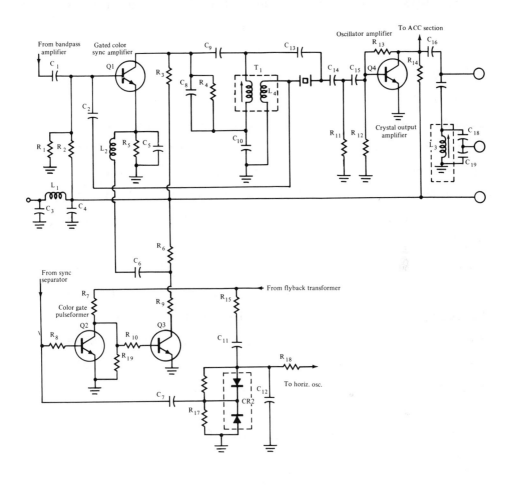

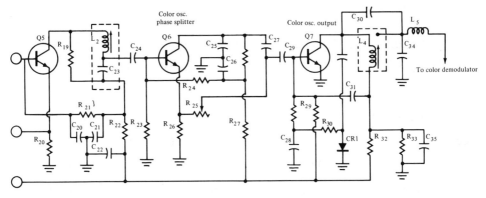

Fig. 14-17 A typical color sync section.

fier. This transistor remains cut off until a flyback pulse
arrives at the emitter and gates the transistor into conduction for the duration of the color burst. Note that if
Q1 should conduct continuously, color sync would be lost
because the chroma sidebands have arbitrary phases. It is
evident that the gating pulse must be correctly timed and
suitably shaped to pass a clean-cut color burst. Accordingly,
wave-processing circuitry is provided, as follows.

Note the locations of transistors Q2 and Q3 in Fig.
14-17. Horizontal sync pulses are applied to the base of
Q2, and flyback pulses are applied to the collector. The
resulting gate pulse produced by Q2 is fed to Q3, which
steps up its amplitude from 1 V to 40 V peak to peak.
Because this gate pulse is applied to the emitter of Q1,
the transistor is gated into conduction, and the collector
output waveform contains the burst signal. This 3.58-MHz
voltage is coupled via T_1 to the quartz crystal CR1. Each
burst shock excites the crystal into a ringing oscillation
which has the same phase as that of the burst signal.
Because quartz crystal has an extremely high Q value, this
ringing voltage decays only slightly from one burst to the
next.

This 3.58-MHz output from Q1 represents the recon-
stituted color subcarrier which was suppressed at the color
television transmitter. Transistor Q4 operates as a
3.58-MHz amplifier. It steps up the subcarrier amplitude
to 20 V peak to peak. Observe that the output from Q4 is
fed to the ACC section which controls the gain of the bandpass amplifier. From Q4 the subcarrier is applied to Q5,
which operates as a limiter.   That is, Q5 slices 3 V from
both excursions of the subcarrier signal and reduces its
amplitude from 20 V to 14 V peak to peak.   In turn, the

3.58-MHz output sine wave from Q5 has a precisely constant
amplitude. This constancy is essential for proper operation
of the color demodulators.

Limiter Q5 is followed by a phase splitter, Q6, which
develops a pair of 3.58-MHz outputs 180° out of phase with
each other. These outputs are applied to a series RC circuit
composed of R_1 and C_1. Because R_1 is variable, it provides
an adjustable phase shift in the 3.58-MHz voltage that is fed
to Q7. Thus, R_1 is called the *hue control* because it changes
the hues that are developed by the color demodulators. The
viewer adjusts R_1 to obtain true colors in the image. Transistor Q7 operates as a buffer output stage between the
phase splitter and the color demodulators. There is considerable loss of signal amplitude through the phase splitter,
and the input signal to Q7 has an amplitude of only 1 V peak
to peak. However, Q7 steps up the signal level to 30 V peak
to peak.

14.6 Troubleshooting Color Television Receivers

It follows from previous discussion that troubleshooting
procedures for the black and white portion of a color television receiver will necessarily be the same as in the case of
a black and white receiver. Moreover, much the same approach
is utilized in troubleshooting the chroma portion of a color
television receiver. Picture analysis often provides useful
clues. For example, the image may display weak color or no
color. In such a case, signal-tracing procedures with a wide-
band oscilloscope and low-capacitance probe generally suffice
to provide preliminary localization of the trouble area.

With reference to Fig. 14-12, a symptom of weak or no
color could be caused by component failure in the bandpass
amplifier section. Thus, an output waveform from Q2 that

has subnormal amplitude with respect to the value specified
in the receiver service data might be observed. In such a
case, it is helpful to measure dc voltages in this area, both
in the presence and absence of signal input. Analysis of the
dc voltage patterns will often pinpoint a defective component without further tests. As in most situations, fixed
capacitors are the most likely cause of trouble symptoms.
Operating controls eventually become worn and erratic.
Transistors occasionally develop collector leakage, and semiconductor diodes may deteriorate.

Waveform checks in chroma circuitry can be made on the
basis of station signal reception.   However, it is helpful
to employ a color signal generator, such as illustrated in
Fig. 14-18.   There are two advantages in the use of generator

Fig. 14-18 A widely used type of color signal generator.
(Courtesy, Heath Co.)

signals.   First, the signal level is constant and can be set
to any desired amplitude.   Accordingly, stable waveforms are
displayed on the scope screen, which are analyzed to better
advantage than in the case of changing waveforms. Moreover,
circuit operation can be readily checked for both weak signal

and strong signal conditions. Secondly, a color generator output signal has precisely known phases, which are essential in analysis of phase-responsive circuitry such as color demodulator sections. This topic is explained in greater detail in Chapter 15.

Questions

Short Answer

1. What are the two basic functions of a color television receiver?
2. Draw a block diagram of a color television receiver and indicate the blocks that operate in black and white reception.
3. What is the difference between a color picture tube and a black and white picture tube?
4. Define the term "convergence" as it applies to a color television system.
5. What are static and dynamic convergence adjustments?
6. How does the Trinitron color picture tube differ from the more common three-gun CRT's?
7. What is the first step in signal processing of the composite color signal in Fig. 14-9?
8. Why is the chroma amplifier called a bandpass amplifier?
9. Why does the Y amplifier have an upper frequency response of 3 MHz?
10. In Fig. 14-1, what is the purpose of the delay line in the block diagram?
11. What is the color-killer section of a television receiver?
12. How is the color-killer circuit controlled?

13. During color reception, what is the function of the color-killer circuit in Fig. 14-12?

14. What is the purpose of diode CR1 in Fig. 14-12?

15. What is the purpose of the subcarrier oscillator circuit in Fig. 14-12?

16. What is the purpose of R_6 in Fig. 14-12?

17. What is the purpose of point TP_1 in Fig. 14-12?

18. In Fig. 14-12, what is the source of the switching voltage for the color-killer circuit?

19. With reference to Fig. 14-12, what causes lamp CP_1 to turn on?

20. State three reasons why a subcarrier oscillator is necessary in a television receiver.

21. Basically, what is the function of a color demodulator?

22. How are blips prevented from appearing on the screen when a color picture is being received?

23. How is the 3.58-MHz subcarrier signal prevented from feeding through the demodulator in Fig. 14-14?

24. How does the color sync system tie in with the black and white sync?

25. What is the purpose of Q1 in Fig. 14-17?

26. In Fig. 14-17, why does the oscillator use a quartz crystal?

27. In Fig. 14-17, what is the function of transistor Q4?

28. Discuss the operation of Q4 and Q5 in the circuit in Fig. 14-17.

29. In Fig. 14-17, what is the function of the hue control?

30. Why is it better to use a color-bar generator rather than a station for signal tracing in a color television receiver?

11. In Fig. 14-17, the hue control R_1:

(a) is an amplitude control.

(b) adjusts the phase shift of the 3.58-MHz voltage.

(c) varies the frequency of the 3.58-MHz signal.

(d) adjusts the bias of the color-killer.

Chapter 15

TELEVISION TEST
EQUIPMENT

15.1 Television Test Equipment Survey

Throughout the text mention has been made of certain
basic test instruments, and typical applications have been
noted. The intention of this chapter is to survey television
test equipment in a general manner and observe the fundamental characteristics of various instruments. Test equipment is employed in television servicing procedures which
cannot be properly included in the instrument category,
inasmuch as a measuring function is not performed.   For
example, a picture tube test jig, such as illustrated in Fig.
15-1, is a television test equipment item, although it is
not a test instrument.

From the functional viewpoint, television test equipment can be classified into the following categories:

1. Voltage-measuring and indicating devices.
2. Current-measuring instruments.
3. Resistance-measuring instruments.
4. Waveform display instruments.
5. Signal-generating instruments.
6. Semiconductor test instruments and devices.
7. Picture tube testers.
8. Degaussing coils.
9. Harnesses, cables, and yoke assemblies.
10. Auxiliary test probes for various instruments.

Fig. 15-1 Color picture tube test jig. (Courtesy, RCA Corp.)

15.2 Voltage-Measuring and Indicating Devices

When making quick checks of television circuitry, it is often desired to know whether voltage is present or absent, without making an exact measurement. Various test-lamp devices may be employed for this type of test, such as illustrated in Fig. 15-2. Voltage indicators avoid the possibility of damage to television circuitry which is risked when a "spark" test is made. The dividing line between voltage-indicating

and voltage-measuring devices is not sharply drawn, inasmuch
as neon-lamp devices which are provided with a control and
calibrated voltage scale are available.   However,   their
accuracy of measurement is comparatively poor, and   most
technicians prefer to employ a conventional voltmeter whenever the value of a voltage is to be measured.

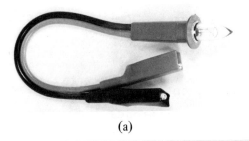

(a)

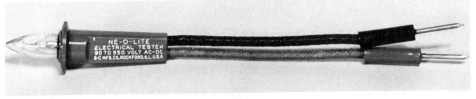

(b)

Fig. 15-2 Test lamp device used in circuit testing:
(a) test light for testing in the 5-to 50-V range, (b) neon
test lamp for testing in the 60-to 550-V range. (Courtesy,
General Cement Co.)

   It is instructive to note that any type of neon-lamp
tester will indicate whether a voltage is direct or alternating. When a dc voltage is being indicated, only one of
the electrodes glows in the neon lamp. On the other hand,
when an ac voltage is being indicated, both electrodes glow.
A neon lamp also indicates polarity of a dc source.   The
negative electrode glows, and the positive electrode remains
dark.   This is the reason, also, why both electrodes glow
when a neon-lamp tester is connected across an ac voltage
source. The ac voltage changes polarity, typically 60 times/
sec., and persistence of vision makes it appear that both

electrodes are glowing steadily.

Voltage-measuring instruments such as the VOM, TVM, and VTVM have been described in previous chapters. A field-strength meter, such as illustrated in Fig. 15-3, is

Fig. 15-3 A field-strength meter. (Courtesy, Jerrold Electronics)

basically a tuned high-frequency voltmeter. When it is connected to a television antenna lead-in, the instrument can be tuned to a desired television channel, and the value of the incoming signal is then measured in μV. Note in passing that voltmeters are often built into bench power supplies, signal generators, and other servicing equipment which is not primarily in the voltage-measuring category.

Although utilized to a minor extent in television service shops, the digital voltmeter (DVM) is widely used in laboratories and often on production test stations. Figure 15-4 illustrates a typical digital voltmeter. The advantages of a DVM over an analog-type voltmeter include its high accuracy, optimum readability, and minimizing of

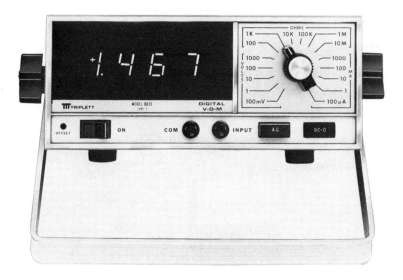

Fig. 15-4 A solid-state voltmeter. (Courtesy, Triplett
Corp.)

operating error among comparatively unskilled personnel.
The chief disadvantage of a DVM is its substantial cost.
Because the accuracy of an elaborate DVM considerably
exceeds the accuracy of highest-quality analog voltmeters,
it is used almost exclusively in research and development
projects which involve high-precision voltage measurements.

15.3 Current-Measuring Instruments

Current-measuring instruments are utilized to a very
minor extent in television test work, compared with voltage-
measuring instruments.   One reason for this disparity is
that most current-measuring instruments require that the
circuit be opened and the instrument connected in series
with the circuit.   As this is a time-consuming procedure,
technicians avoid current measurements whenever it is possible to do so.   Although there are current probes available for both dc and ac voltmeters, which permit current

measurements to be made without disconnection of the circuit lead, these are seldom used outside of laboratories. These probes are called clamp-around current probes, and as the name indicates, are applied by clamping the jaws of the probe around the circuit lead. Such current probes can measure current values from 1 mA to many A. One disadvantage of a current probe is its comparatively high cost. Moreover, a current probe is not practical for application in printed circuitry.

15.4 Resistance-Measuring Instruments

Resistance-measuring instruments find very wide use in television circuit and component testing. Thus, the ohmmeter is second only to the voltmeter as a basic test instrument. An ohmmeter is as convenient in application as a voltmeter. Of course, a voltmeter is always used in a "live" circuit, and an ohmmeter is always used in a "dead" circuit. The chief disadvantage of an ohmmeter is its lack of accuracy, compared to more precise types of resistance-measuring instruments. For this reason, a capacitance bridge often includes a Wheatstone bridge, which provides comparatively accurate resistance measurements, and also serves as a calibrator for ohmmeters (see Fig. 15-5).

Although used to a minor extent in service shops, impedance bridges are almost universally employed in television laboratories. An impedance bridge, such as illustrated in Fig. 15-6, measures inductance, capacitance, and resistance values. All measurements are made by the bridge method, with a Wheatstone bridge for resistance measurements. An impedance bridge enables the user to make resistance measurements which cannot be made by means of an ordinary ohmmeter. For example, the internal resistance of an elec-

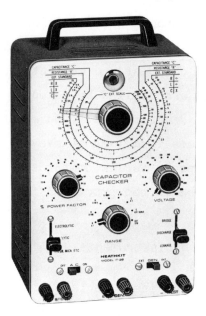

Fig. 15-5 A capacitance bridge that includes a Wheatstone bridge. (Courtesy, Heath Co.)

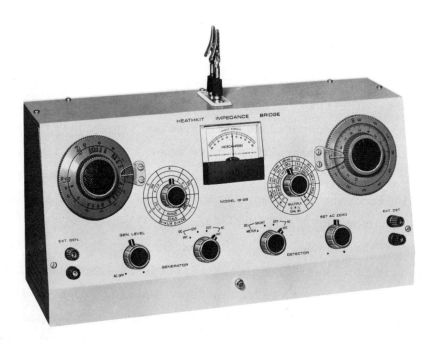

Fig. 15-6 An impedance bridge that includes a Wheatstone bridge. (Courtesy, Heath Co.)

trolytic capacitor can be measured in terms of its power

factor with an impedance bridge. The internal ac resistance of a battery can be measured with an impedance bridge but cannot be measured with an ohmmeter.

15.5 Waveform Display Instruments

This section will consider waveform display instruments used in television technology. In the service area, these instruments are all based on the CRT and are termed oscilloscopes and vectorscopes. Service-type oscilloscopes have been described previously. The vectorscope is used only in color television tests. A vectorscope such as illustrated in Fig. 15-7 is basically an oscilloscope with a special

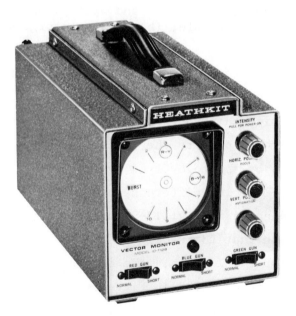

Fig. 15-7 A typical vectorscope. (Courtesy, Heath Co.)

graticule. The graticule layout and a typical vectorgram are depicted in Fig. 15-8. This form of vectorgram is based on a keyed rainbow color-bar signal, which will be explained in greater detail subsequently. Development of the vectorgram pattern can be summarized as follows.

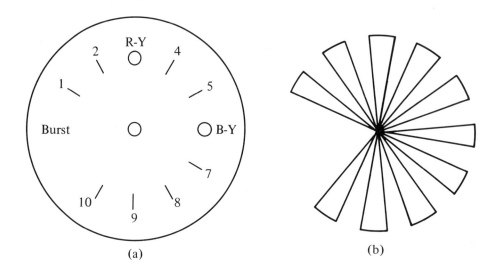

Fig. 15-8 Vectorscope graticule layout and vectorgram:
(a) typical appearance of graticule, (b) ideal vectorgram
pattern.

With respect to Fig. 15-9, the output signal   from a
keyed rainbow color-bar generator consists of 11 color bursts
between consecutive horizontal sync pulses.   Each burst has
a 30° phase advance with respect to the preceding burst.   The
first burst is utilized by the color sync system in the receiver, and the following 10 color-difference bar signals produce
the color pattern indicated in Fig. 15-9 on the picture tube
screen.   We will assume that the receiver employs R - Y and
B - Y chroma demodulators.   In turn, the demodulator output
signals have the waveforms depicted in Fig. 15-10. When these
signals are applied to the vertical and horizontal deflection
plates in a CRT, a vectorgram pattern will be displayed on the
screen.

Because the response of practical circuits is less than
ideal, the vectorgram patterns observed in practice depart
significantly from perfection.   For example, the vectorgram

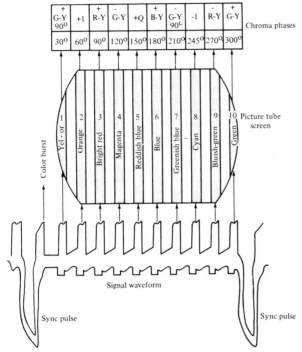

+ G-Y 90°	+1	- R-Y	+ G-Y	+Q	+ B-Y	- G-Y 90°	-1	- R-Y	+ G-Y	
30°	60°	90°	120°	150°	180°	210°	245°	270°	300°	Chroma phases

Fig. 15-9 Characteristics of a keyed rainbow color-bar signal.

shown in Fig. 15-11 is produced by a typical color television receiver in normal operating condition. Substantial departures from the reference waveform indicate various types of receiver malfunctions. Detailed analysis of vectorgrams is an involved topic, and interested readers are referred to specialized texts. Although keyed rainbow color-bar generators are used in most service shops, television broadcast stations utilize NTSC color-bar generators. A characteristically different form of vectorgram is produced by the NTSC signal, as depicted in Fig. 15-12.

15.6 Signal-Generating Instruments

In this section the principal types of signal generators used in television receiver testing will be discussed. Align-

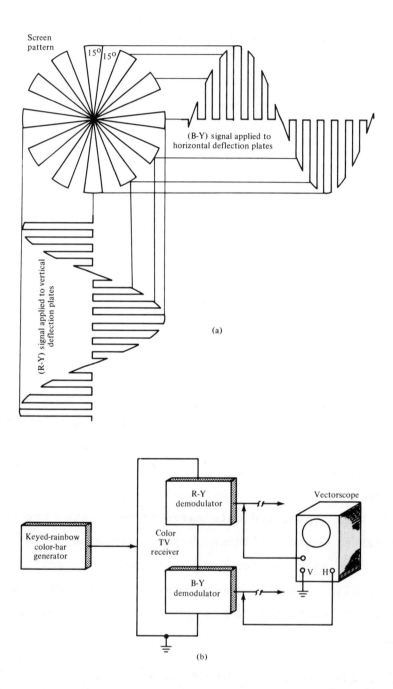

(a)

(b)

Fig. 15-10 Idealized vectorscope operation: (a) development of vectorgram pattern, (b) connection of vectorscope to television receiver.

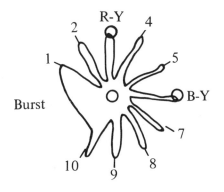

Fig. 15-11 Actual vectorgram pattern produced by a normally operating color television receiver.

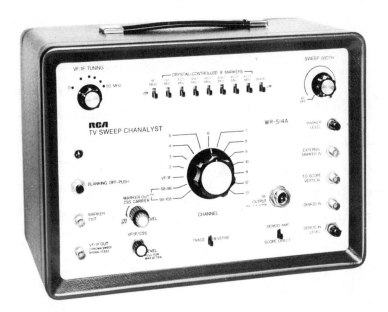

Fig. 15-12 Vectorgram characteristics produced by an NTSC color-bar signal.

ment of RF, IF, and video-frequency circuits requires conventional signal generators, and alignment procedures are greatly facilitated by sweep frequency techniques. Figure 15-13 illustrates widely used types of television signal generators. A VHF-IF marker generator is basically an accurately calibrated signal generator. It is called a marker generator because it

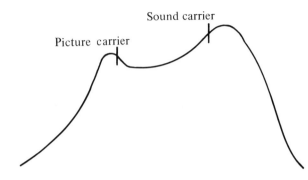

Fig. 15-13 Beat markers at picture and sound carrier points on a sweep alignment curve.

is generally used to place beat markers (also called "pips" or "birdies") on a sweep alignment curve, as illustrated in Fig. 15-13.

A sweep alignment curve is obtained by application of a sweep frequency generator, and the pattern is displayed on the screen of an oscilloscope. The essential distinction between a marker generator and a sweep generator is that the former is an AM generator, whereas the latter is an FM generator. Figure 15-14 depicts output signal waveform from both types of generators. A marker generator can supply either a continuous wave (CW) signal or an amplitude-modulated (AM) signal. On the other hand, a sweep generator can supply a CW signal, or a frequency-modulated (FM) signal. To display a visual alignment (sweep alignment) curve, an FM signal is applied to the input of the circuit under test, with an oscilloscope connected by the output of the circuit. Markers are placed on the curve by mixing a CW signal from the marker generator with the FM signal from the sweep generator.

Color-bar generators can be classified into rainbow and NTSC types, as noted previously. A keyed rainbow color-bar generator such as illustrated in Fig. 15-12(c) produces the signal waveform shown in Fig. 15-9. This is a chroma or color-difference signal. In addition, most keyed rainbow

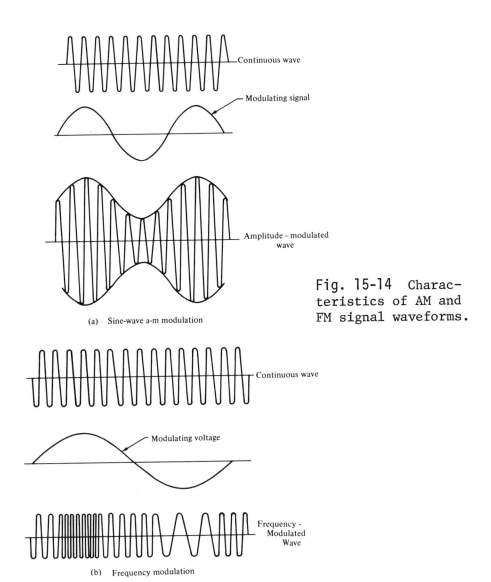

Continuous wave

Modulating signal

Amplitude - modulated wave

(a)   Sine-wave a-m modulation

Fig. 15-14 Charac-
teristics of AM and
FM signal waveforms.

Continuous wave

Modulating voltage

Frequency - Modulated Wave

(b)   Frequency modulation

generators also supply white dot and crosshatch signals. Figure 15-15 depicts dot and crosshatch patterns as they appear on the screen of a color picture tube.   These patterns are used as a guide in adjusting the maintenance controls in the convergence section of a color television receiver.   If a color picture tube is misconverged, a white dot is split

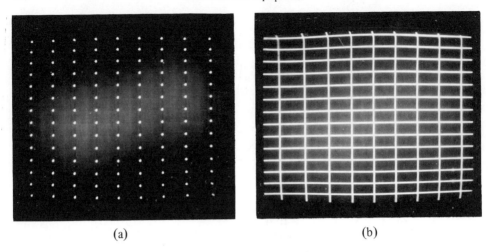

(a)   (b)

Fig. 15-15 Appearance of (a) white dot and (b) crosshatch patterns.

up into two or three colored lines. Convergence adjustments are concerned with merging the red, green, and blue dots to form white dots.

Television laboratories and broadcast stations generally use NTSC-type color-bar generators. These generators typically provide the primary and complementary color signals, and the R - Y, B - Y, G - Y, I and Q color-difference signals. Some television service shops also utilize this type of generator, although its cost is often considered prohibitive. NTSC color-bar generators designed for service application generally include white dot and crosshatch signal outputs. The rated accuracy of a service-type generator is considerably less than that of a laboratory-type generator. Accuracy ratings concern chroma phase, signal amplitude, waveform characteristics, modulation linearity and percentage, and level of spurious output signal components.

Test pattern generators also find considerable application, both in television service procedures and in laboratory work. The most common type of test pattern generator is the flying-spot scanner, which generates a video signal as noted previously. Television laboratories generally employ a monoscope type of test pattern generator. This instrument utilizes a special CRT which has an "Indian-head" pattern deposited on the screen surface. The advantage of a monoscope is its higher resolution and contrast. Television research and development laboratories also use elaborate types of test pattern generators with comparatively complex screen patterns. The advantage of this type of generator is the large amount of information which it can provide concerning the characteristics and operation of circuits under test.

15.7 Semiconductor Test Instruments and Devices

Transistor testers, such as illustrated in Fig. 15-16,

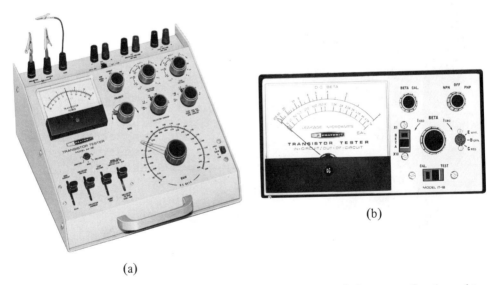

(b)

(a)

Fig. 15-16 Semiconductor test devices: (a) out-of-circuit transistor and diode tester, (b) in-circuit transistor tester.

are used to make basic operating tests. Both in-circuit and out-of-circuit testers are available. Although an in-circuit tester provides considerable operating convenience, it is

quite limited in its ability to determine transistor characteristics. It provides a go/no-go test. On the other hand,
an out-of-circuit tester generally provides measurements of
beta and leakage current under various circuit conditions.
Because transistors are usually soldered into receiver circuits, an in-circuit type of tester is attractive.   Many
technicians feel that an analysis of dc voltages in the operating circuit can provide as much or more information than an
in-circuit tester.

     Television laboratories and semiconductor factories
generally employ semiconductor curve tracers, such as illustrated in Fig. 15-17.   This type of instrument displays the

Fig. 15-17 A semi-
conductor curve
tracer. (Courtesy,
Tektronix Corp.)

collector family of characteristics for a transistor on the
screen of an oscilloscope.   Base families of curves can also
be displayed.   Thereby, this type of transistor tester

provides the maximum amount of generalized information. Of course, it cannot determine anything concerning alpha frequency cutoff or switching characteristics. Therefore, various other test instruments are employed, such as pulse generators. A typical pulse generator is illustrated in Fig. 15-18.

Fig. 15-18 A pulse generator, used in semiconductor testing laboratories. (Courtesy, General Radio Corp.)

15.8 Picture Tube Testers

Various types of picture tube testers are in use. They provide an indication of the ability of an electron gun to provide adequate electron emission. The most common type of picture tube tester is the picture tube test jig noted previously. This jig is utilized in color television service and provides a practical operating test of a color picture tube. Its chief advantage is that it provides a preliminary localization of the trouble area. That is, when the technician is doubtful of the picture tube, but not certain, a jig test will show immediately whether the picture tube or the receiver is at fault. This method is not used in black and white receiver servicing because a substitution test can be made without objectionable difficulty.

15.9 Degaussing Coils

A degaussing coil is not a test equipment item in the
strict sense of the term because it is essentially a corrective device. A degaussing coil consists of a large ring-
shaped coil which is energized by 60-Hz ac voltage. It has
an extensive ac magnetic field which is used to demagnetize
color picture tubes. That is, if there is residual magnetism present in the metal structure of a color picture tube,
it will display poor screen purity. This means that a normally white screen appears tinted or splotched with various
colors. When the residual magnetism is removed by placing
the picture tube in the field of a degaussing coil, normal
screen purity can be obtained.

15.10 Harnesses, Cables, and Yoke Assemblies

As noted previously, various interconnecting leads,
cables, plugs, and receptacles are utilized in various test
procedures. Bias boxes, substitute yokes, adapters, and
picture tube jigs are included in this same general category.
They are basically accessories and not test equipment items.

15.11 Auxiliary Probes

Probes for meters and oscilloscopes have been discussed
in preceding chapters. These devices fall into both the
accessory and the test equipment categories. For example, a
high-voltage probe classifies as an accessory, but if it is
designed with an indicator or meter on its handle, it is
obviously a test equipment item.

Questions

Short Answer

1. Give an example of each of the categories of measuring instruments listed on page

2. Why do most technicians prefer to use conventional volt-meters rather than a neon-lamp indicator?

3. Describe the operation of a field-strength meter.

4. What is the advantage of the DVM?

5. Why are current-measuring instruments seldom used in television repair?

6. What is the chief disadvantage of using an ohmmeter for television repair?

7. Describe the function of the vectorscope.

8. What are the components of the output signal from a keyed rainbow color-bar generator?

9. Discuss the application of a sweep generator in tele-vision circuit alignment.

10. How are markers placed on a sweep alignment curve?

11. Draw a block diagram of a test set up for the align-ment of a television receiver.

12. What are white dot and crosshatch signals?

13. Explain how a dot and crosshatch pattern can be used to adjust the convergence of a color picture tube.

14. What is the purpose of the flying-spot scanner?

15. Compare the in-circuit and the out-of-circuit tran-sistor testers.

16. What function does a picture tester serve?

17. What is the purpose of a degaussing coil?

True-False

1. A field-strength meter is basically a voltmeter with a tuned circuit.
2. A field-strength meter can be used to measure the signal strength at the antenna.
3. The oscilloscope is the most commonly used instrument for television repair.
4. The digital voltmeter is often used in television service shops.
5. Current-measuring instruments are often used for television service.
6. The output signal from a keyed rainbow color-bar generator consists of the three basic color bursts between consecutive horizontal sync pulses.
7. A vectorscope requires both a vertical and a horizontal sync signal.
8. The VHF-IF marker generator is basically an accurately calibrated signal generator.
9. A sweep frequency generator is used to develop a sweep alignment curve.
10. If a color picture tube is misconverged, a white dot is split up into two or three color dots.
11. NTSC color-bar generators designed for service application do not include a white dot or crosshatch signal output.
12. The flying-spot scanner develops a test pattern.
13. Both in-circuit and out-of-circuit transistor testers are available.
14. A picture-tube test jig is used to replace the CRT for a substitution test.
15. A degaussing coil is used to magnetize a color picture tube.

Multiple Choice

1. The most commonly used test instrument for television repair is the:
   (a) oscilloscope.
   (b) field-strength meter.
   (c) voltmeter.
   (d) ohmmeter.

2. The purpose of a Wheatstone bridge is to measure:
   (a) dc voltages   (c) resistance values
   (b) ac voltages   (d) inductance values.

3. When an electrolytic capacitor is suspected of being faulty in a television receiver, the technician would most probably:
   (a) replace the capacitor.
   (b) check the capacitor with a voltmeter.
   (c) check the capacitor on an impedance bridge.
   (d) check the capacitor on a Wheatstone bridge.

4. The beat markers from a marker generator are called:
   (a) notches. (c) indicators.
   (b) pips.   (d) references.

5. The in-circuit transistor provides a:
   (a) beta test.   (c) temperature test.
   (b) go/no-go test.   (d) leakage test.

6. A picture tube test jig is not used for black and white receiver servicing, because:
   (a) a substitution test is simple.
   (b) it would not indicate the correct response.
   (c) a test jig cannot replace a black and white CRT.
   (d) a black and white receiver will not operate correctly when loaded with a test jig.

INDEX